LANGUAGE AND INFORMATION

Selected Essays on their Theory and Application

ADIWES INTERNATIONAL SERIES

This book is in the
ADDISON-WESLEY SERIES IN LOGIC
Hartley Rogers, Jr., Consulting Editor

To Shulamith

Language and Information

SELECTED ESSAYS ON THEIR THEORY AND APPLICATION

BY YEHOSHUA BAR-HILLEL

Professor of Logic and Philosophy of Science
The Hebrew University of Jerusalem

ADDISON-WESLEY PUBLISHING COMPANY

Reading, Massachusetts · Palo Alto · London · Don Mills, Ontario

Preface

At one time or another many authors must have faced the dilemma of whether to gather their articles published on a certain topic and republish them as a collection of essays or whether to rework them into an entirely new book. I decided in favor of the first course with regard to the articles I had written during the last fifteen years on language and information, in particular on the more technical and applied aspects, leaving for some future occasion my papers on the philosophy of language.

This decision was probably motivated by sheer laziness (though writing a new book would have, after all, taken me less time than revising and adapting the older articles). But if I have to rationalize, my excuses are that some of the papers collected here were rather influential in their time and might still exert some influence (beneficial, I hope) when they now become more easily available, that other chapters might deter newcomers to the field from falling into the same traps I had fallen into and had such a hard time getting out of again, while some chapters seem to me still fresh enough to need hardly any revision.

Though, in general, I did not hesitate to omit whole paragraphs or sections in order to reduce the overlap which is almost unavoidable in a collection of independently written essays, on two occasions a considerable overlap was deliberately left. The first two-thirds of Chapter 17 contain little that is new relative to what is contained in Chapter 15, but I am quite sure that there will be a considerable number of readers who will not have the necessary patience and will-power to go over Chapter 15 carefully, and they will, I presume, welcome the shorter and less formal presentation given in Chapter 17. The overlap in the presentation and discussion of categorial grammars in Chapters 2, 7, 8, 11, and 14 is due to my feeling that the reader might profit from following the historical development of the work in this field, even if the progress was by no means in a straight line.

For the same reason, he might on occasion come across an inconsistency in the treatment of the same topic in different chapters. There is a good chance that the later the date of the original publication of the respective chapter, the closer is the opinion expressed in it to my present views.

vii

The references have been consolidated and many items omitted which, though relevant at the time, are no longer so today. Misprints and minor mistakes have been corrected. The number of footnotes has been greatly cut down to allow for smoother reading. Citations in the text will be illustrated rather than explained: '[17: 185; 76 : 12, n. 3; 88: 45, ch. 3]' would mean that relevant material is to be found in item no. 17 (of the References) on p. 185, as well as in footnote 3 of page 12 of item no. 76, and on p. 45 as well as in chapter 3 of item no. 88.

My warmest thanks are extended to Professor Rudolf Carnap for his consent to have a joint Technical Report republished here as Chapter 3, and to my associates, Prof. Eliyahu Shamir, Dr. Chaim Gaifman and Mr. Micha Perles, for their consent to the republication of jointly written papers as Chapters 7, 8, and 9.

I would also like to extend my thanks to the following for their kind permission to reprint:

Chapter 1	The Board of Editors of the **Journal of Symbolic Logic**
Chapters 2 and 5	The Linguistic Society of America
Chapter 3	The M.I.T. Press, Massachusetts Institute of Technology, Cambridge, Mass., U.S.A.
Chapters 4 and 16	The Williams and Wilkins Company, Baltimore, Maryland, U.S.A.
Chapters 7 and 8	The Weizmann Science Press, Jerusalem, Israel
Chapters 6 11 and 12	Academic Press, Inc., New York, U.S.A.
Chapter 9	The Board of Editors of the **Zeitschrift für Phonetik, Sprachwissenschaft und Kommunikationsforschung**
Chapters 10, 18 and 20	John Wiley and Sons, Inc., New York, U.S.A.
Chapter 13	The Times Publishing Company, London, England
Chapter 14	The NATO Scientific Affairs Division, Paris, France
Chapter 15	The Research Laboratory of Electronics, Massachusetts Institute of Technology, Cambridge, Mass., U.S.A.
Chapter 17	The Josiah Macy, Jr. Foundation, New York, U.S.A.
Chapter 19	The Friedr. Vieweg & Sohn Verlag, Braunschweig, Germany

Finally, I wish to thank my assistants Mrs. Elaine Robinson and Mr. David Louvish for their tireless help in preparing this volume for print and reading the proofs, Miss Miriam Balaban, Director of the Jerusalem Academic Press, for her unfailing readiness to go through one more set of proofs in order to come still closer to technical perfection, Mr. Henry S. Stanton, of the Addison-Wesley Publishing Company, for the interest he has shown in the publication of this volume, and Dr. Marshall C. Yovits, Mr. R. H. Wilcox and Mr. Gordon D. Goldstein, of the Information Systems Branch of the U.S. Office of Naval Research, whose generous and no-strings-attached support of the Applied Logic Branch at the Hebrew University of Jerusalem enabled me and my associates to do much of the research presented in this volume.

Jerusalem, August 1963   Y. B-H.

Contents

Introduction

In the autumn of 1935, I left the kibbutz I had joined the year before, in order to continue at the Hebrew University my studies which I had disrupted for the year. While still pondering on the question whether to major in mathematics or in philosophy, I happened to get hold of the first three volumes of *Erkenntnis*, edited by Carnap and Reichenbach, the two most prominent members of the Vienna Circle and the Berlin Group, respectively, and the spiritual leaders of logical positivism at the time. For two weeks I devoured these volumes, hardly doing anything else beyond the absolute necessities. The effect of this "reading period" was nothing short of a revelation. Never before had I come across such an unrelenting strife toward clarity and testability in matters philosophical as in the articles of Carnap in these volumes; never before did I see such a powerful denunciation of metaphysical obscurantism combined with a thorough understanding and analysis of its seductive appeal and with the techniques of combatting this appeal as in the contributions of Carnap, Neurath, Schlick and Reichenbach published there. My future was clear.

The year after, in 1936/37, Professor Abraham A. Fraenkel conducted a seminar on Carnap's **Logische Syntax der Sprache** [22]. For the next couple of years, I was seldom seen without a copy of this book under my arm. My fellow students dubbed it "Bar-Hillel's Bible". It was doubtless the most influential book I read in my life, and a good part of my work is directly or indirectly related to it. Never since has my interest in language abated for a minute.

It was while working in 1938 on my Master's Thesis on *The Antinomies of Logic* that I came across Ajdukiewicz's article "Die syntaktische Konnexität" [1], which was later to become a major factor in my work on logical and algebraic linguistics. In 1938, however, my knowledge of linguistics was precisely nil, so that I did not realize the importance of this article for that field. Neither, I gather, did Ajdukiewicz himself fully grasp its linguistic potential at the time.

In the following years, while teaching mathematics at various high schools

1

in Jerusalem, I began working on my Doctor's Thesis. The first blue-covered booklets of the **International Encyclopedia of Unified Science,** and the contributions there by Carnap, Morris and Bloomfield, kept the fire of my interest in language burning. I had already written a few dozen pages on the pragmatics of adult learning of a totally new language—a subject that used to fascinate Carnap and which he had treated, though for illustrative purposes only, in his contribution to the Encyclopedia, **Foundations of Logic and Mathematics** [25], and which was again taken up by Professor W. V. O. Quine in his discussion of "jungle linguistics" in his **Word and Object** [127]—when the Africa Corps of Fieldmarshal Rommel came, in 1942, uncomfortably close to the gates of Palestine.

After four years of service with the Jewish Brigade Group, I returned to teaching high school and to my thesis. Much of what I had planned to say in it had been said in the meantime by other people. The chapters of Moore and Black in **The Philosophy of Bertrand Russell** [106; 14] gave my thoughts a new turn. The question of the amount of philosophical insight one can obtain from direct analysis of natural languages and ordinary speech, with common sense and linguistic sensitivity serving as the main tools of investigation, in comparison with what can be done by an indirect approach through logically rigorous constructed language systems, the approach favored by Carnap and the "logical reconstructionists" in general, came to the fore [2] and remained since then in the center of my interest. Strange to say, at that time it never seriously occurred to me that there could be a third approach, namely the one attacking natural languages and ordinary speech with the best methods of theoretical and statistical linguistics, respectively. But then both these disciplines were still in a rather poor state in the late forties [76].

Some of Black's remarks on Russell's Theory of Logical Types [14] made me go back to what Carnap had to say in his **Der logiche Aufbau der Welt** [21] on the topic of *Sphärenvermengung* (a type of philosophically important fallacy which was rediscovered twenty years later by Ryle as "category mistake", apparently without being aware of Carnap's prior profound investigations) and on the relations Syntactically Related and Isogenous (in [24]), to his treatment of syntactic categories published between these books, to Ajdukiewicz's discussion of syntactic connexity based on a theory of semantic categories adapted from Leśniewski who in his turn departed from Husserl's *Bedeutungskategorien* which could be partly traced back to ideas of Aristotle, and to many related investigations. This whole topic of "syntactic categories" fascinated me to such a degree that I decided to write my Doctor's Thesis on a **Theory of Syntactic Categories** (in Hebrew), a task I barely finished when the Israeli War of Independence broke out and it was my turn again to do a couple of years of soldiering. As a matter of fact, when the clouds began to gather after the United Nations decision, in November 1947, to establish a Jewish State in part of Palestine, my advisor, Professor S. H. Bergmann, was kind and thoughtful enough to let me submit my thesis without its prospective third chapter, which was to contain a discussion of the philosophical relevance of the theory of syntactic categories, whose history was discussed in the first chapter and whose formalism was developed and illustrated in the second chapter. A greatly revised version of the second chapter, together with some of the philosophical discussions left out of my thesis, was later, in 1950, published as "On syntactical categories", reprinted here as Chapter 1.

I am afraid that my linguistic views of that time, though probably not more naive than those of any other contemporary philosopher or logician, were still deplorably naive. I thought that by going over large texts in any given unknown language, segmented into sentences and words, not only should it be possible to arrive at a categorization of the word sequences occurring in the text, which is trivial, but that this procedure would also yield a grammar of the whole language, whose adequacy would increase with the length of the text and in some cases converge to "the" grammar of the language. I think I did grasp some of the difficulties in such an approach, but certainly not all. I realized, for instance, that in order to obtain a more economical grammar one would have, on occasion, to split up one word into two or more, i.e., to assign typographically equiform word-tokens of the text to one or more word-types belonging different syntactic categories, but probably did not realize that there exists no good reason to believe that increasing the text might not lead to a reversal of this procedure or to a different splitting up, with no convergence seriously in sight.

But worse, I was then—and still for some years to come—under the illusion, shared with all logicians and most linguists who cared to think on this issue, that all sentences of natural languages are "parsible", i.e., can be split up, according to definite rules, into two or more consecutive and contiguous immediate constituents. Each of these, unless already itself a final element (a word, or a similar unit), is again segmentable into its immediate constituents until the final nested segmentation is obtained so that by this procedure the whole syntactic structure of these sentences is exhaustively determined.

To put my linguistic view of 1950 in slogan terms, which have become fashionable since the epoch-making appearance of Professor Noam A. Chomsky's **Syntactic Structures** [34] in 1957, I then believed both that natural languages are adequately representable by *context-free phrase structure grammars* and that there exist approximative and self-correcting procedures for discovering these grammars, procedures that are now known in the trade as *discovery procedures*. I am afraid that both these beliefs were rather strengthened by talking with Professor Zellig S. Harris during his visit to Palestine in 1947 and by reading in manuscript some chapters of his classic **Methods in Structural Linguistics** [62], whose first edition was to appear only three years later. As a matter of fact, if I have the facts straight, around 1948 Harris began his investigations into what he called *discourse analysis* [63], which led him later [64] to the development of *transformational grammars* that transcend not only the framework of context-free phrase structure grammars but even that of phrase structure grammars in general, including their *context-sensitive* type, and thereby present a clear departure from *immediate constituent* type grammars, which at that time dominated linguistic thinking in the United States and many other countries.

I was to learn of all these developments only after coming to the States in 1950. In the meantime, however, the talks with Harris shattered my linguistic naiveté and convinced me that the neglect of linguistics, so conspicuous in the works of such authors as Carnap, Ajdukiewicz and Tarski in the field of logical syntax and semantics, as Wittgenstein, Ryle and Austin in so-called linguistic philosophy, and as Morris (though to a lesser degree) in semiotics, could not but lead to distorted and partly irrelevant results in philosophy of language. Even Reichenbach's famous Chapter VII, entitled "Analysis of Conversational Language", of his **Elements of Symbolic Logic** [160], presenting in its more than one hundred pages the by far most extensive treatment of the grammar of natural languages from the standpoint of a modern symbolic logician, owes its not inconsiderable shortcomings mostly to linguistic innocence — the only linguist of stature quoted in it being Jespersen. I think that the only work by a modern professional linguist I had studied in some depth before these talks was Bloomfield's little contribution [15] to the **Encyclopedia of Unified Science,** published in 1939. This booklet showed a surprising convergence between ways of thinking of at least certain circles of American linguists and those of say, Carnap, and I made a mental note to pursue this issue further sometime. But only in 1951 did I find the time to do so.

A fellowship from the Hebrew University enabled me to go with my family to the United States in the autumn of 1950. We spent the winter term of 1950/51 in Chicago, where the philosophy department of the University of Chicago was so kind as to grant me guest privileges. It was there that I met Rudolf Carnap in person for the first time, having already corresponded with him on and off since 1940. Since I came to know his writings, I had always regarded him as one of the greatest philosophers of all time, but now I became equally impressed with his personality. He was kind enough not only to allow me to attend his classes, in which he revealed himself as an incredibly masterful lecturer who could imperceivably turn the most stupid question of a student into an intelligent remark leading to some additional clarification, but also to dedicate one afternoon each week to discussing with me, or sometimes together with Professor Arthur W. Burks, who also spent that term in Chicago, whatever problems interested him or me at the time.

During these discussions, in connection with certain ideas Carnap intended to incorporate in the second volume of his **Logical Foundations of Probability** [28], he called my attention to Information Theory, in the sense of Statistical Theory of Communication, as discussed in the two classics **Cybernetics** [151] by Wiener and **The Mathematical Theory of Communication** [136] by Shannon and Weaver that had appeared during the two preceding years, and indicated that some of the formulations developed in these new fields should be transferred to a rigorous treatment of *semantic information*. I don't quite remember in what form Wiener's revolutionary ideas had come to my attention in 1949 while I was still in Jerusalem. I might have seen the book **Cybernetics** itself; more likely it was some review of it. I was greatly attracted to these ideas and am quite sure that I became their first prophet in Israel. Bergmann was then giving a course on the mind-body problem, as he had done many times before and after, and I still remember the excitement with which I tried, shortly before my departure for the States, to convince him that the impact of cybernetics must be taken into account in any future fruitful discussion of the problem.

The ideas of cybernetics fitted in rather well with my general utter distrust of metaphysics and speculative philosophy, which has never wavered, and with my increasing interest in the use of mechanical methods in logic and linguistics. I already mentioned that at the time I still believed in the possibility of finding a mechanical discovery procedure for grammars, given long enough corpora, and I had already heard from Harris that he considered using the newly developed electronic computers for just this purpose. I myself had always regarded it of great importance, for testing the validity of some consideration, to perform the *Gedankenexperiment* of telling a machine how to carry out this consideration, and I was enchanted by the idea that some such experiments could now be performed in the flesh rather than only in the spirit.

As a matter of fact, the two persons, after Carnap, I wanted to meet most in the States were Quine and Wiener. With this aim in mind, I left Chicago for Cambridge, Massachusetts, in March 1951. Unfortunately, I had little luck with either of them. Though I attended one of Quine's courses, no real personal contact was established, and our meetings remained restricted to a few seminars and discussions at the strong Greater Boston Unity of Science group, which at that time also included the physicists P. W. Bridgman and Phillip Frank, the mathematician Richard von Mises, the linguist Roman Jakobson, the psychologists S. S. Stevens and B. F. Skinner, the biophysicist Walter Rosenblith, and many other illustrious scientists. As to Wiener, I had hoped to establish contact with him, when I was offered a research associateship in the Research Laboratory of Electronics (RLE) of the Massachusetts Institute of Technology by Professor Jerome B. Wiesner, later to become Director of the Office of Science and Technology to the President. This offer came a couple of months after my arrival in Cambridge, just when my fellowship money was touching bottom. I had been introduced to Wiesner by Walter Pitts who was a former student of Carnap's and whom Carnap had advised me to contact. Unfortunately, Wiener's connection with the work at RLE was less close than I had thought so that the expected contact did not immediately materialise. Only many months later did I meet Wiener over a chess board at the MIT Faculty Club, and though we then had some extremely stimulating talks, my interests had in the meantime switched to fields in which Wiener was less interested.

The two years and three months I spent at RLE were doubtless the most stimulating and creative in my life so far. In spite of my bad luck with Quine and Wiener, there was enough genius concentrated in those few square miles between Harvard and MIT to turn every day of my stay in Cambridge into an intellectual feast full of the excitements of exploring new frontiers of knowledge and understanding. Just to illustrate the all-pervasive spirit of international collaboration that marked RLE at that time, and probably still does so today, let me mention that for a time the six people occupying the desks in my office came from six different countries, none of them the United States. This was also the time when Cybernetics and Information Theory reached their common heydays and created among many of us the feeling that the new synthesis heralded in them was destined to open up new vistas on everything human and to help solve many of the disturbing open problems concerning man and humanity.

Though I did not really neglect logic and philosophy of science during this period, my appointment at RLE was mainly for the study of the application of computers to linguistic work. I had complete freedom in my doings and often "misused" it in order to delve into many other directions, as often as not into fields in which I had known nothing, or close to nothing, before. I was not the only one at RLE who did so. Few among my friends and colleagues were working in the field in which they got their degree.

The major linguistic application I set out to study was *machine translation*

(MT). Nobody at MIT was working at it, and Wiener's reaction to Weaver's famous memorandum of 1949 [148] had been definitely negative. Nevertheless, there was plenty of lunch talk on this topic. Within a few hectic months, I tried to get acquainted with the relevant linguistics, mostly American structural linguistics, to pick up the elements of statistical information theory, to understand the principles of computer operation, and, of course, to go through the literature on MT. The last one was the simplest task, since no more than six or seven papers and reports had by then been published on this topic. (Only many years later did we learn that P. P. (Smirnov-)Troyansky in the USSR and G. B. Artsouni in France had given thought to MT already in the early thirties.)

Though MT was always primarily a purely intellectual challenge for me, a testing ground for the validity of the attempts at formalizing natural languages and the exhibition of the limitations of such attempts, I was also greatly attracted by its possible effect on international communication. I had read a great deal about International Auxiliary Languages and gotten acquainted with two or three of them. (I was pleased to learn in Chicago that Carnap had spent quite some time on them, was fluent in Esperanto from his youth, and had been active in the creation and propagation of Interlingua.) Though convinced that the lack of any such a universally accepted auxiliary language was an enormous handicap for scientists (and, for that matter, almost everybody else), I had few illusions about the prospects of coming to an agreement on this point. MT looked like a promising surrogate.

Naturally, it was not the prospective internationally unifying character of MT which drew rapidly increasing financial support from U. S. governmental and military agencies, but rather the much more prosaic fact that the number of students of Russian in the U. S. did not keep pace with the increase in Russian printed output. There was a feeling that training more people in Russian would be a deplorable waste of time and talent which could be used for better purposes. Scientific output outside the U.S. began to increase at a higher rate than inside, for perfectly obvious reasons, and it was rather natural to think that the supremacy of the U.S. in computer technology and financial resources could and should be used to counteract, at least partially and temporarily, the menaces inherent in this development.

My progress at first was rather rapid. Less than three months after I began working on MT, I was already asked to deliver a few lectures on this subject before the participants in an MIT Summer Course on Communication Theory. In addition to a not too successful repetition of an experiment by Professor Abraham Kaplan, in which he had demonstrated the reduction of semantic ambiguity through context [74]—I am afraid, in hindsight, that the relevance of this demonstration for MT purposes was greatly overestimated at the time — and some general remarks on the formal approach to language, only a review of the meager literature was given and some home-made hand-simulated mechanical translations into English of a few sentences from a German scientific text were described. Among the participants in this course was Professor C. F. Hockett, a linguist from Cornell University, whose interest in MT has not since abated.

A few months later, in October 1951, I toured the U.S. in order to visit the few places where MT research was going on, which were Los Angeles, where Professor Victor A. Oswald Jr. and Professor William E. Bull were exploring the field at the University of California, while Kaplan and Dr. Olaf Helmer were performing experiments at RAND Corporation, and Seattle, where Professor Erwin Reifler was doing his pioneering work, developing and exploring the vital conceptions of the pre-editor and the post-editor and beginning to attack the central problem of semantic ambiguity. I also lectured on MT before various mixed audiences at the University of California at Berkeley, the University of Michigan at Ann Arbor, and other places. Mathematicians and electrical engineers tended to accept MT as a serious endeavor much more than linguists. However, if these cautious linguists turned out to have been right after all, I don't think that this was due to a better understanding of the obstacles on their part. I would rather regard it as an outcome of conservatism, which in this case, by accident so to speak, turned out to be right. In 1951, and for a few years to come, the situation was so little understood that accepting or rejecting the MT challenge was much more a question of temperament than of sound scientific judgment.

After the tour it was decided to hold a conference on MT at RLE in June 1952. Some twenty people were invited to participate. Every research group working on MT at the time was represented, including the British group, which was the first to do serious work in MT problems as far back as 1948, and which was represented by Professor A. D. Booth, giving our little conference an international touch. (I myself, though Israeli, was usually regarded as an MIT man, hence a kind of honorary American.) In addition to most of the people already mentioned, the list of participants also included Professor Leon Dostert from Georgetown University, who was invited as an expert on simultaneous human translation, Dr. Victor H. Yngve, who, originally a cosmic ray physicist, just at that time became interested in MT, and, for good measure, a few observers from government and industry. It was one of the most exciting conferences I had ever participated in, and I shall never forget the pervasive feeling of euphoria which I felt and thought that everybody else shared. It was originally planned to publish the proceedings verbatim, but after we got the mimeographed version of the stenographic record, we decided against it. Instead, in 1955, the first collection of essays on MT was published [89], which included most of the formal contributions presented before the conference as well as some later material (Chapter 3).

I myself had prepared a state of the art report for the conference (Chapter 10), which served as a kind of background for our discussions. In addition, I talked about Operational Syntax, which talk remained unpublished, and gave an outline of a quasi-arithmetical description of syntactic structure which could serve as a basis for the mechanization of syntactic analysis (Chapter 5).

According to the stenographic notes, I used the phrase "if a human being can do it, a suitably programmed computer can do it too" more than a dozen times during the conference. Though this slogan is doubtless correct, "in principle", its value lies more in its being an expression of willingness to work toward a certain goal than in exhibiting a deep philosophical insight. Its practical content is close to nil. The problem of how much of the translation effort can be taken over by machines has never ceased to interest me. During the conference, I regarded a man–machine partnership, in which the human partner would play the role of a post-editor, as the only sensible goal to aim for. I believed that the role played by the mechanical partner could be steadily increased, without any definite limit to the convergence of this process. It did not take me too long to come to a more realistic evaluation of the situation, and recently I have come to the conclusion that even machines with learning capacities, as presently envisaged, will not be able to become fully autonomous, high-quality translators (Chapter 14, Fourth lecture). In a different vein, after careful consideration of the economics of the situation, I became increasingly skeptical as to the economic feasibility of advantageously using computers in translation to any considerable measure (Chapter 13).

Having been dubbed "the first full-time paid research worker in the field" [89: 5], it is perhaps of some importance to point out that I never wrote a program for MT, never collaborated with a group that designed mechanical translators, and never induced a student to write a thesis on MT. I don't think that I have become more "pessimistic" in time, as some of my colleagues like to put it; I would simply say that I became more knowledgeable in the field and therefore came to realize that the MT problem was much harder than I had anticipated.

I am not really sorry for having contributed to the MT boom that is only now beginning to subside. Many linguists were induced to give their thinking a different twist, with results that were sometimes definitely enlightening. Others were able to carry out a good amount of highly interesting basic research in theoretical linguistics through financial support supplied by agencies primarily interested in the application to MT and other types of linguistic data processing. The fact that the easy money attracted also a lot of fakes and operators is deplorable but perhaps also unavoidable. I hope that my later criticisms contributed to cut down the waste.

While the 1952 MIT Conference, by bringing together for the first time all workers on MT at the time, was a turning point in the development of MT research in the U.S., the Seventh International Congress of Linguists, which convened a few months later in London, gave an opportunity to many linguists, in particular from European countries, to get acquainted for the first time with the ideas of MT. A Rockefeller Foundation grant had enabled me to attend this Congress, and though I registered too late to get on the regular program, I was allowed to present a special talk before interested participants. It is perhaps symptomatic that the Eighth Congress of Linguists, which convened in 1957 in Oslo, dedicated a whole session to MT (which I was asked to chair), while the Ninth Congress, which took place in 1962 in Cambridge, Mass., one of the major world centers of MT research, listened to a large number of talks on this topic. I wonder how MT will fare in the next Congress. I should not be surprised if it will just be forgotten.

Simultaneously with my work on MT, I attacked the problem of *semantic information*, in collaboration with Carnap. This collaboration took a somewhat curious form. Carnap was at the time a member of the Princeton Institute of Advanced Study. During a couple of visits there, the plan for a joint Technical Report (Chapter 15) was worked out, and then Carnap sent me his contribution dictated onto a magnetic tape. I had little to do but to add part of the Introduction, work out a few details and write the last third of it. Carnap, of course, saw the last draft.

Though we, and some others, thought at the time that our treatment of semantic information was a good beginning, surprisingly little has been done since to develop it further. I myself did not pursue this topic at all. Carnap, though, did so, and I understand that in a series of monographs, the publication of which is planned by him and his collaborators, there will be one or two that will deal with this topic and will be prepared by Professor John G. Kemeny and Professor Richard Jeffrey. Kemeny had already in 1953 published a paper on information measure functions [77], written independently of, and partly overlapping, our Technical Report, improving upon it in various directions. Professor Karl R. Popper's later treatment of semantic content [119], again done independently, contains little which is technically new relative to our treatment, but his informal exploitation of this treatment for purposes of the methodology of science is highly interesting though not always watertight. Of other more recent contributions, I would like to mention here those by Professor Rulon S. Wells [149] and Professor David Harrah [61].

The words 'cybernetics' (and its derivatives) and 'information' were surely two of the most used, and misused, members of the scientific vocabulary of the fifties. While the popularity of 'cybernetics' declined rather quickly in the States, probably due to its having been usurped there by overt or covert science-fiction (though its popularity is still on the increase in Europe in general and Russia in particular), 'information' is still going strong and doing its share in the creation of the lunatic fringe that surrounds the Theory of Information. Since my first days at MIT, I was greatly irked by what seemed to me an almost deliberate misuse of this term and by the confusions created thereby. Certain curious expressions of Wiener, von Neumann, Weaver and others did nothing to disperse these confusions or the halo of mystery which sometimes surrounded this newly discovered "commodity" whose importance was put on a par with that of "energy", for instance. True enough, Shannon explicitly dissociated himself from those who interpreted his measures of information as measures of meaning or semantic content, but few were thereby discouraged from making just this interpretation, though they occasionally paid lip-service to Shannon's disclaimer.

My attempts to clarify the issue went in three directions: First, I worked out a whole new terminology for the elementary parts of what I proposed to call Theory of Signal Transmission (instead of the so utterly misleading Theory of Information, a term which seems to have been created, by what turned out to be a very unfortunate ellipsis, from Theory of Information Transmission, in correspondence with Hartley's pioneering paper of 1928 [66]). But this terminology never really caught on, and I did not even bother to publish my proposal. I still think that this is a pity.

Second, I substituted at the last minute for Carnap in the Tenth (and last) Macy Foundation Conference on Cybernetics that took place in Princeton in April 1953. In the talk I gave there, I combined a short presentation of our Theory of Semantic Information with an admittedly very tentative critique of the use of Information and related concepts such as Entropy in certain presentations of modern physics, in particular those connected with Maxwell's demon. Many physicists, among them a man no less eminent that John von Neumann, were in the habit of expressing themselves, at least occasionally, as if entropy, as it occurs in statistical mechanics, was a measure of ignorance, of the lack of knowledge of one who observes a physical system. I could never accept this attitude, nor even really understand it. Talks with some of my physicist friends did not help, and I still remember with a shudder an almost traumatic experience, shared with Carnap. During one of my visits to him in Princeton, in 1952, von Neumann also came to see him, and we started discussing the talk I had heard von Neumann deliver shortly before at an AAAS meeting in St. Louis, in which he had proclaimed, among other things, a triple identity between logic, information theory and thermodynamics. Carnap and I wondered with what degree of seriousness this "identity" was to be taken. We were quite ready to agree that there existed a certain formal analogy, up to a common partial calculus, and had indeed ourselves shown, in our **Outline** (Chapter 15), how entropy-like expressions, such as the famous $-\Sigma p_i \log p_i$, occurred in (inductive) logic, but could not see how any stronger relationships could possibly be supposed to exist. After all, inductive logic was a formal and thermodynamics a real science. We tried to convince von Neumann that his way of presenting the analogy as an identity must lead to confusion. His calm reply was that he could see how logicians and methodologists might be worried by his statements but that *no* physicist would misunderstand them. I know that Carnap decided, after this talk, to postpone *sine diem* the publication of a long paper he had almost finished on the role of inductive logic in statistical mechanics. In this paper he had made some forceful and, to my mind, very illuminating criticisms of certain standard formulations in this theory. I myself omitted some of my remarks on physics in the printed version of my Princeton talk (Chapter 17). This might not look very courageous, but if methodologists are to retain any impact on the thinking of physicists, they can ill afford to claim confusion in things which *no* physicist finds confusing, if von Neumann was right in his blunt declaration. I still wonder whether he really was.

Third, I wrote a paper examining in some detail the foundations of statistical information theory and its supposed semantic interpretation (Chapter 16). I still regard this paper as one of the best I ever published and tend to believe that it did succeed, at least in part, in clarifying the issue. Sad to relate, however, that its last section, in which the status of information theory in physics was to be discussed at length, was greatly shortened, for reasons described in the preceding paragraph.

At the same time I was working at MIT on the use of computers in translation and the determination of syntactic structure, Professor James W. Perry (who was also greatly interested in MT, was one of the participants in the 1952 MIT Conference, and published a few articles on this topic), was there doing his utmost to advocate the use of computers for what became known as *information retrieval* (IR), in constant rivalry with Calvin N. Mooers, an MIT graduate, who, however, did not pursue an academic career but had rather decided to combine his knowledge with his ingenuity and inventive spirit for the establishment of a commercial company.

The main idea of Perry and Mooers was to automate the preparation of reference lists of documents containing material relevant to a given query. Perry was struck by the fact that both punched card equipment and electronic computers were very good at performing Boolean operations, while Mooers was attracted by the possibilities inherent in edge-notched cards for superimposed coding. Mooers began advocating the use of very simple and cheap equipment for the search of small document collections, while Perry quickly began thinking in terms of larger collections, of national documentation centers, etc., and therefore concentrated on digital computers.

In a very short time, due at least in part to the relentless propagandizing of Perry, IR became a multimillion dollar affair. Whatever the future prospects of the mechanization of IR—and I think both that there are such prospects and that they are rather limited — the issue became quickly beclouded in two respects. In order better to sell the new ideas, many people followed Perry's lead and started to push the panic button and flooded the country with endless statistics on the "documentation explosion". During the last ten years, I have seen many hundreds of articles and listened to scores of lectures and after-dinner speeches which all began with some such statistics. In Chapter 20, I try to show the irrelevance of these statistics and the baselessness of this propaganda-induced generalized fear of the information flood.

The second respect in which IR tended to get bogged down was a premature and extremely crude theorizing, often based on an utterly inadequate analysis of the situation. I was amazed, for instance, to find out, rather early in my critical investigations into this field, that most people working in it literally did not quite know what they were talking about and failed to make the trivial distinction between systems that provided information or data, in the form of specific answers to specific questions, and systems that provided reference lists as their output. Of course, these two types of systems are not entirely unrelated and one can think of various ways of combining them, but just for this purpose one has first to understand clearly their difference.

This investigation was mostly done during my short second visit to MIT in 1955/56 (Chapter 18). In July 1953, I had returned to Israel to take up my new post as Assistant Professor of Philosophy at the Hebrew University of Jerusalem. In these two years, between 1953 and 1955, I was too busy with my teaching duties to do much research outside philosophy proper but still managed to do my share in propagating in Israel cybernetics, communication theory, automata theory, automation of various intelligent activities, etc., through public lectures, summer courses, radio talks and other such means. But it was only when I returned to research at RLE that I found the time to go into information retrieval.

On my second return to Israel, in March 1956, I took with me a modest research grant from the National Science Foundation which enabled me to take some time off my teaching duties and spend it on keeping up with further developments in the field of the mechanization of information retrieval. After the termination of this grant, the Information Systems Branch of the U.S. Office of Naval Research, headed at that time by Dr. Marshall C. Yovits, gave me a research contract for the study of the mechanization of linguistic data processing, in a rather broad interpretation which included practically everything now investigated under the heading of Artificial Intelligence, with the exception of pattern recognition. In particular, it was understood that I should take upon myself a critical investigation of the state of machine translation and its prospects as well as of the theoretical aspects of reference providing systems.

The material for these studies was gathered during the years 1957/60. A third two-months trip to the States in the fall of 1958, mainly in order to participate in the International Conference on Scientific Information which took place in Washington, D.C., allowed me to visit once more the major study centers in MT and IR and to regain personal acquaintance with what was going on in these fields in the U.S. and England whither I went after the ICSI meeting for a Conference on the Mechanization of Human Thought, organized by the National Physical Laboratories in Teddington [8]. These meetings, together with innumerable private, public and semi-public talks, greatly strengthened my feelings about the utter inadequacy of the theoretical basis of MT and IR, and in particular about the poverty of the logico-mathematical underpinnings.

The results of my studies were presented in two Technical Reports later published in considerably revised versions. Parts of the first of these reports are reprinted here as Chapters 11 and 12. The second is reprinted here, with some omissions, as Chapter 19.

Both reports raised a good amount of objections. I had trodden on the toes of quite a number of individuals and research groups and had not really supposed that they would take it lying down. But I can't say that I was particularly impressed by the rebuttals. Nor was my attitude changed during the sabbatical year I spent in 1960/61 at the University of California at Berkeley and, once again, at the RLE of MIT, with the chances it gave me to take part in a Lake Arrowhead Conference, organized by the University of California at Los Angeles, and the meeting of the American Documentation Institute in Berkeley, as well as the opportunity of consulting with various major research institutions. If at all, I became more and more convinced of the futility of most approaches to MT and the mechanization of IR. As already mentioned above, I realized at that time the fallacy behind the "information flood" argument (Chapter 20), lost my belief of ten years' standing that computers should at least be able to become money-saving partners in translation (Chapter 13), and finally became disenchanted with the thought that computers should be in a position to improve their output in translation—or in many other linguistic data processing performances—through learning (Chapter 14). These disenchantments were presented in talks given before an ONR Colloquium in Washington, D.C., in February 1961, a NATO Summer Institute of Automatic Translation in Venice, Italy, July 1962 (Chapter 14), the Second IFIP Congress in Munich, August 1962, and on many other occasions. The various negative reactions to these presentations remained unconvincing (to me), but for the first time, there was now a considerable number of experts who tended to accept my criticisms, perhaps with some reservations as to their formulation.

I can't say that I am uncompromisingly enamored of the status of the devil's advocate as which many of my friends and colleagues tend to see me and which status I have indeed many times taken upon myself even without having been specifically asked to. It may be true what one of my friends jokingly said about me on one occasion, that I have an extremely low threshold for nonsense and loose formulations, but the constant vigil for sense and responsibility can become quite tiresome. From time to time, I try to rid myself of the bickering and fault-finding and do some honest piece of productive scientific work myself. However, this is not as easy as it sounds. I am not a very good mathematical logician and not even a mediocre mathematician, and am fully aware of these shortcomings. Without a mastery of these two fields and without the patience to overcome this handicap by sheer dogged work, I very often quickly find out that I am not in a position to work out by myself the ideas I might have on one topic or the other. During the last few years, I have been lucky in finding associates and assistants who are my betters in these fields and willing to cooperate with me. Most of the more important theorems in the publications of my research group in algebraic linguistics and automata theory are due to them, while I can take credit at most for some of the basic ideas.

It is almost certain that I would not have gone into these two fields—though my 1953 paper (Chapter 5) may well be counted as one of the forerunners of algebraic linguistics—were it not for the immense stimulation I received during these last twelve years from talks with Chomsky and from reading his publications, very often while still in draft form. Chomsky is a professional linguist, a competent mathematical logician, and a trained methodologist with a keen critical sense and an uncanny ability to follow the most abstruse mathematical argument or, if necessary, to produce one himself. All this combined to make him the founder of algebraic linguistics and by far the best man in this exciting new field (though Chomsky himself would probably claim that it is not really new at all, but just plain good old linguistics, pursued with the best means available at our time, which happen to be of algebraic nature). It was my privilege to meet him in Cambridge in 1951 and to discuss with him linguistics, logic and methodology in endless talks since, as well as to carry on a rather voluminous correspondence between visits to the States. His influence on our publications on algebraic linguistics (Chapters 6, 7, 8, 9, 14) is too obvious to need pointing out, but equally strong was his influence on my philosophy of language, in particular as a kind of counterbalance to that of Carnap, though this might not show in the present volume.

I already mentioned my luck in finding for the Applied Logic Branch I am heading at the Hebrew University the best associates and assistants I could wish for. Eliyahu Shamir was with this Branch since its origination and has just temporarily left it to become an Assistant Professor of Mathematics at the University of California in Berkeley. Chaim Gaifman was with us only for one year, during which period he proved the main theorem of Chapter 8, and then, in 1959, went to the States to serve as a research assistant for Carnap, afterwards wrote his Thesis under Tarski, and has now rejoined the Branch, having been appointed an Instructor in the Mathematics Department of the Hebrew University. Micha Perles, the youngest of the three and still short of his doctorate, was responsible for the enormously complex combinatorial constructions by which the main theorem of Chapter 9 was proved. I hope that these gifted mathematicians will keep their interest in mathematical linguistics alive and continue to enrich the field.

PART I

Theoretical Aspects of Language

On Syntactical Categories*   1

1. Up to now, most constructed calculi had the following common property: Whenever the rules of formation of a calculus laid down that expressions of the designs 'Pa', 'Qa', 'Pb' were sentences—'P' and 'Q' being first-level one-place predicates, 'a' and 'b' individual-symbols— 'Qb' was a sentence too, according to the same rules. This self-imposed restriction of the logicians is historically understandable, since calculi of this common feature have a certain simplicity which differently constructed calculi will not have. So far, calculi of this type have proved to be sufficient for the formalization of mathematics and small parts of other sciences. We may ask ourselves, however, whether such a restriction will still be desirable when attempting to construct calculi covering more ground. It is quite possible that insistence on this kind of simplicity will involve a greater complexity in other respects. Inquiry into types of calculi which do not possess this simplicity should therefore be of some interest. To such an inquiry we are led also from another point of view. More and more stress has been laid in recent researches on the construction of calculi which should show close connection with ordinary languages, and it is obvious that ordinary language does not have the mentioned property. To use an example given by Carnap [21:41]: Whereas 'This stone is red,' 'Aluminum is red,' 'This stone weighs five pounds' are all meaningful sentences of ordinary English, 'Aluminum weighs five pounds' is not and it does not matter in this connection whether we formulate this fact by saying that 'Aluminum weighs five pounds,' though grammatically an impeccable sentence, is logically meaningless, or whether we prefer the more modern formulation that this word-sequence does not form a sentence at all.

Carnap[1] was apparently the first to investigate this neglected possibility, but his treatment is admittedly too short and sketchy. His terminology, though far superior to any other existing so far, is not elaborate enough,

---

* First appeared in **The Journal of Symbolic Logic,** vol. 15 (1950), pp. 1–16.
  [1] Not in [21] — there this possibility was explained away—but only in [24:169].

and no model-language has been constructed to illustrate the complicated relations which may be involved.

The purport of this article is to enlarge Carnap's definitions into a preliminary *theory of syntactical categories*, to state some theorems in this theory and to exemplify the importance and fertility of the new terminology by the construction of five simple model-calculi.

2. The following abbreviations will be used in formal rules, definitions and theorems:

symbol(s)	s(s)
expression(s)	e(s)
sequence(s)	sq(s)
class(es)	c(s)
sentence(s)	st(s)
genus (genera)	gn(a)
maximum	m
isogenous	isg
related	rel
sibbed	sib
brotherhood(s)	bh(s)
family (families)	fy(s)
the genus of	Gen'
the relationship of	Rel'
the family of	Fam'
individual(s)	ind(s)
predicate(s)	pr(s)
functor(s)	fu(s)
isotypous	ist
calculus (calculi)	C(i)
level	lev

Expressions like 'maximum symbolic genus' or 'expression classes' will be abbreviated by the sequence of the corresponding abbreviations, with or without hyphens, like 'msgn' or 'e-cs.'

What is customarily called 'expression' will be called here 'symbol-sequence,' whereas our 'expression' corresponds approximately to the customary 'well-formed expression.'

We define '*expression (of C)*':

Any non-void symbol-sequence (of C) such that there is (in C) a sentence of which it forms part will be called an expression (of C).

Elementary knowledge of Carnap's Logical syntax of language is assumed. We shall use the "arch" ' ⌒ ' to designate *concatenation* of expressions. The expressions 'in C,' 'of C,' etc., will be omitted whenever misunderstandings will not be likely to arise. Logistic symbolism will be avoided.

3. Theory of genera. Definitions and theorems.

D3.1. e_1 and e_2 are called (syntactically[2]) *isg* if (and only if[2]) for any st_1 which contains e_1 the result of the replacement in any place in st_1 of e_1 by e_2 is a st, and for any st_2 which contains e_2 the result of the replacement in any place in st_2 of e_2 by e_1 is a st.

D3.2.   A c of es is called a *gn* if every two es belonging to this c are isg.

D3.3.   A gn is called a *mgn* if no e belonging to this gn is isg with an e not belonging to it.

D3.4.   A gn is called a *sgn* if all es belonging to it are ss.

D3.5.   A sgn is called a *msgn* if no s belonging to this sgn is isg with a s not belonging to it.

D3.6.   The c of all es isg with an e_1 is called $Gen'e_1$.

D3.7.   A gn is called *generated* by e_1 if this gn is identical with $Gen'e_1$.

D3.8.   The c of all ss isg with a s_1 is called $sGen's_1$.

D3.9.   An e is called *isolated* if it is not isg with any different e.

We shall now state some simple theorems which follow immediately from the given definitions (and general syntax). No formal proofs will be given.

T3.1.   isg is a reflexive, symmetric, and transitive relation, i.e., an equivalence.

T3.2.   The mgna are the abstractive cs with respect to isg.

T3.3.   Different mgna have no members in common.

T3.4.   Every e (s) belongs to exactly one mgn (msgn).

T3.5. $Gen'e_1$ is a mgn.

T3.6. $Gen'e_1 = Gen'e_2$ if and only if e_1 and e_2 are isg.

T3.7. $sGen's_1$ is a msgn.

T3.8. $sGen's_1 = sGen's_2$ if and only if s_1 and s_2 are isg.

T3.9.   Every mgn (msgn) is generated by any of its members.

T3.10. $Gen'e_1$ is identical with the unit-c of e_1 if and only if e_1 is isolated.

T3.11.   If in an e_1 some of its partial expressions are replaced by isg es, the resulting e is isg with e_1.

T3.12.   If in a st_1 some of its partial es are replaced by isg es, the resulting e is a st isg with st_1.

---

[2] These parenthesized expressions will be omitted hereafter.

T3.13.   All sts of C_1 are isg if (but not only if) C_1 is extensional with respect to partial sts.

T3.14.   All sts of C_1 which do not form partial es of other sts in C_1 are isg.[3]

4. Let C_1 be defined by the following two *rules of formation*:

RF1–1A (*Rule of Vocabulary*): The following twelve ss form the vocabulary of C_1: 'a',[4] b, c, d, f, g, i, j, p, q, r, t.

RF1–2A (*Rule of Sentence-Enumeration*): The following forty-seven s-sqs only are sts in C_1: 'ap', bp, cq, dq, ar, br, cr, dr, at, bt, ft, gaq, gbq, gar, gbr, cic, cjc, cid, cjd, dic, djc, did, djd, gaic, gaid, gajc, gajd, gbic, gbid, gbjc, gbjd, ciga, diga, cjga, djga, cigb, digb, cjgb, djgb, gaiga, gaigb, gajga, gajgb, gbiga, gbigb, gbjga, gbagb.

There are no rules of transformation, deduction, or refutation in C_1.

T4.1.   Every s (of C_1) belongs to exactly one of the following nine msgna:

$$\text{msgn}_1 = \{\text{'a',b}\} \qquad \text{msgn}_2 = \{\text{p}\} \qquad \text{msgn}_3 = \{\text{c,d}\}$$
$$\text{msgn}_4 = \{\text{q}\} \qquad \text{msgn}_5 = \{\text{r}\} \qquad \text{msgn}_6 = \{\text{t}\}$$
$$\text{msgn}_7 = \{\text{r}\} \qquad \text{msgn}_8 = \{\text{g}\} \qquad \text{msgn}_9 = \{\text{i,j}\}$$

C_1 might have been defined alternatively by the following three rules of formation:

RF1–1B: identical with RF1–1A.

RF1–2B (*Rule of Symbol-Classification*): identical with T4.1.

RF1–3B (*Rule of Sentence-Formation*): A s-sq is a st if and only if it fulfils one of the following twelve conditions:

The s-sq has the form 'x $\frown$ y'

and	(1) x belongs to msgn_1 and y belongs to msgn_2
or	(2) ....msgn_1 ....msgn_5
or	(3) ....msgn_1 ....msgn_6
or	(4) ....msgn_3 ....msgn_4
or	(5) ....msgn_3 ....msgn_5
or	(6) ....msgn_7 ....msgn_6

---

[3] The restrictive phrase in this theorem 'which do not form partial es of other sts' may look strange at first sight. The need for it will soon be exemplified. Cf. note 5.

[4] For the sake of economy, quotes will be printed only around the first member of a list of expressions, wherever misunderstandings will not be likely to arise.

or it has the form 'x $\frown$ y $\frown$ z'

and   (7) x belongs to $msgn_8$, y to $msgn_1$, z to $msgn_4$

or   (8) .... $msgn_8$, ... $msgn_1$, ... $msgn_5$

or   (9) .... $msgn_3$, ... $msgn_9$, ... $msgn_3$

or it has the form 'x $\frown$ y $\frown$ z $\frown$ u'

and (10) x belongs to $msgn_8$, y to $msgn_1$, z to $msgn_4$, u to $msgn_3$

or (11) x belongs to $msgn_3$, y to $msgn_9$, z to $msgn_8$, u to $msgn_1$

or it has form 'x $\frown$ y $\frown$ z $\frown$ u $\frown$ w'

and (12) x belongs to $msgn_8$, y to $msgn_1$, z to $msgn_9$, u to $msgn_8$, w to $msgn_1$.

T4.2.   Every e belongs to exactly one of the following seventeen mgna:

mgn_1 = {'a',b} mgn_2 = {p} mgn_3 = {c,d,ga,gb}

mgn_4 = {q,ic,id,jc,jd,iga,igb,jga,jgb} mgn_5 = {r}

mgn_6 = {t} mgn_7 = {f} mgn_8 = {g} mgn_9 = {i,j}

mgn_{10} = {ai,bi,aj,bj} mgn_{11} = {ci,cj,di,dj,gai,gaj,gbi,gbj}

mgn_{12} = {aq,bq,aic,aid,bic,bid,ajc,ajd,bjc,bjd,aiga,ajga,biga,bjga,
          aigb,ajgb,bjga,bjgb}

mgn_{13} = {ig,jg} mgn_{14} = {aig,ajg,big,bjg}

mgn_{15} = {cig,cjg,dig,djg,gaig,gajg,gbig,gbjg} mgn_{16} = {ar,br}

mgn_{17} = {all sts except the two belonging to mgn_{16}}[5]

T4.3. C_1 contains five isolated es, all of them ss.

C_1 might have been defined alternatively by the following three rules of formation:

RF1–1C: identical with RF1–1A.

RF1–2C (*Rule of Expression-Classification*): The following is a complete member-list of seven mgna in C_1:

mgn_1 = {'a',b} etc., up to mgn_7, as in T4.2.

RF1–3C (*Rule of Sentence-Formation*): A s-sq is a st if and only if it fulfils one of the following six conditions:

The s-sq has the form 'x $\frown$ y'

and (1) x belongs to mgn_1 and y belongs to mgn_2

or   (2) ....mgn_1 ....mgn_5

or   (3) ....mgn_1 ....mgn_6

or   (4) ....mgn_3 ....mgn_4

or   (5) ....mgn_3 ....mgn_5

or   (6) ....mgn_7 ....mgn_6.

---

[5] This exemplifies T3.13. The oddity involved could, of course, have been avoided by the use of auxiliary symbols such as parentheses, or by making use of additional rules of scope.

Another alternative set of formation-rules consists of the following three rules:

RF1–1D: identical with RF1–1A.

RF1–2D (*Rule of Expression-Classification*): The following is a complete member-list of three mgna in C_1:

$$mgn_3 = \{...\} \quad mgn_4 = \{...\} \quad mgn_5 = \{...\} \text{ (as in T4.2)}.$$

RF1–3D (*Mixed Rule of Sentence-Formation*): A s-sq is a st if and only if it fulfils one of the following three conditions:

(1) The s-sq is identical with 'ap', or 'bp', or 'ar', or 'br', or 'at', or 'bt', or 'ft',
    or the s-sq has the form 'x ⌒ y'
and (2) x belongs to mgn_3 and y belongs to mgn_4.
or (3)...........mgn_3...............mgn_5.

This last set is probably the pragmatically simplest one. It is of much greater general interest than the first one, since complete sentence-enumeration is a rule-form appropriate to the most primitive calculi only; on the other hand, partial sentence-enumeration, say for all or certain atomic sentences, is a quite customary procedure.

5. Theory of brotherhoods. Definitions and theorems.

D5.1. e_1 and e_2 are called *rel* if there exists a st_1 which contains e_1 such that the result of the replacement in some place in st_1 of e_1 by e_2 is a st.

D5.2.   A c of es is called a *bh* if every two es belonging to this c are rel.

D5.3.   A bh is called a *mbh* if no e not belonging to this bh is rel with every e belonging to it.

D5.4.   A bh is called a *sbh* if all es belonging to it are ss.

D5.5.   A sbh is called a *msbh* if no s not belonging to it is rel with every s belonging to it.

D5.6.   The c of all es rel with an e_1 is called $Rel'e_1$.

D5.7.   The c of all ss rel with a s_1 is called $sRel's_1$.

D5.8.   An e is called *completely isolated* if it is not rel with any different e.

D5.9.   e-c_1 and e-c_2 are called *c-rel* if at least one e belonging to e-c_1 is rel with at least one e belonging to e-c_2.

D5.10.   A mgn (msgn) is called *c-isolated* if it is not c-rel with any different mgn (msgn).

D5.11.   Two bhs are called *connected* if they have common members.

T5.1.   rel is a reflexive and symmetric relation, i.e., a similarity.

T5.2.   The mbhs are the similarity-circles with respect to rel.

T5.3.   Every e (s) belongs to at least one mbh (msbh).

T5.4. $Rel'e_1 = Rel'e_2$ if (but not only if) e_1 and e_2 are isg.

T5.5. $sRel's_1 = sRel's_1$ if (but not only if) s_1 and s_2 are isg.

T5.6.   If gn_1 and gn_2 are c-rel then every e belonging to gn_1 is rel with every e belonging to gn_2.

T5.7.   If two es are isg then they are rel. Every gn is a bh.

T5.8.   The sum of n c-rel gna is a bh.

T5.9.   The sum of n c-rel mgna is a mbh if and only if no different mgn is c-rel with every one of the n mgna.

T5.10.   Every mbh can be uniquely described as a sum of n ($\geq$ 1) mgna.

T5.11.   The product of n mbhs, every two of which are connected, is either the null-c of es or a sum of m ($\geq$ 1) mgna.

T5.12. $Rel'e_1$ is identical with the unit-c of e_1 if and only if e_1 is completely isolated.

T5.13. $Gen'e_1$ is a sub-c of $Rel'e_1$.

T5.14. $Gen'e_1 = Rel'e_1$ if and only if $Gen'e_1$ is c-isolated.

T5.15.   All sts are rel.

T5.16.   The c of all sts is a mbh.

Whereas the definitions of this section show considerable analogy to those of Section 3, the analogy with respect to the theorems is much smaller, owing to the non-transitivity of rel. This analogy will be restored by introducing the relation sib in Section 7.

6. T6.1.   There are exactly six non-trivial pairs of c-rel msgna in C_1, viz:

$msgn_1$, $msgn_3$ $msgn_1$, $msgn_7$ $msgn_2$, $msgn_5$

$msgn_2$, $msgn_6$ $msgn_4$, $msgn_5$ $msgn_5$, $msgn_6$.

T6.2.   There are exactly seven non-trivial pairs of c-rel mgna in C_1, viz: the six pairs of mgna corresponding to the six pairs of msgna mentioned in T6.1 and, in addition:

$$msgn_{16}, \ msgn_{17},$$

i.e., the pair of the two st-mgna.

T6.3.   There are exactly six msbhs in C_1, viz:

$msbh_1 = msgn_1 + msgn_3$ $msbh_2 = msgn_1 + msgn_7$

$msbh_3 = msgn_2 + msgn_5 + msgn_6$ $msbh_4 = msgn_4 + msgn_5$

$msbh_5 = msgn_8$ $msbh_6 = msgn_9$

T6.4.   There is only one completely isolated e in C_1, viz: 'g'.

T6.5.   There are exactly two c-isolated msgna in C_1, viz: $msgn_8$ and $msgn_9$.

7. Theory of families. Definitions and theorems.

D7.1. e_1 and e_2 are called *sib* if there exists a rel-chain between them, i.e., a series of n (≥ 0) es, $e_{j_1}, e_{j_2}, ..., e_{j_n}$ such that e_1 is rel with e_{j_1}, e_{j_1} with $e_{j_2}, ..., e_{j_{(n-1)}}$ with e_{j_n}, e_{j_n} with e_2.

D7.2.   A c of es is called a *fy* if every two es belonging to this c are sib.

D7.3.   A fy is called a *mfy* if no e belonging to this fy is sib with an e not belonging to it.

D7.4.   A fy is called a *sfy* if all es belonging to it are ss.

D7.5.   A sfy is called a *msfy* if no s belonging to this sfy is sib with a s not belonging to it.

D7.6.   The c of all es sib with an e_1 is called *Fam'e_1*.

D7.7.   A fy is called *generated* by e_1 if this fy is identical with Fam'e_1.

D7.8.   The c of all ss sib with a s_1 is called *sFam's$_1$*.

D7.9.   Two cs of es are called *c-sib* if at least one e belonging to the one is sib with an e belonging to the other.

T7.1.   sib is an equivalence.

T7.2.   The mfys are the abstractive cs with respect to sib.

T7.3.   Different mfys have no members in common.

T7.4.   Every e(s) belongs to exactly one mfy (msfy).

T7.5.   Fam'e_1 is a mfy.

T7.6.   Fam'e_1 = Fam'e_2 if and only if e_1 and e_2 are sib.

T7.7.   sFam's$_1$ is a msfy.

T7.8.   sFam's$_1$ = sFam's$_2$ if and only if s_1 and s_2 are sib.

T7.9.   Every mfy is generated by any of its members.

T7.10.   If two es are rel then they are sib. Every bh is a fy.

T7.11.   If gn_1 and gn_2 are c-sib then every e belonging to gn_1 is sib with every e belonging to gn_2.

T7.12.   Every gn is a sub-c of exactly one mfy.

T7.13.   The sum of n c-sib gna is a fy.

T7.14.   The sum of n c-sib mgna is a mfy if and only if no different mgn is c-sib with one of the n mgna.

T7.15.   Every mfy can be uniquely described as a sum of n (≥ 1) c-sib mgna.

T7.16.   Fam'e_1 is identical with the unit-c of e_1 if and only if e_1 is completely isolated.

T7.17.   Rel'e_1 is a sub-c of Fam'e_1.

T7.18.   Gen'e_1 = Fam'e_1 if and only if Gen'e_1 is c-isolated.

8. T8.1. There are exactly nine non-trivial pairs of c-sib msgna in C_1, viz., the six pairs mentioned in T6.1 and, in addition:

$$\text{msgn}_3, \text{msgn}_7 \qquad \text{msgn}_2, \text{msgn}_4 \qquad \text{msgn}_4, \text{msgn}_6.$$

T8.2. There are exactly ten non-trivial pairs of c-sib msgna in C_1, viz., the nine pairs of mgna corresponding to the nine pairs of msgna mentioned in T8.1 and, in addition:

$$\text{mgn}_{16}, \text{mgn}_{17}.$$

T8.3. There are exactly four msfys in in C_1, viz:

$$\text{msfy}_1 = \text{msbh}_1 + \text{msbh}_2 = \text{msgn}_1 + \text{msgn}_3 + \text{msgn}_7$$
$$\text{msfy}_2 = \text{msbh}_3 + \text{msbh}_4 = \text{msgn}_2 + \text{msgn}_4 + \text{msgn}_5 + \text{msgn}_6$$
$$\text{msfy}_3 = \text{msbh}_5 = \text{msgn}_8$$
$$\text{msfy}_4 = \text{msbh}_6 = \text{msgn}_9.$$

T8.4. There are exactly eleven mfys in C_1, viz., the four mfys corresponding to the four msfys mentioned in T8.3 and, in addition:

$$\text{mfy}_5 = \text{mgn}_{16} + \text{mgn}_{17},$$

and six more mfys identical with $\text{mgn}_{10}, \text{mgn}_{11}, \text{mgn}_{12}, \text{mgn}_{13}, \text{mgn}_{14}, \text{mgn}_{15}$, respectively.

9. Let C_2 be defined by the following three rules of formation:

RF2–1: identical with RF1–1A.

RF2–2: identical with RF1–2A.

RF2–3 (*Rule of Type-Classification*): 'a', b, c, d, f, are ind-ss, type 0; p, $\hat{q}$, r, t are $^1\text{prs}^1$, type (0); g is a $^1\text{fu}^1$, type (0:0); i, j are $^1\text{prs}^2$, type (0,0); any e isg with one of these twelve ss is ist with it.

Since C_2 differs from C_1 only by containing an additional rule of formation all theorems of C_1 are theorems in C_2. For the sake of simplicity, we shall not distinguish typographically between the corresponding expression-classes whenever misunderstandings will not be likely to arise. Thus, we shall use 'msgn_1' as a sign for that—in C_2 which corresponds to msgn_1 in C_1.

According to RF2–3, all expressions of C_2 belong to one or the other of the 4 types. To the same types belong also several other expressions. But there are expressions in C_2 which do not belong to any type.

T9.1.
$$\text{type } 0 = \text{mfy}_1 \qquad \text{type (0)} = \text{mfy}_2$$
$$\text{type (0:0)} = \text{mfy}_3 \qquad \text{type (0,0)} = \text{mfy}_4.$$

10.   Let C_3 be defined by the following two rules of formation:

RF3-1: The following fourteen ss form the vocabulary of C_3: 'a', b, c, d, f, g, i, j, p, q, r_1, r_2, t_1, t_2.

RF3-2:   The following forty-seven s-sqs only are sts in C_3: 'ap', bp, cq, dq, ar_1, br_1, cr_2, dr_2, at_1, bt_1, ft_2, gaq, gbq, gar_2, gbr_2, cic, (and the rest typographically identical with the sts mentioned in RF1–2A after 'cic').

T10.1.   Every s (of C_3) belongs to exactly one of the following eight msgna:

$$\text{msgn}_1^3, \text{msgn}_3^3, \text{msgn}_7^3, \text{msgn}_8^3, \text{msgn}_9^3,$$

all of them identical with the corresponding msgna in C_1,

$$\text{msgn}_2^3 = \{p, r_1, t_1\}, \text{msgn}_4^3 = \{q, r_2\}, \text{msgn}_6^3 = \{t_2\}.$$

The reader will be able to compile by himself the member-list of the maximum genera of C_3 and to construct the alternative sets of formation-rules for C_3. The pragmatically simplest will consist in a symbol-enumeration, a member-list of mgn_1^3, mgn_2^3, mgn_3^3, mgn_4^3, the rule that 'x $\frown$ y' is a sentence if x belongs to mgn_1^3 or mgn_3^3 and y to mgn_2^3 or mgn_4^3, respectively, and the rule that 'ft_2' is a sentence.

T10.2.   Every mgn in C_3 is c-isolated.

It follows from T10.2 that there is no non-trivial application of the theory of brotherhoods and families in C_3.

11. C_3, though containing the same number of sentences as C_1 and two more symbols, is nevertheless syntactically simpler than C_1, in some sense of the word 'simple.' The procedure which brought us from C_1 to the "simpler" but "equivalent" C_3—the equivalence, in our case, is a reversible transformation with respect to all sentences and an irreversible transformation with respect to all symbols—may be generalized for any C_i. To fix our ideas, let us assume that C_i contains a $^1\text{pr}^1$, pr_1, which forms sentences with arguments belonging to n different maximum genera. Then we can construct the "parallel" C_j which contains n different predicates, instead of pr_1, each of which has arguments belonging to one maximum genus only, so that there should be a one-one correspondence between all the full-sentences of pr_1 in C_i and all the full-sentences of the n predicates in C_j.

12.   Let C_4 be identical with C_3 except in containing an additional type-classification-rule RF4-3, identical with RF2-3, except in assigning to type (0) the symbols 'r_1', 'r_2', 't_1', and 't_2', instead of 'r' and 't'. The thus determined types will be identical with sums of maximum genera, but these sums will no more form maximum families, the trivial cases excepted.

13.   Let C_5 be identical with C_3 except in containing an additional type-classification-rule:

RF5–3: 'a', b are ind-ss, type 0; c, d are ind-ss, type *; f is an ind-s, type □; p, r_1, t_1 are $^1prs^1$, type (0); q, r_2 are $^1prs^1$, type (*); t_2 is a $^1pr^1$, type (□); g is a $^1fu^1$, type (0:*); i, j are $^1prs^2$, type (*,*); any e isg with one of these fourteen ss is ist with it.

In C_5, the various types are identical with some of its maximum genera. There are four *systems of levels* in C_5:

R_1—contains 'a' and b as ^0lev, p, r_1, t_1 as ^1lev;
R_2—contains c and d as ^0lev, q, r_2, i, j as ^1lev;
R_3—contains f as ^0lev, t_2 as ^1lev;
R_4—contains g as ^1lev.

14.   All the five constructed calculi are, to a certain degree, "natural" formalizations of a fragment of ordinary English. The following dictionary will make this clear.:

a	New-York	i	is-divisible-by
b	Chicago	j	is-the-square-of
c	three	p	has-a-harbor
d	nine	g	is prime
f	the-Italian-language	r	is-large
g	the-population-of	t	is-beautiful

The forty-seven sentences of ordinary English corresponding to the forty-seven symbol-sequences mentioned in RF1–2A will probably be the only sentences resulting out of any combination of these twelve expressions recognized by an English grammarian with a logical touch—I mean a grammarian who would not recognize 'Three has a harbor' as a genuine English sentence.

15.   The construction of calculi "conforming as far as possible to ordinary languages" is certainly a task of exceptional importance. This does not mean that we should try to construct a series of calculi converging toward an ordinary language. We cannot do that, because the goal itself is changing, ambiguous, and vague, in current slogans, because ordinary languages are "dynamic" and calculi are "static". The divergence of even the best approximations will therefore be quite considerable, though we cannot estimate its degree, for the time being.

It is obvious that this approximation is a multi-dimensional affair. It is quite possible that we should be able to construct calculi which approximate an ordinary language *in some respect* in the highest imaginable degree— but then, they might fall short of this goal *in some other respect*. It should turn out to be rather difficult to define the degree of approximation in such a manner that calculi belonging to different lines of approach should be comparable.

Our five model calculi illustrate some of the different possible approaches with regard to the formulation of the rules of formation. The usual higher functional calculi have a rather low degree of approximation to ordinary languages, since, for instance, all individual symbols in them belong to the same type and the same genus[6]. If such a calculus should be rich enough to contain the equivalents of the 'Caesar is great' and 'three is prime' and if 'is great' and 'is prime' are to be both ^{1}prs^1 in it (which would be the case in a calculus where number expressions as well as names of men are individual symbols), then 'Caesar is prime' will be a meaningful sentence in it. This does not deprive such calculi of their value, and there need not be any disastrous consequences of recognizing the meaningfulness of 'Caesar is prime.' All we can say is that, on the rather doubtful assumption that such word combinations are commonly regarded as "meaningless," calculi of this kind would give a rather poor approximation to ordinary languages; and even this only if explicit definitions alone are allowed in them. In this case, namely, the predicate 'is prime' will be defined, say, by 'x is prime if and only if x is a natural number divisible, without remainder, only by itself and by 1,' which would cause 'Caesar is prime' to be a meaningful false sentence. So would be 'Caesar is compound' — 'prime' and 'compound' would not be contradictory properties. 'Caesar is not prime' and 'Caesar is not compound' would both be meaningful true sentences. But even these consequences, hardly acceptable to common sense, the monopolist of ordinary languages, though theoretically completely harmless by themselves, can be avoided by allowing conditional definitions of *bilateral reduction*

---

[6] I am not sure whether the geometrical calculus dealt with by Hilbert-Ackermann, **Grundzüge der theoretischen Logik**, 2nd ed., p. 82, is an exception. This model-calculus contains two ^{1}prs$_2$: '$\Lambda(x,y)$' ('x lies on y'), where x belong to the maximum genus of point-names and y belongs to the maximum genus of straight-line names, and '$\equiv(x,y)$', the predicate of identity, where x and y may belong to both maximum genera. "Of course, the assertion of the identity of a point with a straight line is always to be regarded as false." But there are no hints as to whether we are to look on the symbol sequence '$\Lambda(x,y)$' where, say, both variables belong to the maximum genus of point-names as an always false sentence or as a non-sentence. In the first case, all individual expressions would be not only isotypous but also isogenous; in the second case, the two maximum genera forming the type of individual expressions would be class-related.

Later on, pp. 83ff., Hilbert and Ackermann show how to construct for every calculus which contains more than one domain of individual expressions an equivalent calculus with one domain of individual expressions only.

Cf. also A. Schmidt, *Über deduktive Theorien mit mehreren Sorten von Grunddingen*, **Mathematische Annalen** vol. 115 (1938), pp. 485–506.

sentences [23:442–443]. If one introduces 'is prime' by, say, 'if x is a natural number then x is prime if and only if x is divisible, without remainder, only by itself and by 1', then 'Caesar is prime,' though not meaningless, would be paralyzed, and neither truth nor falsehood could be predicated of this sentence, so long, at least, as 'is prime' is not further introduced by other bilateral reduction sentences.

The first line of approach to increasing the degree of approximation of the usual higher functional calculi to ordinary languages would therefore consist in allowing for more liberal types of definitions while keeping the principle that all individual expressions may serve as arguments for all $^1\mathrm{prs}^1$, in other words, that all symbol sequences of the design $^1\mathrm{pr}^1$ (ind-e) should be sentences. Bilateral reduction sentences would be the starting point in this line, then would come reduction pairs, then perhaps definitions in which the conditional and biconditional symbols will be replaced by the corresponding probability connectives, etc. [73].

Another line might start from abandoning the stipulation that all individual expressions should belong to the same maximum genus, while insisting on their belonging to the same type. Several maximum genera would then correspond to the same type, and according to whether individual expressions belonging to different maximum genera can serve as argument-expressions to the same $^1\mathrm{pr}$ or not, we shall get different kinds of calculi, exemplified by our C_4 and C_2. Abolishing the type distinctions altogether and transferring their function to the maximum genera, as exemplified by C_3, or to the maximum brotherhoods, as exemplified by C_1, would mean a further loosening of the chains imposed on calculi by their adherence to the customary rule of types, but the dangers of this approach are only too well known. Abandoning the stipulation that all individual expressions should belong to the same type, on the other hand, and working with several systems of levels would give another point of departure, but this line, exemplified by C_5, might perhaps converge with the C_3-line. The maximum genus classification is, of course, more comprehensive than the type classification, since the latter applies usually to individual expressions, predicates, and functors only, whereas the former applies to all expressions, indifferently, but whether the relevant classes of individual expressions, predicates, and functors are called maximum genera or types is a matter of name giving only, so long as they fulfil exactly the same syntactical functions.

Complete abolishment of type distinctions might be approximated by changing the customary rule of types so as to allow for infinite types, for typeless variables[7] (restricted by some other means), etc.

---

[7] Cf. [26: Section 12], with further references there.

We may summarize as follows: The usual calculi deviate from ordinary languages by being both more liberal and more strict than are ordinary languages. The customary rule of types denies sentence character to many symbol sequences whose analogues in ordinary language would normally be looked upon as meaningful sentences. And though this restriction is apparently not too serious, since it is possible to find ways to reproduce important sentences of an ordinary language, ostracized by the type rule, through some artificial device — "artificial" from the point of view of common sense — such as translation from the material mode of speech to the formal mode etc., it is worth while to explore calculi with looser rules. On the other hand, restriction to type classification only lends sentence character to many symbol sequences whose analogues in ordinary language would now normally looked upon as meaningless word sequences. And though the effects of this liberalism are apparently not too serious, either, since the "superfluous" sentences are of no scientific importance (Who cares whether 'Caesar is prime' is true, false, or meaningless? What matters is not the syntactical character of this word sequence but only the syntactical decisions which might be entailed by any convention regarding this point.) and can be immobilized by allowing bilateral reduction sentences, it is worthwhile to explore calculi with additional stricter classifications.

The naturalness of this approach has been exemplified, I hope, by the investigation of the five formalizations of a living part of the English language. The fact that such an extremely rudimentary language torso shows syntactical structures which, in some respects, exceed in their complexity the most developed higher functional calculi shows clearly the vastness of the task which stands before the modern logician in this field.

16.   The theory of syntactical categories has been developed in accordance with the procedures of general syntax. We assumed that a set of formation-rules was given which defined 'sentence in C.' In case this term should turn out to be indefinite for a certain calculus, the syntactical categories defined with the help of 'sentence' would be indefinite too.

The procedure in the construction of some special calculus will normally be the inverse. One starts from a classification of the symbols—up to now, usually into types—, defines 'elementary sentences' as certain ordered sequences of symbols belonging to certain symbol classes, determines a set of operations for the formation of sentences, and finally defines 'sentence' as the result of a finite number of applications of these operations on the elementary sentences.

The aim of a calculus construction will normally be the formalization of a certain body of knowledge, whether already systematized as a semantical system or in a presystematic, more or less vague and ambiguous status. (Only exceptionally will a calculus be constructed without such an interpretation in mind, and then usually for didactical purposes only, "model calculi" such as our calculi.) In the latter case, it is not always determined from the outset which word sequences shall be "meaningful", and still less which sentences shall be valid. We may concentrate here on the latter case, because in the former one, analogous problems arise with regard to the construction of the semantical systems. Very often, not the intention that certain sequences shall be meaningful will direct our construction of the rules of sentence-formation and thereby indirectly the classification of the symbols, but rather the intention that certain symbols shall belong to the same genus will direct our construction of the rules of classification and thereby indirectly the rules of sentence-formation.

To give an example: Should somebody be interested in having in a calculus which he is about to construct the literal equivalent of 'James is the black sheep of his family' as a sentence, but to deny this syntactical property to the equivalent of 'James is the green sheep of his family,' he would have to lay down formation-rules from which it will follow that the equivalents of 'black' and 'green' will not be isogenous. Should, on the other hand, somebody be interested in constructing a calculus in which 'black' and 'green' will belong to the same genus, for certain intuitive reasons perhaps, his decision to this effect would entail one of the following alternative decisions: Either both of the above-mentioned 'James'-sentences may have their equivalents recognized as sentences or neither. Another possibility would be to look on 'black' in 'black sheep' as a word different from the normal 'black' but homonymous with it, and to render its equivalent by a symbol syntactically distinguishable from the equivalent of the normal 'black.' Still another way would be to look on 'black sheep' as a single symbol not to be divided and to render its equivalent accordingly. This last possibility is superior to the former in so far as it disposes at the same time of analogous difficulties which will arise in connection with 'sheep.' (What about 'James is the black fly of his family'?)

The usual intuitive background of a calculus construction will probably be a mixed one: One will be interested in having certain symbols in the same genus and, at the same time, in having certain symbol sequences recognized as sentences and others deprived of this character. These intuitions may be consistent and therefore realizable in a consistent calculus, but it may turn out that they are not. We have already seen some possible resolutions of this often occurring state of affairs.

17. As far as I know, there exists no satisfactory analysis of the reasons which lead philosophers, or even ordinary people, to declare certain "gram-

matically impeccable" sentences as "logically meaningless." The purpose of avoiding antinomies explains only a small part of these decisions, but is not a sufficent reason for ostracizing either 'Caesar is prime' or 'This stone is now thinking about Vienna'—this is clear from the fact that the latter sentence, for instance, was looked upon as meaningless by the members of the Vienna Circle twenty years ago, but was regarded as meaningful, though factually false, by Carnap, ten years later [23:5]. This lack of analysis is perhaps the cause of that strange assertion of a well-known modern philosopher [144:198]: "Thus the proposition "Caesar is a prime number" is not only untrue but meaningless." Would he also have said that "Caesar is not a prime number" is not only true but meaningless? The mere fact that this word-sequence is looked upon as fantastic, as absurd to the highest possible degree, since its terms are taken from widely different domains or universes of discourse, that this combination sins against our sense of plausibility and intelligibility —all these reasons together are still insufficent to declare it as meaningless [144:647–648, 651].[8]

I think that in the verdict "meaningless" is embodied much more than

---

[8] It is very hard to reconcile the various apparently contradictory evaluations which Urban gives of this sentence. The confusion seems to me symptomatic of the still prevalent neglect of the all-important distinction between pragmatical description of certain linguistic usages and the syntactical (or semantical) proposals to reform or unify these usages by construction of artificial language-systems.

Here are two more examples of confusions arising out of this neglect which have immediate relevence to our subject.

In his article *Meaningfulness*, **Mind**, vol. 46 (1937), pp. 347–364, A. C. Ewing opposes the generally held view that statements such as 'Quadratic equations go to race meetings' or 'Virtue is a fire-shovel' are meaningless. He is right in so far as calculi may be constructed in which the corresponding symbol-sequences will be sentences. But when he continues to assert dogmatically that these statements are self-contradictory, he is wrong, when his assertion is interpreted pragmatically as a description of common usage, since this usage is far from being univocal in this respect—no statistical investigations have been made, as far as I know, but I am sure that each of the mutually exclusive predicates 'meaningless,' 'self-contradictory,' and 'factually false' will find its followers among common people and philosophers alike—, and this interpretation is the only possible one in our case.

In conformance with the three mentioned possible evaluations, various language-systems may be constructed in which the corresponding symbol-sequences will have *one* of these properties. A discussion of the advantages and disadvantages of these language-systems will be important and fruitful, but only when held without any dogmatic prejudices.

Belief in the uniqueness of a "logical grammar" corresponding to a given language leads Josef Schaechter to make several mistakes in his otherwise interesting and stimulating book **Prolegomena zu einer kritischen Grammatik**, Vienna, 1935. On this assumption is based his distinction between "essential" and "inessential" grammatical rules, between that. It is not merely a pragmatical statement of fact, it is a *decision*: He who gives this verdict declares by it that he is ready not to bother about the semantical properties of a certain word-sequence and simultaneously advises his hearers or readers to do the same. Expanded, his verdict would be: "Don't bother about the truth or falsity of 'Casear is a prime number'— it's useless, a waste of time. There are many more important things to do, many real problems to solve. This word-sequence looks like a sentence, I admit, and I tried hard to find some possibility of confirming or disconfirming it, but I failed completely and see no chance that somebody else might have better luck. So hark to me and spend your time on other investigations." I believe that this economy factor is the important one. Against the postulate of syntactical liberalism to allow foι a maximum of word combinations stands the postulate of pragmatical ecconomy to narrow down the liberty of combinations to such sequences as can possibly be confirmed[9] (in addition, of course, to analytic and contradictory sentences). Where to draw the limit, how to find the compromise, these are, of course, matters for practical decision. It is the task of the general semiotic to supply the tools for the

the "grammar of significance" and the "grammar of material." Starting from these distinctions, he concludes that there are not only linguistic usages which are impeccable according to usual grammar but which are meaningless word-sequences according to his logical grammar (p. 26)—his examples 'I am travelling into the past,' 'Virtue is triangular,' 'The leaf wishes,' show, incidentally, that Schaechter fails to make the important distinction between symbol-sequences which are not in conformance with the rules of formation of the language dealt with and symbol-sequences which are sentences whose falseness follows from the semantical rules alone, a distinction which corresponds roughly to that stressed already by Husserl under the names 'nonsense' ('Unsinn') and 'countersense' ('Widersinn')—, but that there are also logically impeccable usages which are nevertheless incorrect according to usual grammatical standards, since they sin against "inessential" rules. This remark is valuable so long as we bear in mind its relativity to the language-systems chosen for this comparison, but Schaechter's insistence on the absoluteness of his "logical grammar" leads him astray.

His example for a logically correct but grammatically incorrect sentence is: "Die Mädchen gehte auf dem Strasse." He points out that this word-sequence, in spite of its three grammatical mistakes, i.e., 'die' instead of 'das,' 'gehte' instead of 'ging,' 'dem' instead of 'der,' is a logically impeccable sentence, since all these mistakes are "inessential".

But how does Schaechter know that the utterer of the original word-sequence intended to say (or write) "Das Mädchen ging auf der Strasse" rather than "Die Mädchen gingen auf der Strasse," or "Das Mädchen geht auf der Strasse," or "Das Mädchen ging auf dem Strand," or just anything else you like, meaningful or meaningless? The original word-sequence is neither grammatically nor logically meaningful, and there is nothing in it which points to its meaningful substitute. But as soon as certain pragmatical considerations induce me to replace it by some logically meaningful sentence, *this* sentence will be meaningful also grammatically.

  9 Or, for a non-empiricist, can possibly be of some importance (in a certain sense to be specified).

erection of the various signposts,[10] to show what decisions are entailed by certain syntactical conventions. I should formulate the attitude of the scientific semiotician, as it should be in my opinion, in the following statements: "If you intend to construct the language of science according to this form of the empiricist principle of confirmability, then certain symbol sequences will be sentences. Are you interested in letting people ask questions about these symbol-sequences and in bothering about problems connected with them? If not, then you have to accept a stricter form of this principle. In this case certain symbol sequences will *not* be sentences. Are you interested in forbidding the asking of a question of this design? If not, then you will have to accept a more liberal form. Or, perhaps, you want to leave the question open and to construct two alternative language-systems, for the time being, until final decision? Whatever your choice, you can avail yourself of our tools and methods."

I have formulated the semiotician's attitude towards an empirical scientist who aims at formalizing a certain body of knowledge. But, of course, this attitude will not change in principle even when a metaphysician asks his advice when starting to construct a general theory of being or something else. As an empiricist, I think the former case the far more important and fruitful, but I wonder what formal grounds could make me judge the metaphysician's theory a product of "bad syntax," "a disease of ordinary language," etc. These expressions have been in favor with logical empiricists for a long time, but it seems that they have been abandoned by most of them. Russell, on the other hand, continues to use them [132:157,831]. According to him, 'The moon is one' is bad syntax, so is 'Scott exists.' Attribution of numbers to individuals instead of to individual properties and of existence to individuals designated by proper names instead of to individuals designated by definite descriptions is declared nonsense. If we interpret these assertions to mean that a semantical system can be constructed, in sufficient connection with ordinary language, in which the corresponding symbol sequences will not be sentences, thus avoiding all the annoying consequences and inconsistencies resulting from their recognition as sentences, then Frege and Russell himself have shown these assertions to be true. This minimum interpretation hardly justifies the use of the term "bad syntax" with its heavy emotional load. But if we are to interpret these assertions to mean that no consistent semantical system can be constructed, in which the corresponding symbol sequences will be sentences—and this interpretation seems to be the natural one—, then they are plainly false. The well-known undesirable logical (and metaphysical, for some people) consequences of the recognition of their sentence-

---

[10] This happy term is Reichenbach's.

character are due not only to this act but also to the acceptance of other syntactical rules commonly regarded as valid in ordinary language. But we may clearly change these rules or drop some of them altogether as well as the rules of the use of number expressions or 'exists.'

I come now to my final remark. It is not the case that a certain theory is false, inconsistent, or even meaningless because it is based on a logical blunder of accepting a meaningless symbol sequence as a sentence—this is apparently still the point of view of Russell—, but rather certain undesirable semiotical features of a theory such as its inconsistency or the inconfirmability of some (or all) of its sentences may lead us to construct a semantical system in which certain symbol sequences will not be sentences, thus avoiding the formulation of those expressions which lead us to the undesirable feature without reducing thereby its desirable properties This may be done in various ways, and I hope that my theory of syntactical categories will add some efficient tools for the erection of the various semiotical signposts.

Logical Syntax and Semantics* | 2

Though considerations of meaning in linguistics can be replaced, up to a point, by rigorous STRUCTURAL procedures, i.e. procedures involving solely the kinds and order of the elements of the language under investigation, they cannot be replaced by DISTRIBUTIONAL procedures, despite the claim recently made by Harris [62: 8, n. 7]. Distributional procedures may be sufficient to establish the rules by which all longer expressions (especially sentences) can be constructed out of the elements, but they are inadequate for the establishment of certain other rules that would mirror the so-called logical properties and relations of sentences and other expressions.

It is worth while to quote at this point what the logician Rudolf Carnap had to say on this topic some twenty years ago [24: 1–2]:

> By the *logical syntax* of a language, we mean the formal theory of the linguistic forms of that language—the systematic statement of the formal rules which govern it together with the development of the consequences which follow from these rules.
>
> A theory, a rule, a definition, or the like is to be called *formal* when no reference is made in it either to the meaning of the symbols (for example, the words) or to the sense of the expressions (e.g. the sentences), but simply and solely to the kinds and order of the symbols from which the expressions are constructed.
>
> The prevalent opinion is that syntax and logic, in spite of some points of contact between them, are fundamentally theories of a very different type. The syntax of a language is supposed to lay down rules according to which the linguistic structures (e.g. the sentences) are to be built up from the elements (such as words or parts of words). The chief task of logic, on the other hand, is supposed to be that of formulating rules according to which judgments may be inferred from other judgments; in other words according to which conclusions may be drawn from premises.

---

* First appeared in **Language**, vol. 30 (1954), pp. 230–237.

But the development of logic during the past ten years has shown clearly that it can only be studied with any degree of accuracy when it is based, not on judgments (thoughts, or the content of thoughts) but rather on linguistic expressions, of which sentences are the most important, because only for them is it possible to lay down sharply defined rules. And actually, in practice, every logician since Aristotle, in laying down sharply defined rules, has dealt mainly with sentences. But even those modern logicians who agree with us in our opinion that logic is concerned with sentences, are yet for the most part convinced that logic is equally concerned with the relations of meaning between sentences. They consider that, in contrast with the rules of syntax, the rules of logic are non-formal. In the following pages, in opposition to this standpoint, the view that logic, too, is concerned with the *formal* treatment of sentences will be presented and developed. We shall see that the logical characteristics of sentences (for instance, whether a sentence is analytic, synthetic or contradictory; whether it is an existential sentence or not; and so on) and the logical relations between them (for instance, whether two sentences contradict one another or are compatible with one another; whether one is logically deducible from the other or not; and so on) are solely dependent upon the syntactical structure of the sentences. In this way, logic will become a part of syntax, provided that the latter is conceived in a sufficiently wide sense and formulated with exactitude. The difference between syntactical rules in the narrower sense and the logical rules of deduction is only the difference between *formation rules* and *transformation rules,* both of which are completely formulable in syntactical terms. Thus we are justified in designating as 'logical syntax' the system which comprises the rules of formation and transformation.

What Carnap in 1934 called 'the prevalent opinion' continues to be prevalent among contemporary linguists. The establishment of the 'statements which enable anyone to synthesize or predict utterances in the language' [62:372] is still regarded as the sole aim of descriptive linguistics, 'as the term has come to be used' [62:5]; Fries's recent book **The Structure of English** [55] has the subtitle *An introduction to the construction of English sentences.* It is the rules of formation which have caught the exclusive attention of the structural linguist[1]; the rules of transformation continue to

---

1 The term 'structural linguist' is used throughout this paper to mean 'some American structural linguists', of whom Bloch, Harris, Hockett, Smith, and Trager are a representative sample.

be relegated—with one notable exception, to be mentioned presently—to the limbo of an extra-linguistic logic.

This unfortunate disregard of Carnap's conception of a LOGICAL SYNTAX is not entirely the linguists' fault. Carnap himself and the logicians who followed his lead were too preoccupied with constructed language systems to devote much time and effort to an application of their views to the description of ordinary languages. Carnap even believed [24:2] that 'the statement of the formal rules of formation and transformation [of natural languages] would be so complicated that it would hardly be feasible in practice'. This belief is certainly correct for a COMPLETE statement of the rules, but fairly good approximations should be achievable with some effort. This effort has been expended, as a matter of fact, for the rules of formation; there is no good reason for not doing the same for the rules of transformation. Indeed, beginnings for such an undertaking exist already; but these are the work of logicians and philosophers, who are often biased by their underlying metaphysical conceptions and their adherence to Aristotelian or Scholastic ways of thinking.

It is the duty of the structural linguist to scrutinize Carnap's conception carefully; after all, Carnap is not a linguist proper. If and when his conception is found to be linguistically sound, as I think it is, we shall have to give up Harris's contention [62:5] that 'the main research of descriptive linguistics, and the only relation which will be accepted as relevant..., is the distribution or arrangement within the flow of speech of some parts or features relative to others'. Instead, LOGICAL ANALYSIS, based upon the relation of DIRECT CONSEQUENCE [24:170] will have to be given equal rights with DISTRIBUTIONAL ANALYSIS.

This will entail, of course, a radical change in the official conception of elicitation techniques. Until now the informant has been required only to supply repetitions of sound sequences, to judge whether two sound-sequences are the same or not, to tell whether certain sound-sequences are sentences or not, and to determine whether 'two items are the "same" in a particular aspect of meaning or "different"' [62: 8, n.6]. It now becomes necessary to develop techniques of elicitation for logical analysis which will have the same degree of reliability and validity as those developed for distributional analysis. Direct questioning ('Do *oculist* and *eye-doctor* mean the same to you?') may serve as a first approximation, to be replaced in time by more objective methods. Notice that Harris himself indicates, at one place, an elicitation technique to this effect when he says, 'one can read the text sentence... in company with an informant, and then stop and say to him, in an expectant and hesitant way, "That is to say,...," waiting for him to supply the continuation' [62:20, n. 13]. However, Harris seems not to be aware that what he gets from the informant by this technique is much more than information about distribution. Since structural linguists have no doubt been using such techniques in their practical work, it is of utmost importance that they make these techniques explicit, become aware of their theoretical function, and analyze and improve upon them.

Most structural linguists seem to have recognized that not all aspects of linguistics can be handled by distributional analysis alone; but there is one who attempted the seemingly impossible. Wishing to exploit this kind of analysis to its utmost, Harris has claimed that he can describe in purely distributional terms both synonymy relations (say between *oculist* and *eye-doctor*) and the active-passive relationship (say between *plays* and *is played by*); and he would probably undertake, if challenged, to do the same with respect to the difference between Latin *aut* and *vel*. According to his basic postulate [62: 7, n. 4], 'It may be presumed that any two morphemes having different meanings also differ somewhere in distribution'. It would then seem to follow that any two morphemes with the same distribution have the same meaning. If we were to grant these presumptions, then indeed many of the transformational aspects of language, if not all of them, would be reducible to the formational aspects. But in spite of some initial plausibility, the presumptions are false. Whatever conviction they carry is due to the fact that many of the terms involved are equivocal. It will be worth while to analyze some of these equivocations.

The first is *language* itself. This term is sometimes understood as the totality of all possible sentence-types (or utterance-types), sometimes as the totality of all actually uttered sentence-tokens,[2] or perhaps as the totality of all sentence-tokens that have been uttered or will be uttered until the extinction of the users of this language.

Now if we consider a language as the totality of all possible sentence-types, Harris's presumption is clearly false. *Green* and *red* are surely different morphemes, but their distribution within this totality (with respect to English, of course) is ALMOST exactly the same, i.e. the same up to a subset of special environments which will cause trouble to any consistent and would-be simple description. This subset, to use a fitting mathematical metaphor—which is meant, however, more to help us dodge the problem than to solve it—, is of measure zero. It would contain, for instance, the environments -*horn*, into which only *green* would fit but not *red*, and -*skin*, into which only *red* would fit but not *green*. Except for such cases, within the totality of all possible

---

[2] Following the usage of Charles S. Peirce, a SIGN-TYPE is the abstract class of all concrete SIGN-TOKENS which (by some criterion) belong-to-the-same-type (Chapter 5 and [32:45, n. 13]).

sentence-types, there is for any sentence containing *red* a (significant) sentence that contains *green* instead, and vice versa.

However, if we take a language to be the totality of all sentence-tokens uttered up to a certain time (or alternatively, the totality of all sentence-types of which tokens have been uttered up to a certain time), then—disregarding a coincidence of cosmic dimensions—no two morphemes will show the same distribution. For this interpretation Harris's presumption would indeed turn out to be true, but in such a trivial fashion that it can hardly be what he meant. The relations between *oculist* and *eye-doctor*, *oculist* and *dentist*, *oculist* and *beauty*, *oculist* and *green* are four different types, each of which must be the concern of the structural linguist. To state only that within a given totality of sentence-tokens all these morphemes exhibit different distributions is surely not the whole truth—in fact only a small part of it. Even to state that *oculist*, *eye-doctor* and *dentist* have almost equal distribution within the totality of all sentence-types, whereas *oculist* and *beauty* have overlapping distribution, and *oculist* and *green* have almost exclusive distribution, though incomparably more revealing, still misses the essential difference between the first two pairs. Sameness of distribution, within the type-totality, is perhaps a necessary but certainly not a sufficient condition for sameness of meaning; hence, difference of meaning is perhaps a necessary but certainly not a sufficient condition for difference of distribution, with respect to the same totality.

Since 'sameness of distribution' and 'sameness of meaning' are certainly not convenient terms, other terms are usually employed instead. Here, however, another equivocation becomes effective. *Oculist* and *dentist* are SUBSTITUTABLE in the sense that any[3] sentence containing the one will turn into a sentence (not necessarily a sentence with the same meaning or even with the same truth-value) when this is replaced by the other. *Oculist* and *eye-doctor* are substitutable in the sense that any sentence containing the one will turn into a sentence with necessarily the same truth-value when this is replaced by the other. For both these essentially different relations the term *substitutable* (or *replaceable*, or *commutable*, or even *equivalent*) is used indifferently, more often than not without even a qualifying adverbial. A consistent use of qualifiers like *distributionally* and *logically* (or, more fancifully, *salva significatione* and *salva veritate*) could assist in avoiding the pitfalls connected with this equivocation; but a convention to use, say, *commutable* for the first sense and *interchangeable* for the second, would be even better.

There has recently been a lively discussion of the degree of interdependence

---

[3] From now on the qualifier *almost* will be omitted.

of the various structural 'layers' [117]. It seems to me that part of the purists' insistence on a sharp demarcation between phonology and grammar is based on the assumption that a treatment of the syntactical-transformational aspects of language is in constant danger of succumbing to an infestation by meaning, an evil from which those aspects of language that can be shown to be independent of syntax can be saved. Indeed, so long as syntax, as traditionally handled, was a MEANING SYNTAX, it was methodologically worth while to adopt the procedure of Trager and Smith in **An Outline of English Structure** (1951), which, based upon purely distributional analysis, rigidly discriminates between ascending levels of complexity of organization. If only one could establish phonemics without recourse to grammar, the danger of letting semantic considerations creep in would be considerably reduced if not completely eliminated. I believe that some of the attractiveness of this attitude is reduced by recognizing that a description of the transformational aspects of syntax can be just as free of meaning as other parts of a linguistic treatment.

The fear of allowing meaning to intrude is of course only one reason for the sharp-level approach. Another, probably more important, is the fear of circularity. If (say) the term 'morpheme' is used in the definition of the phoneme, and vice versa, then certainly this procedure looks viciously circular, and the logical soundness of the science that uses such definitions is gravely jeopardized. Pike, however, has given sound reasons why this fear, in its generalized form, is groundless. Moreover, it is possible to show that certain types of concept introductions which look circular are not so in fact—types in which the elimination of the newly introduced term does not involve an infinite regress. As a matter of fact, concept formations of these kinds are in regular use in mathematics, and especially in mathematical logic, where they are known as special cases of RECURSIVE DEFINITIONS. It seems rather likely (though a detailed proof would require many man-hours of work) that Pike's nine-step procedure [107:120] can be formalized and adequately repiesented by a set of such definitions. Since I have treated this topic elsewhere at some length [3], I shall say no more here.

It is an interesting fact, deserving the attention of sociologists of science, that at approximately the same time, but in complete independence of each other, Bloomfield and Carnap were fighting the psychologism that dominated their respective fields, linguistics and logic. They both deplored the mentalistic mud into which the study of meanings had fallen, and tried to reconstruct their fields on a purely formal-structural basis. I think it is correct to say that the difference between the structural linguist and the formal logician is one of stress and degree rather than of kind. Both are essentially attempting to construct language systems that stand in some correspondence to natural languages—though most linguists would say that they are just describing the latter. But whereas for the linguist the closeness of this correspondence is the criterion by which he will judge the adequacy of the language system he is setting up, which alone entitles him to consider himself as describing a given natural language, the logician will look primarily for other features of his system, such as simplicity of handling, fruitfulness for science, and ease of deduction and computation, with close correspondence to a natural language as only a secondary desideratum. Constructed language systems are judged by the linguist according to the degree to which they approximate a natural language; natural languages are judged by the logician according to the degree to which they approximate efficient, well constructed language systems.

I have gone into these generalities in order to emphasize the following point. A few years after Carnap's elaborate attempt to show that prima facie semantic considerations can be satisfactorily mirrored in formal syntax, he reversed himself completely, reintroduced semantics into logic, and dedicated to it most of his later studies [25; 26; 27]. This development is not surprising if we remember that semantics was no longer, by this time, the hodgepodge that went under this name in the first quarter of our century and so much repelled Bloomfield. In the early thirties, Polish logicians of the Warsaw-Lwów school—mainly T. Kotarbiński, A. Tarski, and K. Ajdukiewicz—gave this science a foundation which made it fully competitive with LOGICAL SYNTAX. This was achieved both through an extensive and skillful use of the symbolism of mathematical logic, and by deliberately abstracting from the users and usages of the signs under study and considering only their relations to what was signified by them. Bloomfield's strictures against semantics and the use of meaning for linguistic description, though valid against the state of that field at the time he wrote, do not hold against this revitalized science, in the form given to it by Tarski [138;139], Carnap, Quine [126], and others. I have no intention of bridging the abyss between those linguists who STILL use semantic considerations in their analyses and those who use them AGAIN, just as I do not wish to minimize the corresponding difference between philosophers. I believe that only those who have followed the syntactical method to its very end will be able to appraise adequately the status of the new semantics in descriptive linguistics.

My plea for the reintroduction of semantics into the theatre of operations of descriptive linguistics will be strengthened, I think, if we follow Carnap and Quine in showing that the term 'semantics' has been understood, traditionally as well as by the Polish school of logicians, to contain two rather separate theories with two different sets of concepts. The one theory deals with the INTENSIONAL or CONNOTATIONAL aspects of language or other sign systems, i.e. MEANING (in a restricted sense of this word), the other with the EXTENSIONAL, DENOTATIONAL, or REFERENTIAL aspects. Carnap calls them[4] THEORY OF INTENSION and THEORY OF EXTENSION respectively, Quine calls them [124] THEORY OF MEANING and THEORY OF REFERENCE. The first member of each pair deals with such concepts as logical truth, logical equivalence, and synonymy; the second member deals with truth, equality in truth-value, and coextensiveness. To find out whether a given statement is logically true, whether two statements are logically equivalent, or whether two expressions are synonymous, one needs to know only their intension (connotation, meaning); to find out whether a certain statement is true, whether two statements have the same truth-value, or whether two expressions are coextensive, one must also make detailed observations, or rely on experience. But it is certainly not the linguist's business, or for that matter the logician's, to find these things out. That *morning star* and *evening star* are coextensive (denote the same physical entity) is hardly of interest to the logician qua logician or to the linguist qua linguist; it is, rather, the astronomer's duty to find this out. Whether the statement *All cats have tails* is true is certainly not an exclusively linguistic problem, but rather one for the zoologist.

A linguist who decides that it is not his concern to find out which English statements are true and which English expressions are coextensive is fully justified; he can safely disregard these (pseudo)-semantic aspects of language. Some linguists, however, have thrown away the baby with the bath water. By totally discarding semantics, they have committed two sins. First, it is very definitely the linguist's concern that *oculist* and *eye-doctor* are not only commutable but synonymous (co-intensive), and a description that contained no statement of this fact would be seriously inadequate. (If this is agreed upon, then it must be equally the linguist's concern to state that from *All Greeks are men* and *Socrates is a Greek*, follows *Socrates is a man*; and he should no longer—except for pragmatic reasons—leave such statements to his colleague the logician.) Secondly, both THEORY OF MEANING (in addition to meaning itself) and THEORY OF REFERENCE (though not reference itself) are of vital importance to him, since—like every other scientist—he has to worry from time to time about methodological questions.

It has been the purport of this paper to establish the following four points. (1) There exists a conception of syntax, due to Carnap, that is purely

---

[4] So far as I know, Carnap has not used these terms in print, but they fit the main argument of [27] and were used by him in correspondence.

formal (structural) and adequate in a sense in which the conception prevalent among American structural linguists is not. This conception entails a certain fusion between grammar and logic, with grammar treating approximately the formational part of syntax and logic its transformational part. The relation of COMMUTABILITY may be sufficient as a basis for formational analysis, but other relations, such as that of formal CONSEQUENCE, must be added for transformational analysis. Since modern techniques of elicitation have been developed mainly with distributional analysis in view, a new approach is required that will yield reliable techniques of elicitation for the establishment of synonymy and the like.

(2) A recent attempt by Harris to reduce the transformational part of syntax to its formational part is based on a series of equivocations in the terms *language, equivalent, commutable,* and their cognates, and so is without foundation.

(3) The tendency exhibited by many contemporary structural linguists to set up sharp demarcation lines between the various linguistic subfields is presumed to be based, first, on the attempt to keep linguistics as far as possible independent of concepts open to the intrusion of meaning and, secondly, on a fear of circularity in the definition of basic terms. But Carnap has shown that even the transformational aspects of syntax can be described without appeal to meaning; and recent methodological studies of concept formation indicate that certain procedures with a circular look are in fact harmless because the terms introduced by them can be finitely eliminated.

(4) The generalized fear of letting meaning intrude into linguistics seems to rest mainly on the fact that in the first quarter of this century the study of meaning was indeed in a bad methodological state. But since then, mainly through the efforts of Polish logicians, semantics has become a well-defined, rigorous field. This change has caused Carnap to reintroduce semantics into logic, and should cause descriptive linguists to follow Carnap's lead[5].

---

[5] For a somewhat different approach to the problems discussed here, see [45].

Idioms*

The number of different word types—where word is understood, for present purposes, to be any letter sequence that may occur in print between spaces (or suitable punctuation marks)—in languages such as English, French, German, or Russian, seems to be of the order of millions. English has about 500,000 lexical entries in its largest dictionary with 2 to 3 "derivatives" per entry on the average. Russian has about 100,000 entries with 10 to 15 derivatives, on the average, per entry. Similarly for the other languages. (One may deplore the nonexistence of any precise counts, or even estimates, of these elementary statistics. It is, however, possible that such counts exist somewhere, without having come to my notice or to the notice of the many linguists I have consulted on this topic.) The number of conceivable word *digrams*, i. e, sequences of two words, in each of these languages would then be of the order of billions. (I am again not aware of any reliable estimates of these.) This means that, unless entirely new principles of information storage and retrieval are discovered, the largest unit with which MT will be able to deal must be a word, in general, although a judicious use of a few hundreds of thousands of larger units might also be taken into consideration.

For existing machinery, a storage of, say, even a million words with suitable coded additional information whose exact nature would depend on the specific method chosen for MT poses a practical problem which has not yet been solved. This is the reason for the attempts either to reduce the size of the machine dictionary (by taking into account that a book or paper dealing with some specific branch of science or technology uses only a small fraction of the total vocabulary), or to deal with units smaller than words (i.e., with "stems" and "affixes," properly defined for MT purposes—the definitions need not coincide with the customary ones) or to do both. It seems, for instance, that, out of a million or so Russian words, less than 50,000 would

---

* First appeared in **Machine translation of languages**, edited by W. N. Locke and A. D. Booth, Technology Press of the Mass. Inst. of Tech., and John Wiley and Sons, Inc., N. Y., London 1955, pp. 183–193 (slightly revised).

cover more than 98 per cent of the words occurring in a mathematical paper, and that these could be treated as a combination of some 5,000 to 6,000 stems with a few dozen affixes, the chopping off of the affix from the word to be performed by the machine itself.

Let us assume then that, by one method or another, a word-by-word machine transformation of a given text from the input language into some output language will be technically feasible in the near future, on a time, cost, and precision scale that can compete with a human translator. The number of possible translations in the output language for a given word in the input language will sometimes be considerable, as can be ascertained from any good bilingual dictionary. For a given sentence in the input language, therefore, there will generally be many suggested word sequences in the output language, with their numbers easily reaching into the billions. However, various methods have been evolved for reducing these numbers to a size that can be handled. I am concerned at the moment not so much with how to select from the huge number of tentative translations the one (or the few) appropriate one (or ones) (cf. Chapter 104, and [6]), as with what to do if *none* of the translations offered is appropriate. When such a situation arises with a human translator, one is likely to explain it by saying that the input-language sentence is somehow *idiomatic,* either grammatically or semantically or both.

I believe that the term *idiom* and its derivatives are very much in need of elucidation, and that thinking in terms of machines will be of great help in this task, as in many other linguistic investigations. Although my remarks here are meant primarily to be a practical contribution in solving MT problems, I hope that the analysis of the concept of *idiom* will also have some theoretical significance.

I do not intend to deal with all the connotations of *idiom* but solely with that expressed in definition 3 of **Webster's Collegiate Dictionary,** 1951, "an expression, in the usage of a language, that is peculiar to itself either in grammatical construction or in having a meaning which cannot be derived as a whole from the conjoined meanings of its elements...". I shall not try to criticize this definition here, since there would hardly be any point in doing so. Let me only stress that an idiom is treated there apparently as an *intralanguage* phenomenon, something occurring within *one* language. Our starting point, however, was that none of the sequences of correspondents (output language translations) of a given input language sentence was a suitable translation; hence we were dealing with an *interlanguage* phenomenon. I maintain that an explication of a *monolingual idiom* might best be given after *bilingual idioms* have been properly understood.

It would be rash, however, to decide that any sentence in a given language is idiomatic, in the sense in which we are interested here if, and only if, none of its word-by-word correspondents, according to some given bilingual dictionary, is a satisfactory translation. This statement may be good enough as a first approximation, but adherence to it would probably cause almost any sentence in the language to be classified as idiomatic. It is therefore certainly too broad a statement. Indeed, the French sentence *C'est un enfant ambitieux* would turn out to be idiomatic, since the correlate sequence that comes closest to being acceptable would be THIS IS A CHILD AMBITIOUS, which is not even grammatical English and obviously not an acceptable translation. Readers who know French might think that I am trying to raise a storm in a waterglass. Though the English sentence is non-grammatical, there can be no doubt at all, they would declare, that the intended meaning is THIS IS AN AMBITIOUS CHILD, and any intelligent reader, even if he does not know French, would make the necessary change auto-matically. Therefore, they would conclude, *C'est un enfant ambitieux* is not idiomatic with respect to English.

Even if we accept this argument, the approximation in the first sentence of the preceding paragraph must still be amended by the addition of the clause "even after some automatic changes are made." But this whole automatic-change business is phony. If the French language were com-pletely unknown to us and the particular sentence were the first and only specimen that had come to our attention, we would be very ill-advised to rush to the conclusion that the intended meaning was THIS IS AN AMBITIOUS CHILD. I can very well conceive of a language X in which a certain two-word sequence, which could be translated "literally" (i.e., word-by-word) into English as A CHILD, might mean, before an adjective, something like A LITTLE, whereas the X expression for AN ADULT, in a similar context, might mean A LOT. The correct translation of the X-language sentence then would be THIS IS A LITTLE AMBITIOUS (perhaps THIS IS SOMEWHAT AMBITIOUS or THIS IS RATHER AMBITIOUS). And a lot of other translations can be envisaged.

I agree that nobody who knows even "A CHILD" French would want to call the sentence *C'est un enfant ambitieux* idiomatic. And this points to the unsatisfactoriness of our first attempt at definition. The proposed remedy in terms of "automatic changes" is unacceptable, but the required amendment is surely available. We obviously must take into consideration not only the given bilingual dictionary but also a list of instructions amoun-ting to a specification of the grammar of the original language. The in-structions we would use here, highly simplified, are:

(*a*) *Enfant* is a noun.

(*b*) *Ambitieux* is an adjective.

(*c*) Whenever an adjective follows a noun, transpose them before translating.

(Instruction (*c*) especially must be strongly qualified for actual use.) If these instructions are kept in mind, interchanging places becomes an "automatic" procedure.

We now make a second attempt at defining *idiomatic sentences*. (The careful reader will have noticed the shift from *idioms* to *idiomatic sentences*.) The second characterization is as follows:

A given sentence in a language L_1 is *idiomatic with respect to a language L_2, to a given bilingual word dictionary from L_1 to L_2, and to a given list of grammatical rules* if, and only if, none of the sequences of the L_2 correspondents of the sequence of words of the given L_1 sentence is found to be grammatically and semantically a satisfactory translation, after perusal of the applicable grammatical rules.

This definition makes *idiomatic* an overtly triply relativized term, with additional relativizations hidden in *satisfactory*. I am afraid that, complicated as this analysis may sound, nothing less is adequate. A sentence of L_1 that is idiomatic for L_2 need not be so for some L_3; a sentence that is idiomatic with respect to a dictionary D_1 need not be so with respect to (some more elaborate) D_2; and a sentence that is idiomatic with respect to a set of grammatical rules G_1 need not be so with respect to (some more painstaking) G_2. Finally, a translation that is unsatisfactory for an individual I_1 and a certain purpose P_1 may well be satisfactory for I_2 and P_2.

According to our definition, the English sentence TRUMAN DECLARED THAT THE WHOLE AFFAIR WAS A RED HERRING would be idiomatic with respect to German, to the standard English-German dictionaries, i.e., that part of them which deals with *single* words (most dictionaries deal also with word sequences, and to this we shall return presently), and to any set of grammatical rules I know of. The best word-dictionary translation would be *Truman erklärte, dass die ganze Geschichte ein roter Hering war* (notice that two grammatical rules have been applied!), and this would be entirely inadequate for the great majority of German readers. Those of us who know both English and German sufficiently well are, of course, perfectly aware of where the culprit is. We know that RED HERRING is an "idiom." Rendering this expression in our context as *Finte* will make the resulting translation perfectly acceptable, but a translating machine would not know this nor, for that matter, would a human translator who knows no more of the original language than is presented to him in the dictionary and the list of rules. The obvious solution to the problem is to have an *idiom dictionary*, in addition to the regular word (or "stem") dictionary, and this is of course the method usually adopted. It does not matter whether these two dictionaries are separate volumes or only one volume with the idioms appearing under one or more of the word entries. Although the idiom dictionary is the obvious solution, it is by no means the only one, and perhaps not even the best one under certain conditions.

It may easily be shown that whatever can be achieved by use of an idiom dictionary can also be achieved with a suitably extended word dictionary. In our previous example, the correct translation would be among the suggested correspondents, if the word dictionary also listed a blank—the *null word* (or *zero morpheme*, as it is known to structural linguists)—under the entry RED and under HERRING the word *Finte*. An analogous method can be used in all cases. Though this method is certainly feasible from a theoretical point of view (it would fall under what has been aptly called "hocus-pocus linguistics"), it no doubt looks rather fishy. Still it requires some thought to make its fishiness quite clear. What makes this method so utterly impractical is that, by unjudicious use of it, many extra renderings will be suggested. Their elimination would cause additional difficulties or might even be impossible without many more ad hoc instructions. For example, the blank as a possible German correspondent for RED would make the choice between *Er trug eine rote Krawatte* and *Er trug eine Krawatte* as possible translations for HE WORE A RED TIE well-nigh impossible, nota bene for somebody who does not understand the original. Too many correspondents for single words are a mixed blessing; a null word among them is a Trojan horse. The *embarras de richesse* caused thereby might prove fatal in some cases, and Buridan's ass should serve as a perpetual warning.

We come to the conclusion that, though in principle one could deal with idioms (with respect to a given dictionary D_1) by doing away with them through extending D_1 into a suitable D_2, reliance on a special idiom dictionary would in general be preferable. This does not mean, of course, that existing dictionaries should be used for MT as they are. There can be no doubt that revisions, rather drastic in many respects, will have to be made before they are given the most suitable form, functionally. Prominent among these revisions would be the elimination of certain word correspondents, coupled with addition of a few idioms; and elimination of certain idioms, coupled with addition of a few word correspondents; in short, a reshuffling of the distribution of word and phrase correspondents. One practical boundary condition for this procedure is, of course, the size of the idiom dictionary. A good rule of thumb would be to insist that the number of idioms should be rather less than the number of words.

There is, however, one interesting complication in this division of labor. When a certain phrase occurs in the idiom dictionary, this does not necessarily mean that *all* occurrences of this phrase within any conceivable context have to be treated as idioms and rendered accordingly. Even our RED HERRING might occasionally, when used in describing a painting by Marc Chagall, for example, have its so-called "literal" meaning, and its translation into German should then be just *roter Hering*. (Notice that *literal*, as an antonym to *idiomatic*, is relativized to exactly the same degree. A bilingual *metaphor*, for our purposes, is a special kind of idiom. More should be said about this topic on another occasion.)

An ordinary translator, in general, would turn to the idiom dictionary if the literal translation somehow did not "sound right", but no translating machine of the type envisaged at present is equipped with a semantic, or pragmatic, organ that could be tuned to discern the right-soundingness of a proposed translation. At the most, it would check the grammatical correctness of the output, but certainly not whether the translation "fits" its general context. So the obvious procedure for MT will consist in checking the idiom dictionary *first*. In those cases where, in addition to the translation of a certain word sequence as an idiom, its literal translation might also be appropriate in some contexts, the particular entry will carry with it a coded instruction to the effect that the word dictionary has to be consulted too. In other cases, where the literal translation is never adequate, this step will be skipped.

So far nothing has been said about the exact form the idiom dictionary will take for a given pair of languages and a given machine. Very many procedures are conceivable, and the choice among them may not always be simple. But these considerations are of such a specialized nature that no more need be said about them in our general investigation.

Though I have given a formal definition only for the expression *idiomatic sentence*, I have been constantly using the term *idiom* also. If a certain sentence is idiomatic, then a word block forming part of this sentence may be regarded as an idiom if a satisfactory translation of the sentence will be forthcoming when this word block, as a unit, is rendered nonliterally while all other words are rendered literally. This characterization is once more only a crude approximation, with the required refinements being tiresome perhaps but not especially difficult.

There is still another method of treating idioms that seems prima facie to be quite different from those treated above, though it is nothing but a variant of the preceding one. With this method, there will be no idiom dictionary, and no grammatical rules will be applied to the original text. The text will always be rendered literally. It is to the rough output-language correspondents of the original language text that certain rules will be applied. In general, the rough output-language version will be only an ungrammatical conglomeration of output-language words of a kind well known to linguists as word-by-word translation. The correspondent (strictly speaking, *one* of the correspondents) of *C'est un enfant ambitieux* would now be simply THIS IS A CHILD AMBITIOUS. By determining the syntactical categories of the words occurring in this sequence, which can, of course, be done mechanically, the machine would discover that in this sequence there occurs a partial sequence of the type noun + adjective. This would lead, through appropriate coding, to the consultation of a corresponding rule that, whenever a sequence of the noun + adjective type occurs in the rough translation of a French text, the order in this sequence is to be reversed. One of the rules in the English–German MT procedure would require envisaging the replacement of *roter Hering* by *Finte*, etc.

It should be clear by now that this method is logically the complete equivalent of the preceding one. In both cases, we have a kind of an auxiliary go-between language: in the first a barbaric input language, in the second a barbaric output language. For practical purposes, however, the difference may be great, perhaps even decisive. Since the perusal of a mechanical word dictionary is a very straightforward affair, whereas the application of grammatical rules, syntactic analysis, and idiom dictionaries is laborious as well as complicated, it might be advisable to have these two kinds of operations rigidly separated and to leave to the post-editor the decision as to whether to use the operations of the second kind at all. Should this post-editor find, for instance, that the rough rendering THIS IS A CHILD AMBITIOUS will not be misunderstood by the prospective readers, he might leave it at that, thereby saving time and cost although adding to the troubles of the reader. For translation of scientific texts from Russian into English, the literal rendering would suffice in the great majority of cases. However, should the post-editor believe that he himself or the prospective reader would be unable to understand this rough version, either grammar or the idiom dictionary or both would be consulted by him.

I am therefore inclined at the moment to think that the following operational setup is the most promising one for MT:

1. (*a*) An input-output word dictionary that has for each input word a few (preferably just one) output correspondents, or

(*b*) An input-output dictionary that has for each input stem a few (preferably just one) output correspondents, together with an input-output affix dictionary comprising a few dozen entries, and an automatic affix analyzer of the sort discussed in [109].

2. A set of instructions indicating the transformations to be performed on the rough output. These instructions will be partly grammatical-

syntactical, such as the following (using a self-explanatory ad hoc symbolism):

noun + adjective→adjective + noun; GO + past tense → WENT

They will be partly idiomatic-semantic, such as

roter Hering → Finte

These instructions will have to be given an *operational* form (see Chapter 10, and [4]).

In general, and for the time being, only part 1, whether in form (*a*) or in form (*b*), will be performed automatically by the translating machine, and part 2 only on special request from the post-editor. This division of labor, we stress again, grows out of purely practical considerations of cost and time. There can be no doubt of the long-run desirability of having part 2 also carried out automatically without human intervention.

Now that we have arrived at a characterization of bilingual idioms which not only is fruitful for MT purposes but also might well contribute to an elucidation of this concept in general, it is almost mandatory that we try characterizing monolingual idioms too. Let us not forget that only monolingual idioms were treated in the definition from **Webster's Collegiate Dictionary**. This definition is surely not of great help in deciding whether a given expression is an idiom or not. How shall we find out whether such an expression is "peculiar to itself in grammatical construction"? And how are we to know whether its peculiarity consists "in having a meaning which cannot be derived as a whole from the conjoined meanings of its elements"? Perhaps it might be mentioned, just in passing, that the whole conception of independent meanings of linguistic elements, which are somehow conjoined, is undergoing a process of radical revision in contemporary linguistic philosophy (cf. [126]).

Let me therefore venture to give a completely different characterization of monolingual idioms, admitting beforehand that this characterization probably deviates more from the presystematic usages than my characterization of bilingual idioms on which it is modeled. This greater deviation may be due, however, not only to an insufficient analysis on my part but also to the greater vagueness of the everyday concept of monolingual idiom.

Here, I shall not go beyond a first approximation: *An expression in a given language L is idiomatic within L, with respect to a given monolingual dictionary and a given list of grammatical rules if, and only if, none of the word sequences correlated to the given expression by the dictionary and the list of rules is (sufficiently) synonymous with it.*

Notice that the expression (*sufficiently*) *synonymous* has additional hidden relativizations similar to those contained in the expression (*semantically*) *satisfactory* in the characterization of bilingual idioms.

I shall not try to show that this definition is sufficiently adequate.

Our definitions of idiomatic sentences and other expressions, both interlingual and intralingual, are of course very one-sided. They are what linguists would call *synchronic*, and disregard historical developments. Ordinarily such developments would be considered highly important for determining whether an expression is idiomatic. I do not wish at all to deny the great value of *diachronic* approaches to the problem of idioms, but for our purposes this approach is completely irrelevant.

Many will think that I am putting the cart before the horse by defining idioms on the basis of dictionary and grammar rules, whereas the procedure that comes naturally to one's mind is the reverse: i.e., the lexicographer prepares a dictionary definition in the way he does because a certain expression strikes him as idiomatic. I do not wish to deny that this is probably the customary procedure. My definitions are offered not in what has been called [129:7] the *context of discovery* but in the *context of justification* and *systematic reconstruction*. Whatever the motives of the lexicographer for setting up his distionary the way he does, once the book is ready, it seems to me that, for our purposes and many otherss, it is most convenient to define the concept of idiom in terms of this dictionary. There is no vicious circle involved, since the concept of idiom that might be in the back of the lexicographer's mind is presystematic, vague, and noncommittal; whereas the final concept is systematic, (relatively) rigorous and, in general, effectively and easily determinable.

Intertranslatability of Natural Languages* | 4

Many linguists and many philosophers have, at one time or another, upheld the thesis of the intertranslatability of all natural languages (sometimes in the form of a sister-thesis, that of the universality of all natural languages). It is, unfortunately, obvious that this thesis is highly ambiguous, due to the ambiguity of both "intertranslatability" and "natural language". Two senses of the thesis come immediately to our attention. I shall show that in one of these senses the thesis is false and in the other true, but in such a trivial fashion that it would hardly justify the attention given to it by so many distinguished scientists. I shall finally inquire into the possibility of other senses in which the thesis would be non-trivially true.

The expression "natural language" can be, and is, understood in at least two mutually exclusive senses. Sometimes it is taken to refer to a *closed language*, sometimes to an *open language*. A closed language is one whose rules, both of syntactic and semantic nature, derived from the behavior of its users at a certain time according to principles which, at least in theory, are well understood, are rigid and unalterable. This implies also a fixed and inextensible vocabulary. For such languages, the mentioned thesis seems to me to be obviously false. Equip somebody with a complete knowledge of the closed language Choctaw (as spoken in) 1953, and he will be unable, even when intelligent to the highest possible degree, to provide a translation of an English treatise on quantum mechanics that would be regarded as satisfactory either by himself or by any group of authoritative judges. And you may replace Choctaw 1953, for this purpose, by English 1890. I think that what I assert here holds not only in the sense that the prospective translator would be unable to complete his task in a reasonable time but even in the much stronger sense that a completion of the task would be theoretically impossible. A defense of this assertion would lead, however, into a discussion of some highly interesting though also highly controversial points made by

* First appeared as Section 2 of *Some linguistic problems connected with machine translation*, **Philosophy of Science**, vol. 20 (1953), pp. 217–225.

recent methodologists of science and will therefore not be undertaken here.

However, with regard to the open language Choctaw that consists of Choctaw 1953 and any additions of vocabulary and rules that are not inconsistent with the rules of Choctaw 1953, the mentioned translation would be an easy task. If we take the possibility of extension seriously, or rather hyper-seriously, the task would become not only easy but utterly and self-defeatingly trivial. We only have to add the whole English language, lock, stock, and barrel, to Choctaw 1953, and the translation would be forthcoming immediately.

Now, this is obviously ridiculous, as it is meant to be. Apparently those who uphold the thesis under discussion have in mind a certain restricted extensibility leading to some kind of *semi-open language*, but I do not know of any attempt to specify these restrictions or to show that under such extensions all natural languages will become intertranslatable.

Those methodological researches which I mentioned earlier may have some impact on our question. But one thing is sure: to save the thesis of intertranslatability from the Scylla of falsity and the Charybdis of triviality, much thinking has to be done by linguists, logicians, and methodologists, and preferably in collaboration.

This result, which should have some debunking value, was obtained even without taking into account the ambiguity of the term *"intertranslatability."* It is difficult to know in what sense this term and its cognates were understood by those who used them in connection with our problem. If they had in mind a relation that is stronger than sentence-by-sentence-translatability, they were probably wrong in every interpretation except the utterly trivial one mentioned above. Under no restricted extensibility does it seem plausible that, in general, smaller units than sentences will turn out to be uniquely translatable. It is not even clear that sentences are large enough units.

Let me present, in a rather dogmatic way, just one situation in which even a sentence-by-sentence translation would not be feasible. This example, to be sure, is probably fictitious, but not necessarily so. Assume that the target-language into which the English sentence "I am hungry" has to be translated does not contain *indexical expressions* [5] equivalent to "I" or "the speaker of this sentence" or "your obedient servant," etc. When John Doe wants to say in this target language that he is hungry, he invariably says something whose English equivalent would be "John Doe is hungry." If introduction of indexical expressions into the target language is not allowed under certain extensions, how would "I am hungry" be translated? To be sure, any translator who would know by whom a certain *token* of this sentence was uttered could easily perform the translation of this token. (Notice that it would still be a somewhat oblique translation even in this favorable case, and that at any rate no translation of the sentence-*type* "I am hungry" exists in the extended target language.) But the requirement that the full context of the production of sentences in the source language should always be known to the translator, at least in principle, would be a very forceful one that, if really necessary, would strongly reduce the impact of our thesis.

PART II
Algebraic Linguistics

A Quasi-Arithmetical Notation for Syntactic Description*

5

The purpose of this chapter is to present the outlines of a method of syntactic description that is new insofar as it combines methods developed by the Polish logician Kasimir Ajdukiewicz [1] on the one hand and by American structural linguists [62; 55] on the other. Such a combination has apparently not been undertaken before, if only for the reason that Ajdukiewicz's paper appeared in a Polish philosophical journal and has therefore remained unknown to most linguists.

We are not interested here in developing a method which a linguist might use to ARRIVE at an analysis of a linguistic corpus, but only in a new way in which he could PRESENT the results of his investigations. The decisive difference between this method and the others prevailing so far lies in the fact that in addition to a list in which each linguistic element (usually each word) is assigned to one or more categories, only a simple rule of a quasi-arithmetical character need be given to enable us to 'compute' the syntactic character of any given linguistic string (sequence of one or more elements) in its context. The main economy produced by this method lies, therefore, in that it enables us to dispense completely, at least in principle, with special syntactic statements.

This should be of value in those situations in which a completely mechanical procedure is required for discovering the syntactic structure of a given string. Such a situation arises, for instance, in connection with the problem of mechanized translation. It has been shown (Chapter 10) that a machine could be constructed which would be able to determine the structure of any sentence in the source language, provided that the syntax of this language were presented to the machine in a certain specific form which we may call OPERATIONAL. It may well be that the preparation of the element-category list will be a decisive step toward the construction of an operational syntax whose instructions could be carried out satisfactorily by a digital computer

---

* First appeared in **Language**, vol. 29 (1953), pp. 47–58.

or, for that matter, by a human being operating in completely mechanical fashion.

Before we proceed to sketch the new method in abstracto, we will discuss one simple example. The English string *Poor John sleeps* would be analyzed, according to one method [62: Ch. 16] recently described, in the following way: *poor* is an A (for adjective), *John* is an N (for noun), *sleep* is a V (for verb), -*s* is a Vv (for morpheme added to a verb to form a verbal phrase), where all these assignments hold at least for the given context. Then, by invoking the syntactic statements, A $\frown$ N $\rightarrow$ N¹ (where the arch designates concatenation and the arrow stands for *yields*) and V $\frown$ Vv $\rightarrow$ V, *Poor John* would be assigned to N, *sleeps* to V, hence finally *Poor John sleeps* to N $\frown$ V which is the most frequent form of English sentences.

According to the notation to be proposed and explained in this paper, *John* will belong to the category *n*, *poor* to *n*/[*n*], *sleeps* to *s*/(*n*), where *n* is to be interpreted, approximately, as the category of name-like strings, *n*/[*n*] as the category of those strings that with an *n* to their right form a string belonging to the same category *n*, and *s*/(*n*) as the category of those strings that with an *n* to their left form a string belonging to the category of sentences, That the string *Poor John sleeps* is a sentence can now be tested mechanically, without recourse to any syntactic statements, by using something like ordinary arithmetical multiplication of fractions on the INDEX-SEQUENCE corresponding to the given string, viz.

$$(1) \qquad \frac{n}{[n]} \, n \, \frac{s}{(n)}.$$

By REDUCING the sub-sequence $n/[n]$ n to n, we obtain the FIRST DERIVATIVE

$$(2) \qquad n \, \frac{s}{(n)},$$

from which, by another reduction, we get the SECOND and LAST DERIVATIVE

$$(3) \qquad s.$$

Let us notice immediately another important advantage of our notation: we have not only a mechanical method of testing the SYNTACTIC CONNEXITY of a given string but also a mechanical method of finding the so-called constituents of any given syntactically connex string. In the given example, we find by quick inspection that *John sleeps* is not a constituent of *Poor John sleeps* (in spite of the fact that *John sleeps* is connex in itself), since by reducing first $n \, s/(n)$ to s we would arrive at the derivative

$$(2') \qquad \frac{n}{[n]} \, s,$$

---

[1] Harris uses an equal-sign instead of the arrow, and juxtaposition instead of the arch.

from which no further derivation is possible, showing (by the fact that the last derivative, or EXPONENT, in this case does not consist of a single index) that the whole string, analyzed in this way, is not syntactically connex. Strictly speaking, we are only entitled to the following conditional statement: If *Poor John sleeps* is a syntactically connex string, then *John sleeps* is not one of its constituents.

Let us also take notice that a complete element-list of the stated character enables us to synthesize all possible sentences of the given language without any additional rules, Let us consider, for instance, a language that contains elements belonging, respectively, to the categories n, $n/[n]$, $n/[s]$, and $s/(n)$ $[n]$ (the category of strings that form sentences out of a left n and a right n). Then we know that any syntactically connex sequence of elements belonging to n, $s/(n)$ $[n]$, $n/[s]$, n, $s/(n)$ $[n]$, $n/[n]$, $n/[n]$, n, in this order, would be a sentence, since the only possible exponent of the corresponding index-sequence is s, as can be seen from the following derivation:

$$
\begin{array}{lllllllll}
(4) & n & s/(n)\,[n] & n/[s] & n & s/(n)\,[n] & n/[n] & n/[n] & n \\
(5) & n & s/(n)\,[n] & n/[s] & n & s/(n)\,[n] & n/[n] & & n \\
(6) & n & s/(n)\,[n] & n/[s] & n & s/(n)\,[n] & & n & \\
(7) & n & s/(n)\,[n] & n/[s] & & s & & & \\
(8) & n & s/(n)\,[n] & & n & & & & \\
(9) & & s & & & & & &
\end{array}
$$

Whether all these categories have instances in a given language is of course an empirical question. With respect to English, for instance, this question could be answered Yes, roughly speaking. Indeed, *John knew that Paul was a poor man* would be a sentence of the type mentioned. (The qualification 'roughly speaking' is necessary, since it is obvious that the categories dealt with so far are too gross to be applicable to ordinary languages; according to such an application, *Man knew that John was poor a Paul* would also have to be considered a sentence, a thing which most people would hesitate to do.) The same holds for French, where we have sentences like *Jean savait que Paul était un pauvre homme*, but not for German, which lacks elements belonging to the category $n/[s]$ (at least on an unsophisticated level, for which *Paul war ein armer Mann* and *Paul ein armer Mann war* are not automatic alternates of the same sentence, but which considers the first string alone as a sentence and the second as syntactically disconnex).

These preliminary considerations should suffice to show that the designation of syntactic categories with the help of such symbols (which carry with them, so to speak, indications of the environments in which members of these categories appear) is a method certainly superior to other prevailing ones in at least one respect, if it can be carried through consistently. Rudiments of this notation already appear in the symbol Vv that was used in our first illustration to designate the category to which -*s* belongs.

Let us begin by stating some assumptions on which our method is based, We assume that with respect to any two given ELEMENT-TOKENS (ink-marks, sounds) it is known whether or not they stand in the relation of EQUIFORMITY, which we take in this context as an undefined primitive relation. Whenever two element-tokens are equiform we shall say that they belong to the same ELEMENT-FORM. The relation of equiformity can be extended, in an obvious way, to hold also between STRING-TOKENS. If all tokens of some form belong to the same category, then this form will be called PURE. If not all tokens of some form belong to the same category, but each token belongs to exactly one of *n* categories, we shall call the form MIXED and consider it as the (set-theoretical) sum of *n* TYPES belonging to *n* different type-categories. A pure form is, of course, its only type. To illustrate: assuming that all tokens of *Paul* belong (in English) to the same token-category (viz. of proper names), then the type *Paul* belongs to the type-category of proper names. Assuming that some tokens of *poor* belong to a certain category, others to another category, still others to a third one, and none to another, we shall consider the form *poor* as mixed and composed of the three types, say $poor_1$, $poor_2$, and $poor_3$.

Observing a given token, we know, in general, to which form it belongs, but not, unless the form is pure, to which type. To find out the type of a a token in a given context, we usually have to take account of the linguistic environment of the token and often also of the extra-linguistic context of its production. In all those cases where linguistic environment alone is sufficient to fix the type of a given token, our notation will facilitate this determination and formalize it in such a way that a suitably constructed machine should be able to carry it out. (Even this statement needs qualification: it seems that the proposed notation will be effective only where the crucial environment is not too extended. When the elements are words, the environment taken into account in our notation does not go beyond an utterance.)

According to the envisaged notation, to each element-form there will be assigned a class of $n\ (\geq 1)$ symbols denoting the categories of the types to which the tokens of this form belong. These symbols will be called the INDICES of the form and their class the index-class of this form. To a sequence of elements the sequence of their index-classes will be correlated. To arrive at the category-system, we make, among others, the following assumptions. Each sentence that is not an element is regarded as the outcome of the operation of one sub-sequence upon the remainder, which may be to its immediate right or to its immediate left or on both sides. ('Left' and 'right' are to be understood here, as in what follows, only as the two directions of a linear order.) That sub-sequence which is regarded as operating upon the others will be called an OPERATOR, the others its ARGUMENTS. In a two-element sentence, for instance, one element will have to be the operator, the other its argument. In this case, having only one argument, the operator is SINGULARY. In other cases the operator may be BINARY, TERNARY, etc. According to the position of the arguments, we have to distinguish between a singulary right operator, singulary left operator, binary right operator, binary left operator, binary right-left operator, etc. The verbal terminology will soon become pretty involved. We shall therefore use in general the following symbolism: an operator that forms a sentence out of m left arguments belonging (from right to left) to the categories $\alpha_1, \ldots, \alpha_m$, respectively, (the α's may be different but need not be so) and out of n right arguments belonging (from left to right) to the categories $\beta_1, \ldots, \beta_n$, respectively, will be said to belong to the category

$$\frac{s}{(\alpha_m)\cdots(\alpha_1)[\beta_1]\cdots[\beta_n]} \quad (m + n \geq 1)$$

If both the operator and the arguments are elements, then the only remaining thing to be done is to assign the arguments to such categories as will yield an over-all simplest description. (The tremendous problems connected with this procedure cannot be discussed here.) If, however, either the operator or some argument, or both, are PROPER STRINGS, i.e. consist of more than one element, they too have to be regarded as the result of the operation of some sub-sequence upon the remainder. The result of the operation in this case will, in general, no longer be a sentence. Whenever an operator, out of m left arguments belonging to $\alpha_1, \ldots, \alpha_m$ and n right arguments belonging to $\beta_1, \ldots, \beta_n$, respectively, forms a string belonging to the category γ (identical with one of the α's or β's or different from all of them), it will be said to belong to the category

$$\frac{\gamma}{(\alpha_m)\cdots(\alpha_1)[\beta_1]\cdots[\beta_n]} \quad (m + n \geq 1)$$

Elements which are operators in a given string may be arguments in another string or even at another place in the same string, and similarly with arguments. It seems plausible, however, that the requirement of over-all greatest simplicity will necessitate, at least with respect to languages with a finite number of elements, the classing of some types as arguments in all contexts. We shall now make the assumption that the languages we are dealing with contain types which are 'absolute' arguments, so to speak.

These types will be said to belong to BASIC CATEGORIES. For purposes of illustration, we shall assume that sentences, proper names, and common nouns belong to basic categories. As the symbol for the category of sentences we shall continue to use s, if necessary with subscripts. As the symbol for the other basic categories we shall use n—again, if necessary, with subscripts. (If the language to which these categories apply is not assumed to be fixed in the given discourse, superscripts can be used to indicate that language relative to which the categorization is to hold.)

Strings which belong to basic categories will themselves be called BASIC. Strings that are not basic are operators, and belong to OPERATOR-CATEGORIES. There is a potentially infinite and elaborately ramified hierarchy of them, but in an effective description of a given language only some of them will be used.

We are now ready to describe that operation upon index-sequences, to be called DERIVATION, on the basis of which the other concepts of our method will be defined. By a derivation of an index-sequence we understand the replacement of any sub-sequence of the given sequence of the form

$$\alpha_m \dots \alpha_1 \frac{\gamma}{(\alpha_m) \dots (\alpha_1)[\beta_1] \dots [\beta_n]} \beta_1 \dots \beta_n \qquad (m + n \geqq 1)$$

by γ. The resulting index-sequence is called the DERIVATIVE of the original sequence.

A given index-sequence may obviously have more than one derivative. We already saw that the index-sequence (1) has both (2) and (2′) as its derivatives. Another example is provided by the string *a very poor man*, to which, among others, the following index-sequence is correlated (the use of the double slant-line should be sufficiently clear):

(10) $\qquad\qquad n/[n] \quad n/[n]//[n/[n]] \quad n/[n] \quad n$

This has two derivatives:

(11) $\qquad\qquad n/[n] \qquad n/[n] \qquad\qquad n$

(11′) $\qquad\qquad n/[n] \quad n/[n]//[n/[n]] \qquad\qquad n$

A derivative may, in its turn, have one or more derivatives. Thus, (11) has the following as its only derivative:

(12) $\qquad\qquad n/[n] \qquad\qquad\qquad n,$

which again has as its only derivative

(13) $\qquad\qquad\qquad\qquad n$

whereas (11′) has no derivative at all. (11) and (11′) may be called the FIRST

DERIVATIVES of (10), (12) its SECOND DERIVATIVE, (13) its THIRD DERIVATIVE, (11') and (13) its LAST DERIVATIVES or EXPONENTS. (13), but not (11'), is a PROPER EXPONENT, i.e. one consisting of a single index, and any derivation leading up to it a PROPER DERIVATION. The terms 'derivative' and 'exponent' will be used not only with respect to index-sequences but also with respect to the strings to which these sequences are correlated.

Since an element may have more than one index correlated to it, a string may have more than one index-sequence correlated to it. If at least one index-sequence of the set of index-sequences correlated to a given string has at least one proper exponent, the string will be called (SYNTACTICALLY) CONNEX. *Poor John sleeps* and *a very poor man* are both connex, each having at least one proper derivation; *poor sleeps John* is not, since neither of its two index-sequences

$$n/[n] \quad s/(n) \quad n$$

$$n \quad s/(n) \quad n$$

has a proper derivation, as can be verified immediately.

Here, however, arises the following interesting situation. A string that is connex by itself need not be CONNEX AS A SUB-SEQUENCE OF SOME OTHER STRING. Before we define this phrase, let us give an example. *John sleeps* is connex by itself but is not connex within *Poor John sleeps*, so far on an intuitive basis.

Let us now give the strict definitions: A string m_1 will be said to be CONNEX AT A CERTAIN PLACE WITHIN A STRING m_2 WITH RESPECT TO THE DERIVATION d_1 if (1) m_2 is connex, (2) d_1 is proper, (3) d_1 includes a subderivation in which the index-sequence of m_1 at the place in question has a proper exponent. An exact definition of the term 'subderivation' would be somewhat tiresome; it is hoped that the illustration given will make its intended sufficiently clear. In the proper derivation (1)—(2)—(3) above, the index-subsequence correlated to *Poor John*, viz. $n/[n]$ n, has the exponent n. *Poor John* is therefore connex within *Poor John sleeps* with respect to this derivation, but *John sleeps* is not connex within *Poor John sleeps* with respect to this derivation.

We now define 'm_1 is connex within m_2' as short for 'm_1 is connex within m_2 with respect to all proper derivations of m_2', and 'm_1 is thoroughly connex' as short for 'm_1 is connex within all m_i of which it is a (proper or improper) part'.

Clearly, not every connex string has to be also thoroughly connex. In English, *John sleeps* is connex but not thoroughly connex since it is not connex within *Poor John sleeps*. That a language should exhibit this character may be deplored, since it introduces complications into its description and into the analysis carried out on the basis of such a description. We shall take up this point again at a later stage.

The complications mentioned are not such as to cause, by necessity, any major ambiguities. The knowledge that a string is thoroughly connex would indeed dispense with the task of testing whether this string is connex within some given context. That this knowledge is not at our disposal might necessitate more complex checking procedures, but the outcome of these procedures can still be unique. Knowing that *John sleeps*, though connex, is not thoroughly connex, we might be interested in finding out whether it is connex within *Paul thinks that John sleeps*, or at least whether it is connex within this larger string with respect to some of its proper derivations. This last question can indeed be answered in the affirmative by exhibiting the following proper derivation:

	Paul	thinks	that	John	sleeps
(14)	n	$s/(n)$ $[n]$	$n/[s]$	n	$s/(n)$
(15)	n	$s/(n)$ $[n]$	$n/[s]$	s	
(16)	n	$s/(n)$ $[n]$	n		
(17)		s			

The relevant subderivation is framed. But is *John sleeps* also connex with respect to all other proper derivations of *Paul thinks that John sleeps*? The derivation given above is the only proper one with (14) as the original index-sequence. But (14) is only one out of many other possible original sequences. *Thinks* may also have at least the indexes $s/(n)$ and $s/(n)$ $[s]$ (as in *Paul thinks* and *Paul thinks John is sleeping*, waiving possible sophistications) and *that* also has the indexes n and $n/[n]$ (as in *Paul believes that* and *Paul likes that girl*). Disregarding other possible indexes, we have therefore before us at least nine original index-sequences for the given string, which we might arrange in the following way:

Paul	thinks	that	John	sleeps
	$s/(n)$	n		
n	$s/(n)$ $[s]$	$n/[s]$	n	$s/(n)$
	$s/(n)$ $[s]$	$n/[n]$		

By systematic testing we can find that only one other original index-sequence out of the possible nine has a proper derivation. The sequence and its derivation are:

(14')	n	$s/(n)\,[s]$	$n/[n]$	n	$s/(n)$
(15')	n	$s/(n)\,[s]$		n	$s/(n)$
(16')	n	$s/(n)\,[s]$		s	
(17')		s			

Since *John sleeps* is not connex within *Paul thinks that John sleeps* with respect to this derivation, it is not connex within this larger string (without qualification). In this case, however, we can describe the situation in a slightly more precise way and say that *John sleeps* is connex within *Paul thinks that John sleeps* with respect to a certain index-sequence of this larger string, since *John sleeps* is connex within *Paul thinks that John sleeps* with respect to every proper derivation starting with this original sequence.

The fact that (14') is far a less likely sequence for *Paul thinks that John sleeps* than (14) is of high importance for what we might call STATISTICAL SYNTAX. Our investigation lies on the level where relative frequencies are not yet taken into account, but only possibilities and impossibilities of occurrence. We also disregard, on this level of approximation, the differences in intonation-patterns which would determine, with high likelihood, whether a given uttered token of *Paul thinks that John sleeps* has the one or the other of the two stated original sequences assigned to it.

Instead of the phase 'is connex within m_2 with respect to d_1' we shall, in general, use the more customary expression 'is a constituent of m_2 with respect to d_1' hence instead of 'is connex within m_2' also 'is a constituent of m_2'. We can now also define the phrase 'is an immediate constituent of m_2 with respect to d_1' as meaning 'is a constituent of m_2 with respect to d_1 but is not a constituent of any m_3 that is a (proper) constituent of m_2 with respect to d_1'. In our last example, for instance, *that John sleeps* is an immediate constituent of *Paul thinks that John sleeps* with respect to the derivation (14)–(17), and also with respect to the derivation (14')–(17'), and this in spite of the fact that it has different exponents in these two derivations.

With respect to the first derivation, the immediate constituents of *Paul thinks that John sleeps* are *Paul*, *thinks*, and *John sleeps*. Of these, the first two are elements and the third a proper string which has, therefore, immediate constituents of its own, with respect to the same derivation, viz. *that* and *John sleeps*, of which the first is an element and the second again a proper string with the immediate constituents *John* and *sleeps*. In a self-explanatory terminology, we may therefore say that, with respect to the given derivation (14)–(17), the elements *Paul* and *thinks* are IMMEDIATE CONSTITUENTS of the given string, *that* is a CONSTITUENT OF THE SECOND ORDER, *John* and *sleeps* are CONSTITUENTS OF THE THIRD ORDER; and we may say that the string itself is OF THE THIRD ORDER. A connex two-element string would then be of the first order with respect to any of its proper derivations, and we might say, if this should prove to be convenient, that any element is OF ZERO ORDER (without qualification).

If two tokens of the same element-form occur in a given string, then explicit reference to these occurrences may have to be made, since even if they belong to the same type they need not be constituents of the same order with respect to a given proper derivation. It is clear that m_1 may be an immediate constituent of m_2 with respect to some proper d_i but not with respect to some different d_j. If, however, m_1 happens to be an immediate constituent of m_2 with respect to all proper derivations, then we shall drop the qualifications and say that m_1 is an immediate constituent of m_2. Under the assumption that the set of index sequences given above for *Paul thinks that John sleeps* is exhaustive, *Paul*, *thinks*, and *that John sleeps* are immediate constituents of this string, without qualifications.

Many of the concepts defined so far are much more dependent than one might at first thought assume upon the specific derivation, and hence upon the form of the original index-sequence. One might tend to believe, for instance, that it would make no appreciable difference whether one regarded a given operator as forming a sentence out of a right *n* and a left *n*, i.e. an operator $s/(n)\,[n]$, or as forming out of a right *n* an operator that forms a sentence out of a left *n*, i.e. an operator $s/(n)//[n]$. But such a belief would be a mistake. It makes a considerable difference in the organization of immediate and other constituents whether we treat *loves* (say) as an operator which out of a left *n John* and a right *n Mary* forms a sentence, *John loves Mary*, IN ONE COMPLEX STEP, or as an operator which out of a right *n Mary* forms an operator, *loves Mary*, which out of a left *n John* forms a sentence IN TWO SIMPLE STEPS. According to the second treatment, *loves Mary* is an immediate constituent of the whole; according to the first, it is no constituent at all. The fact that being-a-constituent-of is a relation which is not invariant even with respect to such 'inessential' transformations as that of $s/(n)\,[n]$ into $s/(n)//[n]$ shows that this relation and its cognates are of somewhat restricted importance. Incidentally, according to the Aristotelian analysis, *John loves Mary* has to be understood as a subject-predicate sentence with *John* and *loves Mary* as its immediate constituents. The categorization which treats *John* and *Mary* on a par, as respectively the left and right arguments of *loves*, though much in favor with modern logicians, for a long time was not regarded as proper.

But leaving philosophical and logical considerations aside, it is an interesting problem to compare the advantages and disadvantages of using only SINGULARY OPERATORS WITH COMPLEX NUMERATORS as against using only *n*-ARY OPERATORS WITH SIMPLE DENOMINATORS, or using both simultaneously. In certain presentations of COMBINATORIAL LOGIC [44], for instance, singulary operators are preferred, in spite of the fact that this involves multiplying the number of operations. Nothing more will be said here on this topic.

It is useful, in certain investigations, to distinguish between operators which out of their arguments form a string belonging to the same category as the arguments, and those which do not. The first kind might be called ENDOTYPIC, the second EXOTYPIC. That type of *poor*, for instance, which belongs to the category $n/[n]$, is endotypic, while *sleeps*, which belongs to $s/(n)$, is exotypic. In certain contexts, it might be profitable to use a slightly different classification and to regard operators belonging to categories of the form $\alpha/(\alpha) \ldots (\alpha) [\alpha] \ldots [\alpha]$ as endotypic. That type of *and*, for instance, which is an $s/(s) [s]$, would be endotypic according to the second conception but exotypic according to the first. We might perhaps, if necessary, distinguish between endotypic in the narrow sense and endotypic in the wider sense.

English adjectives when used in adjectival function, demonstratives when used in adjectival function, articles, adverbs, and conjuctions are endotypic; verbs and prepositions are exotypic; nouns in general are neither, being mostly basic. This is only a rough application of our terminology, since it is obvious that it is unable, as developed so far, to cope with the whole gamut of relationships that exist between the elements in English or in any other natural language. With this provision in mind, adjectives will in general belong to n/n-categories (omitting parentheses and brackets now for the same of simplicity), as will articles and adjectival demonstratives; conjunctions will be s/s (hence endotypic only in the wider sense); adverbs will be $n/n//n/n$ (VERY *good*), $s/n//s/n$ (*sleeps* SOUNDLY), $s/nn//s/nn$ (ARDENTLY *hates*), s/s (UNFORTUNATELY *John died*), etc.

To get a slightly better outlook on the effectiveness of the proposed notation, let us analyze a string with a much more complex structure than that of the strings so far, though still very far from the top of the complexity ladder. The string is taken from a language[2] which most readers will not know. Its rough transliteration is:

1	2	3	4	5	6	7	8	9
mošе	*yada*	*ki*	*pinxas*	*xaxam*	*yoter*	*mеašer*	*axoto*	*haktana*

---

[2] Colloquial Hebrew. For the sake of the simplicity of analysis, however, the common *meaxoto* has been replaced by the (colloquially) much less frequent *meašer axoto*.

Let us assume that by looking up the elements of these strings in the category-list (so far non-existent), we obtain the information given in Table 1.

	1	2	3	4	5	5	7	8	9
a	n	$s/(n)$	$n/[s]$	n	n	$\dfrac{n/(n)}{(n/(n))}$	$\dfrac{n/(n)}{(n/(n))[n]}$	n	n
b		$s/(n)[n]$	$s/[n]$		$n/(n)$	$\dfrac{s/(n)}{(s/(n))}$	$\dfrac{s/(n)}{(s/(n))[n]}$		$n/(n)$
c					$s/(n)$	$\dfrac{s/(n)[n]}{(s/(n)[n])}$	$\dfrac{s/(n)[n]}{(s/(n)[n])[n]}$		

TABLE 1

The list in Table 1 is incomplete even with respect to that very rough approximation which we have set as our standard.) We have before us a set of 216 original index-sequences. Systematic testing for SUITABLE original sequences (i.e. sequences with proper derivations) would be laborious though perfectly feasible for a properly designed machine. We shall use some shortcuts. It is easy to realize that 9a does not fit. 5a does not fit either. Similarly 5b, 6c, hence also 7c, are out. The exponent of 7–9 obviously operates on the exponent of 4–6 and must be s, because of 3. 3b is unsuitable, as is 2a. Exactly one suitable original index-sequence is left:

1	2	3	4	5	6	7	8	9
n	$s/(n)[n]$	$n/[s]$	n	$s/(n)$	$\dfrac{s/(n)}{(s/(n))}$	$\dfrac{s/(n)}{(s/(n))[n]}$	n	$n/(n)$

(20)

Many derivations start from (20). There are already three different first derivatives as a result of operating 5 upon 4, 6 upon 5, and 9 upon 8. It is, however, easy to see that the first derivation leads into a blind alley. We thus arrive at the interesting (though on second thought not surprising) result that only two proper derivations are correlated to the given string, even though it has 216 original index-sequences, many of them with more than one first derivative, We present one of the two proper derivations in the abbreviated scheme of Table 2. The second derivation differs from the one presented in Table 2 only in that steps (21) and (22) change places, a difference which we may safely describe as trivial. If the category-list were constructed so as to contain singular indexes only, the derivation would have contained

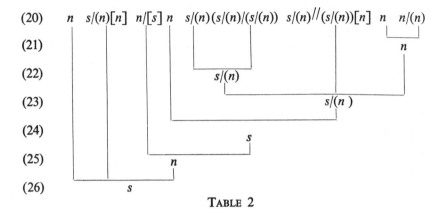

TABLE 2

two more steps, each THREE-FORK being split into a sequence of two TWO-FORKS, and the set-up of immediate and *n*-order constituents would have undergone some changes.

I am fully aware of the inadequacies of the proposed notation. Its shortcomings are many and of various kinds. Some are due to the effort of presenting the main ideas as simply as possible, and can easily be overcome through a less simplified approach. Moreover, the problem of categorization is far from a satisfactory solution, and the proposed notation as such (I repeat) cannot put the linguist in a better position for solving it, though it may well redirect his attitudes.

Two further points should be mentioned. First, we have said nothing about what the linguistic elements are to be in specific cases; in our examples, we used words. It is plausible that other elements might be more suitable, if not for all languages, at least for many. Phenomena like separable prefixes and Harris's 'long components' will pose additional problems.

Another feature, related to the previous, is our deliberate restriction of the range of arguments to the IMMEDIATE environment of the operators. This will prove to be disturbing with regard to languages that have constructions like the English string *Paul strangely enough refused to talk*, where *strangely enough is* probably best regarded as an *s/s* operator, since it is the whole event which is regarded as strange and not the way in which Paul refused to talk. But whether we assign *s/(s)* or *s/[s]* to this string, it will turn out that the larger string will be disconnex, as the reader can verify for himself. However, both *Paul refused to talk* (,) *strangely enough* and *Strangely enough* (,) *Paul refused to talk* will come out all right. The last two sentences are commonly regarded as variants of the first, with hardly any difference in meaning—certainly not in cognitive meaning.

Though this example points to a certain shortcoming of our notation, it also shows that only a small change is needed to make it adequate for handling complications of this type. Using certain auxiliary symbols such as commas would change the picture. If we write *Paul, strangely enough, refused to talk* (which is, incidentally, the common usage) and interpret the function of the commas as giving us license to lift the string between them from its position and deposit it at some other position (within certain limits, of course), we can still adhere to the simple rules of immediate environment. It remains to be seen whether devices of such a simple nature will enable us to retain a notation which takes account only of the immediate environment with respect to all languages.

Some Linguistic Obstacles to Machine Translation*

6

For certain pairs of languages it has been shown experimentally that word-by-word machine translation leads to an output which can often be transformed by an expert post-editor into a passable translation of the source text. However, if one is interested in reducing the burden of the post-editor, as one apparently has to be in order to make the use of machine aids in translation commercially profitable, or if one has to do with pairs of languages for which word-by-word translation is not by itself a satisfactory basis for post-editing, it is natural to think of mechanizing the determination of the syntactic structure of the source sentences. It is theoretically clear, and has again been experimentally verified, that knowledge of the syntactic structure of the sentences to be translated does considerably simplify the task of the post-editor. It is obvious, for instance, that this knowledge tends to reduce, and in the limit to eliminate, those syntactical ambiguities which are created by the word-by-word translation and which are nonexistent for the human translator who treats the sentences as wholes. The task of the post-editor would then consist solely in eliminating the semantical ambiguities and in polishing up the style of the machine output. Whether these steps, too, can be completely taken over by machines of today or of the foreseeable future is still controversial. I myself have strong reasons for regarding this task as hopeless, in general, but this point will be discussed elsewhere (Chapter 12).

A few years ago, I proposed what I called a *quasi-arithmetical notation for syntactic description* (Chapter 5) whose employment should allow, after some refinements, for a mechanical determination of the constituent structure of any given sentence. At that time, I actually demonstrated the effectiveness of the method for relatively simple sentences only, but cherished the hope that it might also work for more complex sentences, perhaps for all kinds of sentences. I am now quite convinced that this hope will not

---

* First appeared as Appendix II to *The present status of automatic translation of languages*, **Advances in Computers**, Vol. I (F. L. Alt, ed.), Academic Press, New York 1960.

come true. As a consequence, the road to machine translation can be shown to contain more obstacles than was realized a few years ago. I think that this should be of sufficient interest to warrant some more detailed exhibition, especially since this insight is due to an important new, not to say revolutionary, view of the structure of language, recently outlined by Chomsky [34], and could perhaps, in its turn and in due time, be turned into a new method of machine translation, which would be more complex than known ones but also more effective.

Let me present the main point of Chapter 5 again briefly, with some modifications in terminology and notation, partly under the impact of a recent article of Lambek [82].

The basic idea, adopted from Ajdukiewicz [1], is to regard every sentence (of more than one word) as the result of the operation of one continuous part of it upon the remainder, these two parts being the *immediate constituents* of the sentence, such that these constituent parts which in general are not sentences themselves, but rather phrases, are again the product of the operation of some continuous part upon the remainder, etc., until one arrives at the final constituents, say words or morphemes. In accordance with this variant of the *immediate constituent model*, which is the standard model with which many modern linguists are working [71: Section 17], all words of a given language are assigned to one or more, but always finitely many, *syntactic categories*.

For the purpose of illustration we shall try to get along, for English, with two fundamental categories, those of *nominals* and (declarative) *sentences*, to be denoted by n and s, respectively. The operator category of *intransitive verbals*, i.e., the category of those words that out of a nominal to their left form a sentence, will be denoted by $n\backslash s$ (read: n sub s); the category of *adjectivals*, i.e., of words that out of nominals to their right form nominals, will be denoted by n/n (read: n super n); the category of *intransitive verbal adverbals*, i.e., of words that out of intransitive verbals (to their left) form intransitive verbals, by $(n\backslash s)\backslash(n\backslash s)$—for which we shall, by means of a self-explanatory convention, usually write $n\backslash s\backslash n\backslash s$—etc. (Nominals, verbals, adjectivals, etc., in my present usage, are *syntactical categories*. They should not be confused with nouns, verbs, adjectives, etc., which are *morphological* (*paradigmatic*) *categories*, in my usage. The connection between these two classifications, as the choice of terms is intended to indicate, is that nouns usually, though by no means always, belong to the syntactical category of nominals, etc., and that most expressions belonging to the syntactical category of nominals, of course only if they are single words, are nouns.) In *Little John slept soundly*, for instance, we would regard *Little* to be an n/n, *John* an n, *slept* an $n\backslash s$, and *soundly* an $n\backslash s\backslash n\backslash s$.

Assuming then, that a category "dictionary" listing for each English word all its categories stands at our disposal, the task of finding out whether a given word sequence is a sentence or, more generally, a *well-formed* (or *connex*) expression and, if so, what its *constituent structure* is, could now be solved according to the following utterly mechanical procedure: We would write under each word of the given word sequence the symbols for all the categories to which it belongs, separated by commas, and then start *cancelling* in all possible ways, according to either of the two following rules:

$$\alpha, \alpha\backslash\beta \rightarrow \beta \text{ and } \alpha/\beta, \beta \rightarrow \alpha.$$

(The reading of these rules should be self-explanatory. The first, for instance, reads: Replace the sequence of two category symbols, the first of which is any category symbol whatsover and the second of which consists of the first symbol followed by a left diagonal stroke followed by any category symbol whatsoever, by this last category symbol.) A series of such symbol sequences where each sequence results from its predecessor by one application of a cancellation rule is called a *derivation*. The last line of a derivation is its *exponent*. If this exponent consists of a single symbol, *simple* when it consists of a single letter, *complex* when it contains at least one stroke, the word sequence with this exponent, and with the constituent structure given by the derivation, is well-formed; if the exponent of a certain derivation is, more specifically, *s*, the sequence is a sentence, relative to this derivation.

To illustrate, let us start with the last analyzed expression:

Little John slept soundly.

Let us assume (contrary to fact) that as a result of consulting the category dictionary we would have arrived at just the following category symbol sequence:

(1) $n/n, \ n, \ n\backslash s, \ n\backslash s\backslash\backslash n\backslash s.$

It is easy to see that there are exactly three different ways of performing the first cancellation, starting off three different derivations, viz.:

(2) $n, \ n\backslash s, \ n\backslash s\backslash\backslash n\backslash s.$

(2') $n/n, \ s, \ n\backslash s\backslash\backslash n\backslash s.$

(2") $n\backslash n, \ n, \ n\backslash s.$

(2′) leads into a blind alley. The other two lines, (2) and (2″), each allow for two continuations, of which one again leads into a blind alley, whereas the other allows for just one more derivation, wtih both exponents being s. Let me write down one of these derivations:

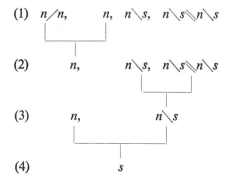

The other derivation differs from the one just presented only in that the two cancellation steps in (2) and (3) occur in the opposite order. These two derivations are therefore *equivalent* in an important sense; in fact, they correspond both to the same *tree expansion*:

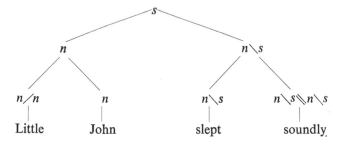

Our second and final example will be:

Paul thought that slept John soundly.

(I hope that the somewhat shaky English of this example will be forgiven; it simplifies making the point without falsifying it.) Copying only the first entry under each word in our fictitious category dictionary, we arrive at

Paul	thought	that	John	slept	soundly
n,	$n\backslash s /\!/ n$,	$n\backslash s$,	n,	$n\backslash s$,	$n\backslash s \backslash\!\backslash n\backslash s$

There are two nonequivalent derivations with a single exponent. I shall again write down only one of these derivations:

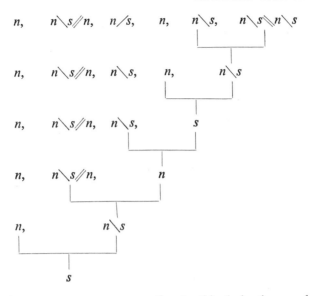

The constituent structure corresponding to this derivation can be pictured in the following parsing diagram:

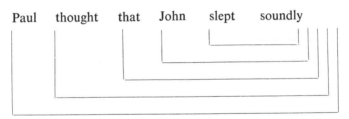

The reader is invited to check that the parsing diagram corresponding to the other derivation is:

Paul   thought   that   John   slept   soundly

If this structure is regarded as unacceptable, this would prove that either the categorization assumed for this illustration is ill-chosen, or else that the whole model is inadequate for English. I shall not pursue this issue further here, since I shall later on proffer stronger reasons for questioning the adequacy of the model.

As said before, the situation actually is more complicated. An adequate category dictionary would contain in general more than one entry per word. *That*, e.g., is often a nominal, n, and even more often an adjectival, n/n; *soundly* could as well be an $n\backslash s /\!/ n\backslash s$ or an $(n\backslash s)/n /\!/ (n\backslash s)/n$, and *thought*, finally, belongs also to categories n, $n\backslash s$, $n\backslash s /\!/ s$ (*Paul thought John was asleep*) and, as a participle, to still others. It can nevertheless readily be seen that our method is capable, at least in certain cases, to determine by purely mechanical operations the specific category to which a given word belongs in its given linguistic context. In our example, e.g., listing all the mentioned categories in column form yields the following scheme:

Paul	thought	that	John	slept	soundly
n	$n\backslash s /\!/ n$	$n\backslash s$	n	$n\backslash s$	$n\backslash s \backslash\!\backslash n\backslash s$
	n	n			$n\backslash s /\!/ n\backslash s$
	$n\backslash s$	$n\backslash n$			$(n\backslash s)/n /\!/ (n\backslash s)/n$
	$n\backslash s /\!/ s$				

It would be a tedious but wholly routine exercise to determine that out of the very many derivations corresponding to this word sequence —notice that there are 36 initial lines alone!—there exist only four essentially different ones with a single exponent, namely, in addition to the two above-mentioned derivations, just

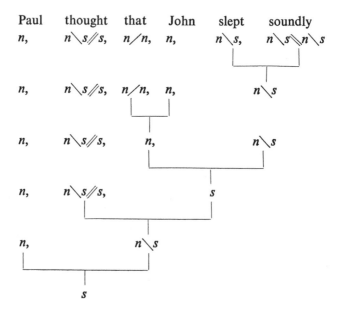

and the one whose parsing diagram would be

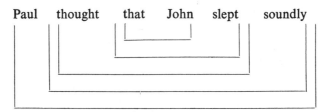

I still remember my surprise a few years ago when I discovered that the third constituent structure is doubtless grammatical, however wildly implausible the conditions under which it would be uttered. I was still less pleasantly surprised when I discovered recently that the second and fourth derivations yield constituent structures whose grammaticalness is highly doubtful. The sentence under discussion is *syntactically ambiguous* (or *constructionally homonymous*).

So far, so good. But, unfortunately, the actual situation is still much more complicated. For categorizing English words, it would be necessary to increase the number of fundamental categories and distinguish various kinds of nominals, for instance, *singular* and *plural*, *animate* and *inanimate*. One would also have to distinguish *declarative sentences*, *question sentences* etc., these being irreducible to each other under the present model. Some additional notational means would have to be found from which it will follow that *John slept*, *The boy slept*, *Boys slept*, *The boys slept* are well-formed but that *Boy slept*, *The John slept* are not, that *The little boy slept* is connex but not *Little the boy slept*—at least not with the parsing diagram

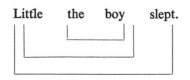

These and thousands of other additional refinements could perhaps still be introduced without blowing up the whole model. But there are many features which make it highly doubtful whether English grammar—or that of any other natural language, for that matter—can at all be forced into the straitjacket of the immediate constituent model and remain workable and revealing. Since the arguments against such a possibility have already been presented by Chomsky [34], I shall not repeat them here in all their generality but restrict myself to the point of view of machine translation.

It takes but little to realize that the four categories mentioned above for *thought* are far from being exhaustive. In addition to its being a participle, which has already been mentioned, there are such phrases as *thought processes, thought thirsty* (not common but definitely grammatical), *thought provoking*, etc. In order to take care of the first two contexts, for example, we would have to assign *thought* also to the categories n/n and $n/n/\!/n/n$. ("In these contexts, *thought* occurs in the function of an adjective or an adverb, respectively" would have been one traditional way of putting the issue.) The third context would have raised the notoriously difficult problem of the status of the participle present, in addition. The task of preparing a category list that would work for all these and many other contexts is certainly much harder than the first successful analyses caused us to believe. Would not the required list become so long that the mechanical determination of the constituent structure of, say, a 30-word sentence might well require trillions of machine operations, hence be totally impractical for machines of today as well as of tomorrow?

It is likely, for instance, that every assignment to a category of the form $\alpha\backslash\beta/\!/\gamma$ (such as the assignment of *thought* to $n\backslash s/\!/s$) will have to be accompanied by an assignment to the category $\alpha\backslash\!\backslash\beta/\gamma$; an attempt to avoid this through unique assignment to $\alpha\backslash\beta/\gamma$ would amount to a change in the notational framework and would require considerable changes in the cancellation rules.

Still worse, it is not clear whether assigning each word to a finite number of categories only would do at all. Should it be requisite to assign some words to an infinity of categories, then the simple mechanical procedure described above of determining the syntactic structure of a given word sequence breaks down, since there is no longer any assurance that the number of derivations is finite at all.

And what about a sentence such as *Playing cards is fun*? On first sight, it seems that one has to arrive at the category n for the phrase *playing cards*. However, it is intuitively clear that this should not be derived from *cards* being an n and playing being an n/n (and not only intuitively so: notice that the next word is *is* and not *are*; *playing cards* in our context is a singular nominal). There are, of course, many other ways of enforcing an assignment of n to playing cards, but none of these, to my knowledge, is such that it would not introduce unwarranted and counterintuitive syntactical resolutions of other sentences. "Hocus-pocus" linguistics—as certain linguistic methods were called whose only purpose was to save certain phenomena, without regard to any intuitive (or psychological) realities—would in our case definitely refute itself by saving also phenomena that are nonexisting.

And what about a sentence like *He looked it up*? We all feel that *looked* and *up* belong together and that in the context *He looked up the table*, at any rate, *up* is an operator that out of an intransitive verbal to its left forms a transitive verbal, hence belongs to the category $n\backslash s\backslash\!\backslash(n\backslash s)/n$. This assignment indeed works well for *He looked up the table*, but would obviously not do for *He looked it up*, since there exists no derivation from

$$n, \quad n\backslash s, \quad n, \quad n\backslash s /\!\!/ (n\backslash s)/ n$$

with an exponent *s*.

Finally, what about a sentence like *John, unfortunately, was asleep*? *Unfortunately*, in the context *Unfortunately, John was asleep*, is clearly an *s/s* but with this category assignment, *John, unfortunately, was asleep* would turn out not to be connex.

If now the present variant of an immediate contituent model is not good enough to serve as a general model for the whole syntax of a given language, the method of mechanical structure determination outlined above can no longer be assumed to be of general validity, either. As a matter of fact, I had already noticed six years ago that the model did not work too well for complex sentences, but had rather hoped that this was due only to lack of refinement that could be partly remedied by increasing the number of fundamental categories, partly by using additional rules. I have now come to realize that its failure in the more complex cases has a much deeper cause: the linguistic model on which this method was based is just not good enough.

The situation is apparently not changed very much by using a more complex model which has been proposed by Lambek [82]. Though he uses in addition to the cancellation rules other rules of a different character which may perhaps allow for a reduction in the number of the machine operations required for a test of sentencehood, it is not clear whether Lambek's model is really more powerful than the one outlined above.

Another model, or rather a whole set of models, for linguistic structure has recently been developed, in outline, by Chomsky [33;34]. (A similar conception has been developed also by Harris [64], but since Chomsky's formulations seem to me much clearer, I prefer to refer to his work in the sequel.) They are incomparably more efficient than the phrase structure models, in all their variants. These so-called *transformational models* do not discard the immediate constituent model but rather supplement it. The former model remains intact for a certain kind of simple sentences, the so-called *kernel sentences* (or rather for their underlying *terminal strings*) —and our method of mechanical structure determination remains therefore valid for these sentences—but has to be supplemented by additional procedures, the so-called *transformations*, in order to account for the synthesis of *all* sentences.

Each sentence, according to the transformational models, is the result of a series of one or more transformations performed one after the other on one or more structured strings—unless, of course, it is a terminal string itself. A complete analysis, mechanical or otherwise, of a given sentence has to tell us what its basic strings are, together with their constituent structure, and what transformations, and in what order, were performed upon them. Assuming that a complete transformational grammar for some given language has been prepared, the preparation of a corresponding *analytical* (or *operational*) grammar is a formidable, though perhaps not necessarily impossible task. There exist here a large number of unsolved problems, partly due to the fact that the nature of the transformations involved have so far been left rather vague, partly to the fact that we find ourselves here within the confines of new and extremely complicated disciplines like recursive function theory, Post canonical systems and the like, the exploration of which has only started. So far, of course, no transformational grammar exists for any language, to any serious degree of completeness.

The recognition that immediate constituent grammars have to be supplemented by transformational grammars makes the task of mechanizing translation look much harder, but the resulting picture is not at all uniformly black. On the contrary, there are reasons to suppose that the additional insight we get on the basis of this model will not only be of decisive importance for theoretical linguistics, but may well turn out to facilitate the mechanization of translation from new angles.

One gain of the transformational model is similar to, but still more effective and more intuitive than the one obtained by Lambek's model: a reduction in the number of categories to which the words will have to be assigned. No longer will *thought* have to be assigned to the categories n/n and $n/n\!\!/n/n$ in order to take care of the connexity of *thought processes* and *thought thirsty*, because sentences containing these phrases are not terminal strings but result from transformations. In addition, the assignment of *thought* to $n\backslash s\!\!/s$ is no longer required, since the sentencehood of *Paul thought John slept soundly* will now be taken care of by our regarding it as the result of a *that*-omitting transformation on *Paul thought that John slept soundly*, which itself is the result of a certain fusing transformation on the two terminal strings *Paul thought this. John slept soundly.* (This description is oversimplified and to that degree misleading. A better description is given in Chomsky's publications. A sufficiently sophisticated treatment would require too much space here.) As a result, the noun *thought* will (perhaps) always be assigned to the syntactical category of nominals, the finite verb *thought* to the syntactic category of transitive verbals, and the participle *thought* to an appropriate syntactical category (with which we shall not bother here), the multiplicity of category assignments to the word *thought* now being considered as exclusively the result of homonymity or homography, as the case may be.

One interesting result of all this will now be that the number of categories of many words will be reduced to — zero. This will happen if no sentence containing these words is regarded as a terminal string. To give an example: *sleeping* will not be assigned to any category, any sentence containing this word being considered as the result of a transformation. (*Interesting*, however, will be assigned to the category n/n, the difference being—to give only a hint—that *very interesting* is connex but not *very sleeping*.) That there might be words which do not belong to any syntactic category will strike many linguists as rather queer, but I am convinced that on second sight they will realize the enormous advantages of such an attitude; innumerable pseudo-problems have in the past been created by the search for the syntactic category (the traditional term is, of course, "part of speech") of certain words or phrases which—under the new model—just do not belong to any category. This is—if I may be allowed one generalization— just one more instance of the very common class of situations where the attempt of applying a model which is very useful within certain limits leads, when pushed beyond them, to pseudo-problems and their pseudo-solutions.

The second gain is somewhat more speculative: it seems likely, but has so far not been seriously tested, that languages will be much more similar with regard to their terminal string structure than with regard to the structure of the totality of their sentences. Word-by-word translation of terminal strings, with some occasional permuting, seems to yield satisfactory results for many pairs of languages, including those for which this kind of translation does not work at all with regard to more complex sentences.

The most remarkable gain, however, would be achieved when it turned out that between the sets of transformations of two languages there existed a close semantic relationship. Should it happen that for certain two languages, L_1 and L_2, there exist two transformations, say t_1 and t_2, such that for any semantically equivalent terminal strings of these languages, k_1 and k_2, $t_1(k_1)$ is semantically equivalent to $t_2(k_2)$, this would allow for a relatively simple mechanization of the translation, provided, of course, that the syntactic analysis of L_1 has been mechanized, whereas a word-by-word translation of $t_1(k_1)$ into L_2 might be highly unsatisfactory.

Of course, there is but little hope that the sets of transformations of two languages which do not stand in any close genetical relationship will do us the favor of exhibiting isomorphism or near-isomorphism with regard to semantic equivalence. So far, there exists to my knowledge no *general* theory of machine translation which would ensure that, if only the precepts of this theory are followed, the target-language counterpart (or counterparts) of any sentence of a given source-language will be no more and no less syntactically ambiguous than the original sentence itself. Current statements to the contrary seem to me palpably false, and any hope for an imminent establishment of such a theory—unsubstantiated. Great progress has been made in this respect with regard to certain ordered pairs of languages, such as French-English, German-English, Russian-English, English-Russian, German-Russian, and French-Russian, partly prior to the appearance of the transformational model and without any conscious use of its methods, and more progress may be expected in the future through a conscious use of these methods. As one almost necessary condition for future success I regard the recognition on behalf of the workers on machine translation that the model with which they were working, consciously or unconsciously, during the first decade of their endeavors was too crude and has to be replaced by a much more complex but also much better fitting model of linguistic structure.

Finite-State Languages: Formal Representations and Adequacy Problems*

7

1. INTRODUCTION

The mechanization of recognizing the syntactic structure (or structures) of a given string of words in some natural language is clearly a worthwhile linguistic aim as such, and probably of decisive importance for applications such as machine translation. In order that the recognition procedure be mechanical it has to rely solely on the *formal* properties and relations of the words under investigation, i.e., on their shape (in case of printed words which alone are considered in this report) and order, to the exclusion of their so-called semantical and pragmatical properties and relations.

For our purposes a *language L* will be understood as a certain subset of the set V^* of all finite non-empty strings of elements of a given finite set, the *vocabulary V*. Each member of the subset will be called a *sentence*. Any language whose vocabulary is V will be called a *language over V*.

By a *grammar* of a language L we understand a finite device (system of rules) which is capable of enumerating the distinguished subset of the set of all strings over V which defines L. A grammar is *formal* if its rules refer solely to the formal properties and relations of the symbols with which it deals.

With regard to *natural languages*, whose grammars are descriptive, in contradistinction to *language systems*, whose grammars are prescriptive, we shall adopt the following view which seems to us a good approximation of the aims we have in mind. The vocabulary of these languages will be regarded as fixed. (This is, of course, not strictly the case; natural languages are not closed but rather "clopen", i.e., partly closed and partly open.) We shall, for simplicity's sake, assume that the speakers of a certain natural language are capable of telling us unanimously whether a given string of words of this language is a definite sentence, a definite non-sentence, or whether they cannot make up their minds. (In order to make this assumption

* First appeared in The Bulletin of the Research Council of Israel, vol. 8F (1960), pp. 155–166.

look less artificial, we may think of a so-called "idiolect", i.e., the dialect of a certain speaker at a certain time.) We shall regard a grammar as *adequate* for this language if (1) every definite sentence of the language is a sentence of the language determined by the grammar, and (2) every definite non-sentence of the natural language is not a sentence in the language determined by the grammar, letting the chips fall as they come on those strings on which the speaker could not make up his mind.

With all due consideration, we hope, of the dangers inherent in a careless use of the unqualified phrase *natural language*, we shall from now on use this short phrase in lieu of other more careful but then also much more long-winded expressions. We hope that the number of misunderstandings arising from our usage will be kept at a minimum.

A mechanical recognition procedure of syntactic structure is possible only if the given language is adequately describable by a grammar fulfilling certain conditions. A new typology of grammars has recently been proposed by Chomsky [33;34;40;35]. The present report further investigates those types of grammars which were called by Chomsky *type 3 grammars* [35], and, more specifically, their adequacy for natural languages.

Our investigations were much influenced by a study of Rabin and Scott on finite automata [128], and we also had the benefit of several stimulating discussions with Dr. Rabin. In fact, we shall show in Section 3 the equivalence of type 3 grammars with finite automata, as defined by Rabin and Scott, and make use in Sections 5, 6 and 7 of some of the results obtained by them.

2. NOTATIONS AND TERMINOLOGY

The vocabulary V, which is a finite set of symbols, will be assumed to be fixed throughout Sections 2–5. We shall use the capital letters B and C (with subscripts, if necessary) for symbols of V and the small letters x, y and z (with subscripts) for nonempty strings of symbols. For the concatenation of the string x and y we shall use xy. V^* is the set of all finite non-empty strings over V, and a language L is any subset of V^*.

We shall deal with certain devices variously called "grammars", "automata" and "machines". These devices will be denoted by bold-face Gothic capitals. Given such a device $\mathfrak{A}$, we shall define when a string x is *accepted* (or *generated*) by $\mathfrak{A}$. Such a string will also be called a sentence of $L(\mathfrak{A})$, the *language determined* by $\mathfrak{A}$. Two devices $\mathfrak{A}_1$ and $\mathfrak{A}_2$ are *equivalent* if $L(\mathfrak{A}_1)=L(\mathfrak{A}_2)$. If a language $L=L(\mathfrak{A})$, we shall call $\mathfrak{A}$ a *representation* of L.

3. THE EQUIVALENCE OF FINITE AUTOMATA AND TYPE 3 GRAMMARS

Definition 1: A *deterministic finite automaton* (DFA) over V is an ordered quadruple $\mathfrak{D} = (S,M,\bar{s},F)$, where S is a finite non-empty set (the *internal states* of $\mathfrak{D}$), M is a function from $S \times V$ into S (the *table of moves of* $\mathfrak{D}$), $\bar{s}$ is a distinguished element of S (the *initial state of* $\mathfrak{D}$), and F is a subset of S (the *final states* of $\mathfrak{D}$). A string $x = B_0 B_1 \ldots B_{n-1}$ is *accepted* by $\mathfrak{D}$ if the sequence of states $s_0, s_1, \ldots, s_n$, defined recursively by:

$$s_0 = \bar{s}, \quad s_{i+1} = M(s_i, B_i) \quad (i = 0, 1, \cdots, n-1) \tag{1}$$

satisfies $s_n \in F$. This sequence is called the *accepting state sequence* of x.

A DFA may be viewed as a machine capable of "reading" the string with which it is fed, say on consecutive squares of a tape in the well-known Turing fashion. The internal state of the machine at each moment is one of the states $s_i \in S$, and specifically $\bar{s}$ whenever it starts scanning the left-most symbol of a string fed to it. It reads the string from left to right, symbol after symbol; the internal state at each moment is uniquely determined by its internal state at the previous moment and the symbol then scanned. The string x is accepted if the machine switches into one of its final states after having scanned the right-most symbol of the string.

Definition 2: A *non-deterministic finite automaton* (NFA) is an ordered quadruple $\mathfrak{R} = (S, M, I, F)$ where S is a finite non-empty set (the *internal states*), M is a function from $S \times V$ into the set of all subsets of S (the *table of possible moves*), I and F are distinguished subsets of S (the *initial* and *final states*, respectively). A string $x = B_0 B_1 \ldots B_{n-1}$ is *accepted* by $\mathfrak{R}$ in case there exists a sequence of states $s_0, s_1, \ldots, s_n$ (an *accepting state sequence*) such that

$$s_0 \in I, \quad s_{i+1} \in M(s_i, B_i) \quad (0 \leqq i \leqq n-1), \text{ and } s_n \in F. \tag{2}$$

We note that the main difference between a NFA and a DFA is: if $M(s_i, B_i)$ is a subset of S which contains several elements, then a NFA has several possible moves in the "configuration" (s_i, B_i). If $M(s_i, B_i)$ is the empty subset, the machine is "blocked." Reading through a string x will, in general, give rise to several state sequences. In order that x be accepted it is (necessary and) sufficient that one of these sequences be an accepting state sequence (i.e., terminate with $s_1 \in F$).

It is clear that the NFA in which $M(s_i, B_i)$ consists, for each i, of a single element, is just a DFA. In the general case, it might seem that the class of languages determined by NFAa would be more extensive than the class of languages determined by DFAa. However, it turns out that this is not the case. In fact, we have

Theorem 1: For every NFA $\mathfrak{R}$ there exists an equivalent DFA $\mathfrak{D}$.

Indeed $\mathfrak{D}$ can be readily (and effectively) obtained from $\mathfrak{R}$ by taking all the sets of states of $\mathfrak{R}$ (including the empty set) as the states of $\mathfrak{D}$. For a detailed proof see [128]. (An analogous theorem concerning FSGs — see next definition — appears in [40].) It should be noted that the proof covers also the case where several $M(s_i, B_i)$ are empty, i.e. where M is in effect a *partial function*.

Definition 3: A *finite state grammar* (FSG) over V is an ordered triple $\mathfrak{F} = (S, \bar{s}, R)$, where S is a finite non-empty set (the *states* of $\mathfrak{F}$), $\bar{s}$ is an element of S (*the initial state*), and R is a subset of the Cartesian product $S \times V \times S$, i.e. a set of ordered triples (s_i, B_j, s_k). Each such triple will be called a *rule* (of the grammar) *associated with* the state s_i.

A string $x = B_1 B_1 \ldots B_{n-1}$ is *generated* by $\mathfrak{F}$ in case there exists a sequence of states $s_0, s_1, \ldots, s_n$ (a *generating state sequence*) such that

$$
\begin{aligned}
&\text{(i)} \quad s_0 = \bar{s} = s_n, \\
&\text{(ii)} \quad (s_i, B_i, s_{i+1}) \in R \quad (0 \leq i \leq n-1), \\
&\text{(iii)} \quad s_i \neq \bar{s} \quad (1 \leq i \leq n-1).
\end{aligned}
\tag{3}
$$

A FSG may be viewed as a machine capable of "generating" strings, say by printing symbols on consecutive squares of a tape. The machine starts operating when in state $\bar{s}$. At each moment it is in one of the states $s_i \in$ S. During the next moment, it switches into one state out of a certain number of states and simultaneously prints one symbol out of a certain number of symbols (say, at random). The machine generates a sentence during each run starting at $\bar{s}$ and ending at $\bar{s}$ (while never at $\bar{s}$ in between).

We picture a FA as a *recognition grammar*, i.e., a device which *accepts* strings in case they are sentences and *rejects* them in case they are non-sentences, whereas a FSG is pictured rather as a *production grammar*, i.e., a device which *produces* sentences (and nothing but sentences) as end-products. This distinction is only of heuristic importance here, but in the next chapter, where we are going to deal with so-called phrase structure grammars, it will become also theoretically important.

Theorem 2: For every NFA $\mathfrak{N}$ there is a FSG $\mathfrak{F}$ such that $L(\mathfrak{N}) = L(\mathfrak{F})$; conversely, for every FSG $\mathfrak{F}$ there is a NFA $\mathfrak{N}$ such that $L(\mathfrak{F}) = L(\mathfrak{N})$.

Proof of the first part: Assume $\mathfrak{N} = (S, M, I, F)$. Let now $\bar{S} = S \cup \{\bar{s}\}$, where $\bar{s}$ is a new state not contained in S, and let R contain the following triples:

$$
\begin{aligned}
&\text{(i)} \quad (s_i, B_j, s_k), \text{ if } s_k \in M(s_i, B_j); \\
&\text{(ii)} \quad (s_i, B_j, \bar{s}), \text{ if for some } m, s_m \in F \text{ and } s_m \in M(s_i, B_j); \\
&\text{(iii)} \quad (\bar{s}, B_j, s_k), \text{ if for some } m, s_m \in I \text{ and } s_k \in M(s_m, B_j); \\
&\text{(iv)} \quad (\bar{s}, B_j, \bar{s}), \text{ if for some } m, s_m \in I \text{ and for some } k, \\
&\qquad\qquad s_k \in F \text{ and } s_k \in M(s_m, B_j).
\end{aligned}
\tag{4}
$$

Let, finally, $\mathfrak{F} = (\bar{S}, \bar{s}, R)$.

It is clear from this construction that if $s_0, s_1, \cdots, s_{n-1}, s_n$ is an accepting state sequence for a string x in $\mathfrak{N}$, then $\bar{s}, s_1, \cdots, s_{n-1}, \bar{s}$ is a generating state sequence for x in $\mathfrak{F}$. (Since $\bar{s} \notin S$, the condition $s_i \neq \bar{s}$ for $1 \leq i \leq n-1$ is fulfilled.) Conversely, if $\bar{s}, s_1, \cdots, s_{n-1}, \bar{s}$ is a generating state sequence for x in $\mathfrak{F}$, then there exist $s_0 \in I$ and $s_n \in F$ such that $s_0, s_1, \cdots, s_{n-1}, s_n$ is an accepting state sequence for x in $\mathfrak{N}$. It follows that $L(\mathfrak{F}) = L(\mathfrak{N})$.

The construction given here may also be applied to convert a general NFA into an equivalent one having a single initial state $\bar{s}$ and a single final state $\bar{\bar{s}}$ (with, if desired, $\bar{s} = \bar{\bar{s}}$). (However, this is not true if we admit the empty string into our languages; cf. remark at the end of this section.)

Proof of the second part; Assume $\mathfrak{F} = (S, \bar{s}, R)$. Let $\bar{S} = S \cup \{\bar{\bar{s}}\}$, where $\bar{\bar{s}}$ is a new state not contained in S, and let M be defined as follows:

(i)   If $(s_i, B, \bar{s}) \notin R$, then $M(s_i, B_j) = \{s' \in S \mid (s_i, B_j, s') \in R\}$;
(ii) if $(s_i, B_j, \bar{s}) \in R$, then $M(s_i, B_j) = \{s' \in S \mid s' \neq \bar{s} \text{ and } (s_i, B_j, s') \in R\} \ldots \{\bar{\bar{s}}\}$;
(iii) for every $B_j \in V$, $M(\bar{\bar{s}}, B_j) = \emptyset$.

$(S, M, \{\bar{s}\}, \{\bar{\bar{s}}\})$ is the required NFA. Indeed, $\bar{s}, s_1, \cdots, s_{n-1}, \bar{\bar{s}}$ is an accepting state sequence in $\mathfrak{N}$ for a string x if and only if $\bar{s}, s_1, \cdots, s_{n-1}, \bar{s}$ is a generating state sequence for x in $\mathfrak{F}$. Note that for all pairs $(s_i B_j)$, $\bar{s} \notin M(s_i, B_j)$, and thus requirement (3) (iii) is automatically fulfilled by the accepting state sequences in $\mathfrak{N}$. Hence dropping it does not effect $L(\mathfrak{N})$. It follows that $x \in L(\mathfrak{N})$ if and only if $x \in L(\mathfrak{F})$. Q.E.D.

Remark: We excluded throughout the empty string 0 from our languages. Rabin-Scott, however, include 0. According to them 0 is accepted by (S, M, I, F) just in case $I \cap F \neq \emptyset$.

Chomsky also includes the empty string. But as he requires, in his definition of FSG, that the initial state $\bar{s}$ be also the final state, the empty string always belongs to $L(\mathfrak{G})$. Thus the equivalence of FSGs and NFAa ceases to be true if we take the empty string into consideration. (Cf. [72: Section 8] for another example where the empty string has to be excluded in order to establish an equivalence theorem between automata.)

If we deviate from Chomsky's original definition by not requiring the final state $\bar{s}$ to be identical with the initial state $\bar{s}$, the full equivalence with NFAa is re-established. The empty string will now be generated by $\mathfrak{G}$ just in case $\bar{s} = \bar{\bar{s}}$.

Note that the exclusion of the empty string makes possible the reduction of a NFA into an equivalent one having a single initial and a single final state. This is not true if the empty string is admitted. Thus the set $\{0, A\}$ is representable only by an automaton having several initial or several final states. (This remark is due to M. Perles.)

4. PROPERTIES OF FINITE STATE LANGUAGES

A language of the form $L(\mathfrak{D})$, where $\mathfrak{D}$ is a DFA, is called a *finite state language* (FSL). It follows, from theorems proved above, that languages determined by NFAa or FSGs are also finite state languages. In this section we shall list several theorems regarding properties of FSLs and their representations, especially some properties of proper linguistic interest arising when the FSG model is applied to natural languages. Proofs of these theorems are not given here; they may be found in [128] or [40].

Theorem 3: A finite set of strings is a FSL.

Theorem 4: (Closure under Boolean operations) The complement of a FSL over V with respect to V^* is a FSL. The intersection and union of two FSLs are FSLs.

Theorem 5: Let L be a FSL over V. Then the language L' obtained by omitting all occurrences of a fixed symbol $B \in V$ in all the sentences of L is again a FSL.

For the next theorem we shall first introduce the notion of a congruence relation.

Definition 4: R is a *congruence relation* in V^* if R is an equivalence relation defined for all pairs of strings and if $x_1 R y_1$ and $x_2 R y_2$ entails $x_1 x_2 R y_1 y_2$.

Being an equivalence relation, R induces a partition of V^* into mutually exclusive equivalence classes which we shall call here *congruence classes*. A congruence relation R is *of finite index* if the number of congruence classes induced by it is finite.

Theorem 6: L is a FSL if and only if L is the union of some of the congruence classes induced by a congruence relation of finite index.

Theorem 6 gives an intrinsic characterization of FSLs which does not rely on a representation by a FA or a FSG. This characterization is quite useful in the investigation of FSLs and, as we shall see in the next section, has interesting consequences.

The next two theorems will assert that for some elementary properties of FSLs, represented by FAa, there are effective decision procedures.

Theorem 7: Given a DFA $\mathfrak{D}$, there exists an effective procedure to decide whether $L(\mathfrak{D})$ is empty, finite or infinite.

Theorem 7 and the possibility of effectively constructing DFAa representing the complement of $L(\mathfrak{D})$ and the intersection of $L(\mathfrak{D}_1)$ and $L(\mathfrak{D}_2)$ entail:

Theorem 8: Given two DFAa $\mathfrak{D}_1$ and $\mathfrak{D}_2$, there exist effective procedures to decide whether $L(\mathfrak{D}_1) = L(\mathfrak{D}_2)$ and whether $L(\mathfrak{D}_1) \cap L(\mathfrak{D}_2)$ is empty.

Since for a given FSG an equivalent NFA was effectively constructed in Section 3, and a DFA equivalent to a given NFA can also be effectively constructed, it follows that the properties in Theorems 7 and 8 can be effectively decided from any of the representations of FSLs treated here.

We shall finally mention still another representation of FSLs, namely by *two-way finite automata* (TFAa). The exact definition of a TFA is given in [128]. Such an automaton can also "move" backward, the movement (backward, forward or stationary) being determined, like the new state, by the configuration (s_i, B_i). A string is accepted by a TFA if the automaton ever reaches the rightmost symbol and, having scanned it, moves forward and winds up in a final state. Rabin and Scott proved that TFAa add nothing new: for every such automaton there exists an equivalent DFA. Another, more elegant proof of this fact has been given in [137].

5. APPLICATION OF FSGs TO NATURAL LANGUAGES

The use of FSGs as models for natural languages has many highly attractive features. We can indeed find some interesting connections between FSGs and many concepts of conventional grammars.

We recall that by Theorem 6 a FSG $\mathfrak{F}$ induces a partition of the class of all strings into a finite number of congruence classes with respect to a congruence relation R, and that the union of some of these classes constitutes the set of sentences $L(\mathfrak{F})$. We may call the congruence class to which a string belong the *syntactical class* of x. Then some syntactical classes are classes of sentences and the others are classes of non-sentences. Because of the congruence, two strings of the same syntactical class are interchangeable in any context without changing the syntactical class of the whole context (especially, without changing its status as to sentencehood). This relation of *commutability* has often been used in modern linguistics as a basis for the definition of "syntactical category" and related terms, for languages in general, whatever the type of their determining grammar. In a FSL *every* string (and not only single words or special combinations) belongs to a syntactical class, the number of these classes is finite, and the commutability of strings of the same category holds universally.

If we represent a FSL by a DFA, then every string is associated with a sequence of states. In case of a NFA or a FSG, every sentence or even every string the machine can read or print (without being blocked) is associated, in general, with several state sequences, namely those sequences the machine assumes while reading, or printing, the string. (These include the accepting or generating state sequences, in case of a sentence.) "Linguistic meaning" can then be given to the internal states. We shall not try to do this here but only note the phenomenon of *constructional homonymity* which appears when the representation is by a NFA or a FSG. The phenomenon arises when a sentence has several representing sequences, i.e., several different "constructions". (Chomsky [33;34] attaches, rightfully, much importance to the ability of a grammar to discriminate homonymities by constructional methods, but he does not seem to have been aware of the fact that this is theoretically possible even in a FSG model.)

The use of a FSG model has the following advantage: Suppose two (or more) grammarians suggest different grammars for the same language. If these grammars are FSGs, we have a mechanical method of checking whether they are equivalent or not (by Theorem 8). This is noteworthy since, as we shall prove in Chapter 9, it is no longer the case for more complex models.

6. CONDITIONAL INADEQUACY OF FSG MODELS FOR NATURAL LANGUAGES

Are FSGs adequate for natural languages such as English?

The answer is trivial if the number of grammatical English sentences is taken to be finite, since in view of Theorem 3 every finite set is a FSL. In this case, the length (number of words) of the sentences is bounded and there exist longest sentences. It follows that certain very convenient recursive grammatical rules such as:

R.1   If x and y are sentences, then x *and* y is also a sentence,

could not be applied without restrictions. The use of unrestricted recursive rules of various kinds for forming sentences or clauses allows for a simpler and more compact formulation of the syntax. If we insist on taking the set of English sentences to be finite, we have to put some bound on the number of times the recursive rules may operate, or renounce their use altogether. None of these procedures looks attractive, and we believe, like Chomsky, that they should be avoided as much as possible.

However, R.1 does not yet transcend the reach of a FSG, as can easily be shown. This reach is however transcended by the following rule:

R.2   If x and y are sentences, then   *If x then y*   is also a sentence.

Indeed we can prove the following conditional

Theorem 9: If R.2 is a rule of English grammar, then English is not adequately representable by a FSG.

Proof: Let n be the number of congruence classes of the congruence relation R induced by a proposed FSG for English. Among any $n + 1$ different strings, at least two are in the same class. Thus, out of the following $n + 1$ strings:

$$if,\ if^2\ (= if\ if),\cdots, if^{n+1}$$

at least two are in the same class. Let $x_1 = if^k$ and $x_2 = if^m (k \neq m)$, and suppose that x_1 is congruent to x_2. Let y_1 and y_2 be any two sentences and let $z = y_1\ (then\ y_2)^k$. Now $x_1 z = if^k y_1\ (then\ y_2)^k$ is a sentence, under the antecedent of our conditional, but $x_2 z = if^m y_1 (then\ y_2)^k$ is definitely not a sentence. Hence $x_1 z$ and $x_2 z$ are in *different* classes. But by the properties of the congruence relation $x_1 R x_2$ entails $x_1 z R x_2 z$, hence $x_1 z$ and $x_2 z$ are in the *same* class. This contradiction proves that the proposed FSG would not be adequate.

[We might as well admit that this proof is not totally convincing since our statement that $if^k y_1 (then\ y_2)^m (k \neq m)$ is *definitely* not a sentence may be challenged. There might be some who would perhaps accept another example which is formally similar but linguistically sufficiently different. If someone is ready to grant that a phrase of the type

$$anti\text{-}^k missile^m \quad (k \geqq 0,\ m \geqq 1)$$

is well-formed if and only if $m = k + 1$, an analogous argument can be carried through.]

Most linguists as well as most ordinary speakers of English—in contradistinction to most logicians—would regard the above conditional as counterfactual. Indeed, very few would want to commit themselves to regarding the string

If if it rains then it pours then if it rains then it pours

as an English sentence. How many would regard this string as a definite non-sentence and how many would hesitate to commit themselves, we do not know. The different attitude of the logicians is conditioned by the fact that counterparts of R.2 are standard formation rules in any formalized language system. Linguists might perhaps be ready to accept a rule like

R.2a If x and y are sentences and x does not start with *if*, then *if x then y* is also a sentence.

However, if we replace in Theorem 9 "R.2" by "R.2a", this theorem can no longer be established by the proof given above.

The argument employed in this proof can also be used to show the unconditional inadequacy of a FSG for English, though only in a restricted and practical sense. The argument shows that whenever $x_1 R x_2$, $z_1 R z_2$ but not $x_1 y_1 z_1 R x_2 y_2 z_2$, y_1 and y_2 are not congruent and have therefore to be put in different classes. For instance, as soon as we can exhibit even a single English sentence which turns into a non-sentence when one of its constituent strings y_1 is replaced by y_2, these two strings are thereby shown to belong to different syntactical classes. Since this can probably be done for almost any pair of English strings, we would no doubt get an enormous number of syntactical classes, probably not much less than the number of words, and conceivably even more, since there need not exist, for every string, a single word belonging to the syntactical class of the string. The number of states of the representing FSG, though much smaller, would still be very large. Altogether the resulting grammar would be inadequate in the sense of being "unrevealing" and impractical.

One might want to prove the inadequacy of a FSG from the following fact: Let the vocabulary of some language contain exactly $2k$ words, say $A_1, A_1', A_2, A_2', ..., A_k, A_k'$. Whenever x is a string over the unprimed words, let x' be the string of the corresponding primed words. Let the sentences be all and only the strings of the form xx'. It can then easily be shown that the resulting language is not finite state. Now, it is not implausible to assume that English does indeed contain constructions of approximately this form. Even linguists might perhaps consent that a string of the form:

John, Mary, David,..., are a widower, a widow, a widower,---, respectively,

is a grammatical sentence if and only if the three dots are replaced by a string of any length of proper names, with repetitions and commas between the names, and the three dashes by a string of equally many phrases of one of the forms *a widower* or *a widow* and such that whenever the n-th proper name is male (or female), the n-th phrase is *a widower* (or a *widow*).

However, one might argue that no English speaker in his senses would want to utter a string of this form containing, say, more than 20 proper names in a row, since neither he himself nor the listener could possibly remember the correct sequence of *a widower* and *a widow*. On the other hand, this argument seems to show that even an unlimited string of this form would be regarded as a sentence *on principle* though not as one that should be used, just as replacing all periods in the present section by commas and putting *and* after them would result in something that would perhaps be regarded as a sentence though not as one to be recommended in English composition classes.

We ourselves tend to regard this second inadequacy proof as almost conclusive in showing that English cannot be adequately described by a FSL. (It shows, incidentally, much more than this. It shows also the inadequacy of the simple phrase structure grammars to be discussed in the next chapter.)

The following point is probably worth making in this connection. The standard Propositional Calculus contains connectives, & and ∨, whose interpretation is approximately *and* and *or*, respectively. The English sentence,

On parents' day, Mary will play the piano and John will recite or Paul will sing,

is ambiguous as is the expression

Five minus three plus one,

whereas the rules of formation of the Propositional Calculus or Formalized Arithmetic would not allow for such ambiguity by requiring, for instance, that whenever p and q are sentences, $(p \& q)$ and $(p \vee q)$ are sentences, and that whenever a and b are numerical terms, $(a + b)$ and $(a - b)$ are numerical terms. Each of the two English strings would then have two formal correspondents, the first $((p \& q) \vee r)$ and $(p \& (q \vee r))$, the second $((5-3)+1)$ and $(5-(3+1))$, respectively, each of which is completely unambiguous.

If there were no other reasons for regarding English as not being adequately describable by a FSG, the above-mentioned rule R.1 and the rule

R.3   If x and y are sentences, then $x \, or \, y$ is also a sentence

would not transcend the finite state character. On the other hand, if the rules for printed English had been

R.1a   If x and y are sentences, then $(x \, and \, y)$ is also a sentence,

R.3a   If x and y are sentences, then $(x \, or \, y)$ is also a sentence,

then English would no longer be a FSL, just as the languages of the Propositional Calculus and Formalized Arithmetic are not. Not transcending the framework of a FSL, at least under certain conditions, can then apparently be obtained by paying the price of additional ambiguity. It has been observed by Pike [116] that English speakers are able to make up to four scope differentiations while uttering arithmetical statements. This would still leave spoken English finite state in this respect, though by increasing the number of states required for producing (and recognizing) these differences, the number of ambiguities is kept at a size which is tolerable in most ordinary communicative situations.

7. FURTHER INADEQUACY PROOFS

In this section we shall use several results listed in Section 4 in order to prove that certain seemingly more powerful grammars can be shown to be equivalent to FSGs and thus to be again (probably) inadequate for the description of English.

FSLs form a Boolean algebra (Theorem 4). It is therefore impossible to represent English by unions and intersections of FSLs and their complements. This is important since for other types of grammars one does obtain stronger models by means of Boolean operations.

The fact that for every TFA there exists an equivalent DFA (end of Section 4) shows that we cannot represent English even by a machine capable of running forward *and backward* in the sense of TWAa. This fact is somewhat more surprising than the fact that (one-way) DFAa are inadequate. From Theorem 5 follows that the addition of special end-markers on both sides of the string, giving the two-way machine a capacity of recognizing the beginning and the end of the strings, does not increase the power of the model. Chomsky and Miller already proved [40] that terminal punctuation does not increase the power of the FSG model, but our present result is slightly stronger.

We shall, finally, prove the following

Theorem 10: Let $L(\mathfrak{F})$ be a FSL over V and let f be a one-valued function from W to V. The inverse functon f^{-1} is then a many-valued function from V to W which induces a mapping of $L(\mathfrak{F})$ on a set of strings over W. This set is a FSL over W.

The proof is immediate. All we have to do is to replace each rule (a_i, B_j, s_k) of $\mathfrak{F}$ by all the new rules $(s_i, f^{-1}(B_j), s_k)$.

Theorem 10 shows that certain replacements of the vocabulary of a FSL do not change the status of the resulting languages. For the representation of English, or some part of it, it is very probably more economical to use the vocabulary of syntactical classes (Nominals, Verbals, Adjectivals, etc.) and only ultimately substitute in the strings of the symbols denoting these classes the actual English words. This change will not cause English to become adequately representable by a FSG. In fact, Theorem 10 shows that the special vocabulary chosen does not play an important role in the proof of the inadequacy.

On Categorial and Phrase Structure Grammars*

8

INTRODUCTION

In Chapter 7, some properties of finite-state grammars (FSGs), in the sense of Chomsky [33; 34; 40; 35], and their relation to finite automata, in the sense of Rabin and Scott [128], were discussed. The present chapter is dedicated to a study of certain more complex types of grammars discussed by Chomsky, which we call *simple phrase structure grammars* (SPGs), and their relation to what we propose to call *categorial grammars* (CGs), certain types of which were discussed by Leśniewski [88], Ajdukiewicz [1] and in Chapters 5 and 6.

The plan of this chapter is as follows. In Section 1, the historical background of these grammar types is sketched. In Section 2, the basic concepts to be discussed in this chapter are introduced. Section 3 contains the proof of the main result of the chapter, viz. the equivalence between SPGs and various kinds of CGs. As a corollary, these kinds of CGs are shown to be equivalent to each other. Section 4 contains a short remark on the adequacy of SPGs for representations of natural languages.

In the next chapter, we shall study the behavior of SPGs under Boolean operations and the relation between SPGs and finite automata; there we shall also deal with various decision problems connected with SPGs.

1. HISTORICAL SURVEY

The Polish logician St. Leśniewski [88] introduced his *theory of semantical categories* for certain logico-philosophical reasons, under the impact of Husserl's *Bedeutungskategorien* on the one hand and Bertrand Russell's logical types on the other. However, this theory remained almost unnoticed outside of Poland until, in 1935, K. Ajdukiewicz [1] presented a more generally accessible version of it. In its full rigor, it was meant to apply not so much to natural languages as to artificial language systems and

---

* First appeared in **The Bulletin of the Research Council of Israel,** vol. 9F (1960), pp. 1–16.

among these more specifically to those written in the so-called Polish (parenthesis-free) notation, i.e., the notation in which the *operators* (or *functors*) are always written to the immediate left of their *arguments*. This notation allows us, for instance, to distinguish without the use of parentheses between arithmetical expressions which in the ordinary notation are distinguishable only by the use of parentheses. Instead of $(a + b) \cdot c$ and $a + (b \cdot c)$, for instance, the Polish notation has $\cdot + abc$ and $+ a \cdot bc$, respectively. In a grammar of the type envisaged by Ajdukiewicz, one distinguishes between *primitive* (or *fundamental*) categories, denoted by simple symbols (such as 's' for the category of *sentences* and 'n' for the category of *nominals*), and *derived* (or *operator*) categories symbolized by complex symbols of the form $[\alpha / \beta]$—read: alpha super beta—, where α and β are any categories, primitive or derived. The only rule of operation in such a grammar is :

C.1 Replace a string of two category symbols of the form $[\alpha / \beta]$, β by α, in (metatheoretical) symbols:

$$[\alpha / \beta], \beta \to \alpha.$$

This operation recalls cancellation of fractions, hence the term *cancellation* for it.

In order to find out, for instance, whether $= \cdot + abcd$ is a sentence (of a certain formalized language of algebra) and, more generally, what the structure of this string is, one would consult the category list of the vocabulary of this language and find, let us say, that a, b, c and d belong to the category n, $+$ and $\cdot$ to the category $[[n/n]/n]$, and $=$ to the category $[[s/n]/n]$. The category string[1] corresponding to the given string would then be

=	+		a	b	c	d
$[[s/n]/n]$,	$[[n/n]/n]$,	$[[n/n]/n]$,	n,	n,	n,	n.

This string can univocally be cancelled, by six applications of C.1, to s, as the reader will readily verify for himself. Thereby the sentencehood of the string is established and its precise internal syntactical structure determined.

If one would like to look upon English intransitive verbs, as seems intuitively plausible, as belonging to operator categories which out of nominals (whether single words or longer strings) form sentences, then a *unidirectional categorial grammar* (UCG) of the type treated by Ajdukie-

---

[1] We shall from now on use the term *category* ambiguously, but (we hope) not confusingly, for both *category* and *category symbol*.

wicz would clearly be inadequate for ordinary English. The category string corresponding to *John died*, for instance, would be $n,[s/n]$ to which the rule of cancellation C.1 is not applicable. Such a UCG would, however, work in this case for a kind of pseudo-English written in Polish notation, as it were, e.g., for the pseudo-sentence *Died John*. Similarly it is not applicable to the English *David loves Marcia*, but would be applicable to the pseudo-English *Loves David Marcia*.

Leśniewski and Ajdukiewicz were primarily philosophers and logicians and as such not directly interested in the problem of the mechanical determination of syntactic structure within natural languages. When this problem became prominent around 1950, both because of developments in linguistic methodology and its central importance for such applications as machine translation, I extended Ajdukiewicz's theory in three ways: (a) assignment of more than one category to words was allowed; (b) a new kind of operator categories was introduced, operating upon arguments at their immediate left, so that now, whenever α and β were categories, $[\alpha \backslash \beta]$—read: alpha sub beta—was regarded as a category too; (c) in this connection an additional rule of cancellation was introduced:

C.2 Replace a string of two categories of the form $\alpha,[\alpha \backslash \beta]$ by β,

in symbols:

$$\alpha,[\alpha \backslash \beta] \to \beta.$$

(As a matter of historical fact, both Ajdukiewicz and myself originally envisaged employing operators with any finite number of arguments together with cancellation rules of a somewhat different kind. In Chapter 5, for instance, I envisaged a rule to the effect that, whenever $\alpha_1, \cdots, \alpha_n, \beta_1, \cdots, \beta_m$, and γ were categories, $[\alpha_n, \cdots, \alpha_1 \backslash \gamma / \beta_1, \cdots, \beta_m]$ was a category, too—though I had used at the time a less expedient notation—and employed a cancellation rule of the form (in effect):

$$\alpha_n, \cdots, \alpha_1, [\alpha_n, \cdots, a_1 \backslash \gamma / \beta_1, \cdots, \beta_m], \beta_1, \cdots, \beta_m \to \gamma.$$

This approach, though in a certain obvious sense more economical, involves dfficulties because of which it was later, in Chapter 6, changed into the one described above.)

In the above English strings, *died* could now be assigned to $[n/s]$ and *loves* to $[[n \backslash s]/n]$, thereby insuring the smooth cancellation to s of the category strings corresponding to *John died* and *David loves Marcia*, in one or two steps, respectively. The examples above show that a quite extensive sub-language of ordinary English can be adequately described by a *bidirectional categorial grammar* (BCG) of the type envisaged in Chapter 5, and this for intuitively natural-looking category assignments. This, of course, is not the case for a UCG, for "natural" category assignments. Thereby, however, the question is not answered whether for any given BCG there does not exist an equivalent UCG, perhaps an "unnatural" one, determining exactly the same set of sentences, hence the same language. This problem, which seems to us of considerable interest, has not been solved before, to our knowledge, and may not have been posed before. Its positive solution follows as a corollary from a theorem proven further on; moreover, an even stronger equivalence statement follows from this theorem, viz., the equivalence of both these kinds of grammars to *restricted categorial grammars* (RCGs) whose categories are restricted to the three forms $\alpha, [\beta \backslash \alpha]$, and $[[\gamma \backslash \beta] \backslash \alpha]$, where α, β and γ are primitive.

On the other hand, it is quite clear that there exist English strings ordinarily regarded as sentences, which would not turn out to be sentences even in a BCG, so long, at least, as the category assignments are natural. Simple examples are: *He looked it up* or *John, unfortunately, died.* Neither of the corresponding "natural" category assignments, viz:

He	looked	it	up	John	unfortunately	died
$n,$	$[n \backslash s],$	$n,$	$[[n \backslash s] / [[n \backslash s] / n]],$	$n,$	$[s \backslash s],$	$[n \backslash s],$

cancels to s, as the reader will easily verify. Each of these two strings can of course be taken care of by some artificial category assignment—the second, for instance, by assigning to *unfortunately* (forgetting for the moment about the commas) the category $[[n \backslash s] / [n \backslash s]]$. But now the highly interesting question arises whether such assignments, artificial, counter-intuitive, *ad hoc*, or whatever other disparaging epithets those who dislike them would use in this context, can at all be made without causing the resulting grammar to be clearly too wide, in the sense that certain intuitively definite non-sentences would be assigned the category s. In addition to this theoretical question, one might, and in certain circumstances has to ask the question whether such a description would be humanly, or machine-wise, manageable; for instance, whether the recognition procedure for sentencehood and internal structure of an English string of some 40 words in length would not require a hyper-astronomical number of operations that could not be performed at all in a reasonable time by even the fastest machines of the present and future.

For these reasons, I did not continue for a time my work on categorial grammars. In the meantime, Chomsky had started his investigations into the general theory of linguistic models, the first generally accessible results of which appeared in 1956 [33]. His approach, partly perhaps under the influence of the then fashionable mode of thinking in terms of Markov processes imported from the statistical theory of communication [136], was to look on grammar as a device for the *generation* (or *production*) of the set of grammatical sentences, rather than as a device for the *recognition* of given strings as sentences.

This approach is the standard one for the *combinatorial systems* conceived much earlier by Post [120] as a result of his penetrating researches into the structure of formal calculi, though Chomsky seems to have become aware of the proximity of his ideas with those of Post only at a later stage of his work.

Chomsky originally distinguished three types of grammars which he christened, in order of increasing strength, *finite-state grammars*, *phrase-structure grammars*, and *transformational grammars*, respectively. Since then he has developed his ideas in a series of publications of which especially the book **Syntactic Structures** [34] has attracted wide-spread attention.

The problem arose of determining the exact relationships between these types of grammars and the categorial grammars. I surmised in 1958 that the BCGs were of approximately the same strength as phrase-structure grammars of the special kind which was later called by Chomsky [35] *type-2 grammars* and which shall be called here *simple phrase structure grammars* (SPGs). A proof of their exact equivalence was found in June 1959 by Gaifman. It was later simplified by Shamir and is given below in Theorems 1 and 2. As a by-product of this theorem the equivalence of various kinds of CGs was obtained.

The equivalence of these different kinds of grammars should not be too surprising. Each of them was meant to be a precise explicatum of the notion of *immediate constituent grammars* which has served for many years as the favorite grammar type of American descriptive linguistics as exhibited, for instance, in the well-known books by Harris [62] and Hockett [71]. (However, it is doubtful whether these explicata were adequate; cf. Chomsky [35:148].)

Still the two explicata were based on different principles, and in many cases different precise explicata of a vague intuitive notion do not turn out to be equivalent. That CGs and PSGs should be equivalent is therefore by no means trivial. Still less trivial is the corollary to the effect that the various kinds of CGs we treat are equivalent among themselves. (Indeed, we were unable to find a direct proof for this corollary.) The difficult part in the proof of the equivalence is to establish that every PSG can effectively be described by a CG. The reader will probably find the proof of this part rather long and tedious.

2. DEFINITIONS AND NOTATIONS

Given a finite set of symbols V, a *grammar* $\mathfrak{M}$ over the *vocabulary* V is a device which singles out (enumerates) a certain subset of the set V^* of all (finite) strings over V. Any such subset of V^* will be called a *language* over V. The language *determined* by a grammar $\mathfrak{M}$ will be denoted by $L(\mathfrak{M})$.

Notational Convention: We shall use capital Latin letters for members of V, and small Latin letters for members of V^*. For the empty string we shall use o, and xy for the concatenation of the strings x and y.

In order to rigorously define the two specific types of grammars the equivalence of which we intend to prove, a series of auxiliary definitions will first be given in each case.

Definition 1a:　A *simple phrase structure system* (SPS) is an ordered couple $\mathfrak{P} = (V, P)$, where V is a finite vocabulary and P is a finite set of *productions* of the form $X \to x$ $(o \neq x \neq X)$ (read: rewrite the symbol X by the nonempty string x).

1b:　A string y *directly generates* a string z $(y \Rightarrow z)$ if y has the form

$$X_0 X_1 X_2 \cdots X_{n-1} X_n \ (n \geqq 0),$$

and z can be given the form

$$x_0 x_1 x_2 \cdots x_{n-1} x_n,$$

such that, for all i, either $X_i = x_i$— in which case X_i is said to be *carried over* — or $X_i \to x_i$, in which case X_i is said to be *rewritten*. (Notice that if z is directly generated by y, then in general it is not uniquely determined which symbols of y are rewritten and according to which productions.)

1c:　A string x *generates* y $(x \overset{*}{\Rightarrow} y)$ if there exists a sequence of strings $z_0, z_1, \cdots, z_r$ such that $x = z_0$, $y = z_r$, and $z_{i-1} \Rightarrow z_i$ $(1 \leqq i \leqq r)$.

1d:　Let $Z \Rightarrow z_1 \Rightarrow \cdots \Rightarrow z_n$, and let it be specified (e.g., by means of a graph, see Figure 1, below), for each direct generation in this sequence, which symbols are rewritten and how. We shall call the sequence $Z, z_1, \cdots, z_n$ together with these specifications *a (generation) tree* with vertex Z and *final string* z_n (or *a tree from* Z *to* z_n) and denote it by $\langle Z, z_1, \cdots, z_n \rangle$.

Obviously, if $\langle Z, z_1, \cdots, z_n \rangle$ is a tree, then $Z \overset{*}{\Rightarrow} z_n$. Conversely, if $E \overset{*}{\Rightarrow} y$, then a generation tree from E to y (in general, several generation trees) can be constructed.

1e: Let $\Gamma = \langle Z, z_1, \cdots, z_n \rangle$ be a tree, and Y a symbol of $z_k (1 \leqq k < n)$. Clearly, there exist $y_1, y_2, \cdots, y_{n-k}$ such that $Y \Rightarrow y_1 \Rightarrow \cdots \Rightarrow y_{n-k}$ and each y_j $(i \leqq j \leqq n - k)$ is a definite (uniquely determined) substring of Z_{k+j}. If we adhere to the specifications of the original tree, we obtain a new tree $\langle Y, y_1, \cdots, y_{n-k} \rangle$, which we call the *subtree formed by* (that occurrence of) Y, or *the subtree of Y in* Γ.

Definition 2a: A *simple phrase structure grammar* (SPG) is an ordered quadruple $\mathfrak{G} = (V, P, T, S)$ where (V, P) is a SPS (see Definition 1a), T (the *terminal vocabulary*) is a subset of V, none of whose elements occurs on the left side of a production[2], and S is a distinguished element of $V - T$ (the *initial symbol*).

2b: A string x is a *sentence of* $\mathfrak{G}$ if x is a string over T (*a terminal string*) and $S \overset{*}{\Rightarrow} x$ in the SPS (V, P). $L(\mathfrak{G})$ is the set of all sentences of $\mathfrak{G}$.

2c: A language L over a vocabulary T is *representable* by a SPG, or is a *simple phrase structure language*, if there exists a SPG $\mathfrak{G}$ such that $L = L(\mathfrak{G})$.

A SPG can be viewed as a *combinatorial system*, as defined e.g. by Davis [47:84], with S as axiom and P as the set of productions. It is, more specifically, a rather special kind of *semi-Thue system*, since in a general semi-Thue system the productions have the form $x_1 \rightarrow x_2$, whereas in SPG the form is $X \rightarrow x$. The restriction that the left-hand side of a production should always consist of a single symbol is the main feature of SPGs, and the general theory of semi-Thue systems is therefore not of much avail for our purposes.

Let $\mathfrak{C}_p = \{\Lambda_1, \cdots, \Lambda_m\}$ be a finite set of symbols.

Definition 3a: A *bidirectional category system* (BCS) over $\mathfrak{C}_p$ is an infinite set of symbols, $\mathfrak{C}$, obtained from $\mathfrak{C}_p$ in the following way:

(0)   (i) $\Lambda_i \in \mathfrak{C}$ $(i = 1, \cdots, m)$;

(ii) if $\Phi_i, \Phi_j \in \mathfrak{C}$, then $[\Phi_i / \Phi_j] \in \mathfrak{C}$;

(iii) if $\Phi_i, \Phi_j \in \mathfrak{C}$, then $[\Phi_i \setminus \Phi_j] \in \mathfrak{C}$.

The elements of $\mathfrak{C}$ will be called *categories*; $\Lambda_1, \cdots, \Lambda_m$ will be called *primitive categories*. We use Capital Greek letters for categories and small Greek letters for sequences of categories. If $\alpha = \Phi_1, \cdots, \Phi_k$ and $\beta = \Psi_1, \cdots, \Psi_l$, then α, β will denote the sequence $\Phi_1, \cdots, \Phi_k, \Psi_1, \cdots, \Psi_l$.

---

2 There is no loss of generality in requiring this. We can always add elements to V and choose P in such a manner that no element of T occurs on the left side of a production and this without changing $L(\mathfrak{C})$.

3b: A *unidirectional category system* is the set of all categories obtained from $\mathfrak{C}_p$, by using, in addition to 0(i), 0(ii) alone or 0(iii) alone.

3c: A *restricted category system* is a (finite) set of categories of the form $\Lambda_i,[\Lambda_i\backslash\Lambda_j]$ or $[\Lambda_i\backslash[\Lambda_j\backslash\Lambda_k]]$.

3d: A sequence α *directly cancels* to β (in a given category system) if

(i) $\alpha = \gamma,[\Phi/\Psi],\Psi,\delta$ and $\beta = \gamma,\Phi,\delta$, for some γ and δ,

or if

(ii) $\alpha = \gamma,\Phi,[\Phi\backslash\Psi],\delta$, and $\beta = \gamma,\Psi,\delta$, for some γ and δ.

3e: A sequence α *cancels* to β if there exist sequences $\gamma_0,\cdots,\gamma_k$ such that $\alpha = \gamma_0$, $\beta = \gamma_k$ and γ_{j-1} directly cancels to γ_j, for $1 \leqq j \leqq k$.

Definition 4a: A *restricted* (*unidirectional, bidirectional*) *categorial grammar* RCG (UCG, BCG) is a quadruple $\mathfrak{R} = (V,\mathfrak{C},\Sigma,\mathfrak{A})$ where V is a finite vocabulary, $\mathfrak{C}$ is a restricted (unidirectional, bidirectional) category system, Σ is a distinguished primitive category of $\mathfrak{C}$ and $\mathfrak{A}$ is a function (the *assignment function*) defined on V, whose values are finite subsets of $\mathfrak{C}$.

4b: A string $x = A_1 \cdots A_k$ of V^* is *accepted* by the categorial grammar $\mathfrak{R}$ if and only if there exist categories $\Phi_j \in \mathfrak{A}(A_j)$, such that the sequence $\Phi_1,\cdots,\Phi_k$ cancels to Σ.

Remark: A string $x = A_1 \cdots A_k$ is called of *type* α if there exist categories $\Phi_j \in \mathfrak{A}(A_j)$ such that $\Phi_1,\cdots,\Phi_k$ cancels to α. Thus we can rephrase Definition 4b and say that x is accepted if and only if x is of type Σ.

As usual, the set of all strings accepted by $\mathfrak{R}$ will be called the *language determined by* $\mathfrak{R}$ and denoted by $L(\mathfrak{R})$.

3. THE EQUIVALENCE OF CGs AND SPGs

The main result of this section is the proof of the complete mutual equivalence of the three kinds of CGs defined in the previous section, and their equivalence to SPGs, where equivalence of two grammars is defined, as usual, by the identity of the languages determined by them.

Theorem 1 states that, for every BCG (hence, for every UCG and every RCG), there exists an equivalent SPG. The proof is rather simple. The corollary to Theorem 2 states that for every SPG there exists an equivalent RCG (hence, an equivalent UCG and an equivalent BCG). The proof of Theorem 2 itself is rather long and requires several lemmas (Lemmas 1, 2, 3, 4).

Theorem 1: For any BCG $\mathfrak{R} = \{V,\mathfrak{C},\Sigma,\mathfrak{A}\}$ it is possible to construct an equivalent SPG $\mathfrak{G}$.

Proof: Let $\mathfrak{C}_V = \bigcup_{X \in V} \mathfrak{A}(X)$ (i.e. the union of all category sets assigned to the elements of the vocabulary). $\mathfrak{C}_V$ is a finite set of categories (the *assigned categories*).

Let $\overline{\mathfrak{C}}_V$ (the *constituents* of $\mathfrak{C}_V$) be defined inductively as follows:

(i) If $\Phi \in \mathfrak{C}_V$, then $\Phi \in \overline{\mathfrak{C}}_V$;

(ii) if $[\Phi \backslash \Psi] \in \overline{\mathfrak{C}}_V$, then Φ and Ψ belong to $\overline{\mathfrak{C}}_V$;

(iii) if $[\Phi \backslash \Psi] \in \overline{\mathfrak{C}}_V$, then Φ and Ψ belong to $\overline{\mathfrak{C}}_V$.

Let $W = V \cup \mathfrak{C}_V$, and let P consist of the following productions:

(i) $\Phi \to [\Phi / \Psi]\Psi$, if $[\Phi / \Psi] \in \overline{\mathfrak{C}}_V$;

(ii) $\Phi \to \Psi[\Psi \backslash \Phi]$, if $[\Psi \backslash \Phi] \in \overline{\mathfrak{C}}_V$;

(iii) $\Phi \to X$, if $\Phi \in \mathfrak{A}(X)$ (for every $X \in V$).

P is clearly finite and $\mathfrak{G} = (W, P, V, \Sigma)$ is the required SPG.

Theorem 2: For every SPS $\mathfrak{P} = (V, P)$, it is possible to construct a RCS $\mathfrak{H}$ and a *finite* assignment function $\mathfrak{A}$ which assigns categories of $\mathfrak{H}$ to members of V, such that to every $E \in V$ is assigned a distinguished category Σ_E and $E \overset{*}{\Rightarrow} x$ in $\mathfrak{P}$ if and only if x is the type Σ_E, i.e., if and only if at least one of the category sequences assigned to x cancels to Σ_E in $\mathfrak{H}$.

Corollary: For every SPG $\mathfrak{G}$, it is possible to construct an equivalent RCG $\mathfrak{R}$.

Proof of the Corollary: Let $\mathfrak{G} = (V, P, T, S)$. Let $\mathfrak{H}$ and $\mathfrak{A}$ be the categorial system and the assignment function which we can construct by Theorem 2 for $\mathfrak{P} = (V, P)$. Let Σ_s be the distinguished category of S. $\mathfrak{R} = (T, \mathfrak{P}, \Sigma_s, \mathfrak{A})$ is the required RCG since a string x over T is of type Σ_s if and only if $S \overset{*}{\Rightarrow} x$ in $\mathfrak{G}$.

Remark: For the corollary we need only the restriction of the assignment function $\mathfrak{A}$ to T. The assignment of categories to members of $V{-}T$ is immaterial for the corollary, but is needed in the proof of the theorem.

Proof of Theorem 2; We shall first prove the theorem for the special case that all productions of $\mathfrak{P}$ are of the form $C \to AB$. The general case will then be reduced to this special case.

Every derivation $E \overset{*}{\Rightarrow} x$ in $\mathfrak{P}$ has a corresponding generation tree $\Gamma = \langle E, \cdots, x \rangle$. For every symbol occurring in this tree it will be important to know the "history" of its generation in the tree. For this purpose we introduce the following

Definition: Let $\langle E, z_1, \cdots, z_n \rangle$ be a tree in $\mathfrak{P}$. The *occurrence* of E in the tree is *left* (or E occurs *left* in the tree). If a symbol C in z_i is rewritten as AB in z_{i+1} then *the corresponding occurrence of A in z_{i+1} is left and that of B is right.* The carry-over of a left [right] occurrence is again a left [right] occurrence.

In this manner, every occurrence of a symbol in a tree is either right or left (but not both).

The next steps in the proof should be the construction of a category system $\mathfrak{H}$ and an assignment function $\mathfrak{A}$ and the verification that these $\mathfrak{H}$ and $\mathfrak{A}$ fulfil the requirement of the theorem. But to make this construction more understandable, we shall first describe informally how we intend to analyze generation trees.

Given a generation tree $\Gamma = \langle E, z_1, \cdots, z_n \rangle$, we look for a subtree of "pure right form" which is cofinal with Γ and whose vertex occurs left in Γ. Such a subtree is drawn in Figure 2, in which, except for its vertex K, only right-occurring symbols $(L_1, \cdots, L_{r-1})$ are rewritten.

The main idea of the proof is to choose for left-occurring and right-occurring symbols different kinds of categories, *left categories* and *right categories*, respectively. (Each symbol-token will of course be assigned, in general, several left and several right categories.)

Consider the subtree in Figure 2 and suppose that for every left category Ψ of K we can find left categories $\Phi_1, \cdots, \Phi_r$ for $K_1, \cdots, K_r$ and a right category Θ_r for L_r such that the sequence $\Phi_1, \cdots, \Phi_r, \Theta_r$ cancels to Ψ. Then, since K occurs left in the "truncated" tree obtained by cutting the subtree of Figure 2 from the tree in Figure 1 (leaving only K and repetitions of K—Figure 3), we can clearly repeat the same procedure in the truncated tree. In other words, we can carry out a proof by induction (Lemma 1).

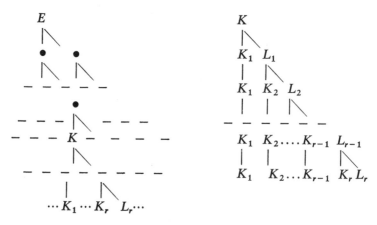

Figure 1   (the original tree Γ)   Figure 2   (the subtree of K)

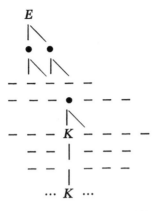

Figure 3 (the "truncated" tree)

We shall be able to choose $\Phi_j = [\Delta_s \backslash \Delta_{j+1}]$ $(j = 2, \cdots, r)$, $\Phi_1 = \Delta_1$, and $\Theta_r = [\Delta_{r+1} \backslash \Psi]$ where the Δ's are primitive categories. But the real problem now is not to obtain "too much", i.e., to take care that such Φ_j, Θ_r are assigned to K_j, L_r *only* if there actually exists a subtree from K to $K_1, \cdots, K_r L_r$, as exhibited in Figure 2. Only thus we shall be able to prove that if a cancellation works then a suitable generation tree can be reconstructed (Lemma 2). The exact description of the technique of how this is performed will be provided in the detailed proof.

After this informal description, we continue with the proof of the theorem. We introduce a fixed enumeration of the productions of P:

$$P = \{C_1 \overset{(1)}{\to} A_1 B_1, \; C_2 \overset{(2)}{\to} A_2 B_2, \cdots, C_m \overset{(m)}{\to} A_m B_m\}$$

This enumeration induces a convenient notation of the symbols of the vocabulary. Thus C_j shall always denote the symbol rewritten in the j'th production. This notation is *not* unambiguous. C_j may equal some A_i, B_i or even C_i.

Let Q be the set of triplets (k, p, q) of natural numbers $\leqq m$ such that:

(1)   (i) $k = p$ and $B_p = C_q$

or

             (ii) $C_k \overset{*}{\Rightarrow} u C_p$ for some u and $B_p = C_q$.

Remark: Given the SPS $\mathfrak{P}$, we can effectively construct the set Q. This follows from the easily provable fact that the relation "$C_k \overset{*}{\Rightarrow} u C_p$ for some u" is effectively decidable. (A general treatment of the decision properties of SPGs will be given in the next chapter.)

We shall now construct the RCS $\mathfrak{H}$ and the assignment function $\mathfrak{A}$.

Construction: The primitive categories of $\mathfrak{H}$ are: Σ_E, for every $E \in V$, the natural numbers $1, 2, \cdots, m$, and all the triplets of Q.

The assignment function $\mathfrak{A}$ is determined by six rules:

Assignment rules: I. $\Sigma_E \in \mathfrak{A}(E)$, for every $E \in V$,

II. $r \in \mathfrak{A}(A_r)$ $(r = 1, \cdots, m)$,

III. if $(p,p,r) \in Q$, then $[p \backslash (p,p,r)] \in \mathfrak{A}(A_r)$,

IV.   if $(k,p,q) \in Q$ and $(k,q,r) \in Q$ then
$[(k,p,q) \backslash (k,q,r)] \in \mathfrak{A}(A_r)$.

The categories assigned by rules I–IV will be called *left categories*. Note that rules II, III, and IV assign categories to the A_r. The next two rules assign *right* categories to the B_r.

V.   If C_r was assigned a left category Ψ by rules I–IV, then $[r \backslash \Psi] \in \mathfrak{A}(B_r)$,

VI.   if C_r was assigned a left category Ψ and $(k,p,r) \in Q$, then $[(k,p,r) \backslash \Psi] \in \mathfrak{A}(B_r)$.

By this construction every $E \in V$ is assigned a finite number of categories. The most complex form of a category is $[\Lambda_i \backslash [\Lambda_j \backslash \Lambda_k]]$, where the Λ are primitive. This form can be assumed only by the right categories. For later purposes we note that no triplet of Q was assigned to a *single* symbol.

Now it remains to be proven that the constructed $\mathfrak{H}$ and $\mathfrak{A}$ fulfil the requirements. This we shall do in two lemmas.

Lemma 1:   Let $\langle E, y_1, \cdots, y_p \rangle$ be a generation tree and $y_p = D_1 \cdots D_p$. There exists a sequence of categories $\alpha = \Psi_1, \cdots, \Psi_n$ such that $\Psi_j \in \mathfrak{A}(D_j)$ and such that α cancels to Σ_E. Moreover, Ψ_j is a right category if and only if the occurrence of D_j in the tree is right.

Remark: An assignment of categories fulfilling the last conditions will be called *proper*.

Lemma 2: If $\Phi_j \in \mathfrak{A}(D_j)$ and $\alpha = \Phi_1, \cdots, \Phi_r$ cancels to Σ_E, then $E \overset{*}{\Rightarrow} D_1 \cdots D_n$.

Proof of Lemma 1:   The proof is by induction with respect to the *power* w of the tree (i.e., the total number of symbols in the tree). Since the case $w = 1$ is trivial, we assume that $w > 1$, and that the lemma holds for trees of power smaller than w. Let q be the greatest number such that for some K, $y_q = xKy$, where the occurrence of K is left and K is rewritten in y_{q+1}. Such q and K always exist if at least one symbol in the tree is rewritten, for then the first symbol which is rewritten must occur left. If no symbol in the tree is rewritten, then this is a "trivial" tree which can be reduced to a tree with power $w = 1$. From the maximality of q it follows that all the symbols in y_t for $t \geq q + 1$ which are rewritten are right-occurring symbols. Thus, the subtree formed by K is, except for repetitions, of a pure right form (see Figure 2):

(2) $K \overset{(\bar{1})}{\Rightarrow} K_1 L_1 \overset{(\bar{2})}{\Rightarrow} K_1 K_2 L_2 \overset{(\bar{3})}{\Rightarrow} \cdots \overset{(\bar{r})}{\Rightarrow} K_1 K_2 \cdots K_r L_r$ $(1 \leqq r \leqq p - q)$.

The numbers in parentheses over the arrows denote the ordinal number of the production used[3].

If $q > 1$, consider the "truncated" tree $\langle E, \cdots, y_q, y'_{q+1}, \cdots, y'_p \rangle$ which is obtained from the original one by carrying over k from y_q onward. Clearly y'_p and y_p have the forms:

$$y'_p = z K z_1, \quad y_p = z K_1 K_1 \cdots K_r L_r z_1.$$

The tree $\langle E, \cdots, y_q, y'_{q+1}, \cdots, y'_p \rangle$ has a smaller power than $\langle E_1, \cdots, y_p \rangle$, hence, by the induction hypothesis, there exists a proper sequence of categories α for y'_p which cancels to Σ_E. Therefore, in order to prove the lemma in case $q = 1$, or to finish the proof in case $q > 1$, it suffices to show that for every left category Ψ of K, there exists a proper sequence of categories $\beta = \Phi_1, \cdots, \Phi_r, \Theta_r$ for $K_1 \cdots K_r L_r$ which cancels to Ψ.

But from (2) it follows that

(3) $K = C_{\bar{1}}, K_1 = A_{\bar{1}}, K_2 = A_{\bar{2}}, \cdots, K_r = A_{\bar{r}}$ and $L_1 = B_{\bar{1}} = C_{\bar{2}}, \cdots, L_{r-1} = B_{\overline{r-1}}$

$= C_{\bar{r}}, L_{\bar{r}} = B_{\bar{r}}$.

It follows similarly that the occurrences of K, $K_1, \cdots, K_r$ in the original tree as well as in the subtree formed by K are left, and that the occurrence of L_2 is right. It also follows from (2) and (3) and the definition of Q (see (1)) that:

(4) $(\bar{1}, \bar{1}, \bar{2}) \in Q$, $(\bar{1}, \bar{2}, \bar{3}) \in Q$, $(\bar{1}, \bar{3}, \bar{4}) \in Q, \cdots, (\bar{1}, \overline{r-1}, \bar{r}) \in Q$.

Hence, by assignment rule II, $\Phi_1 = \bar{1} \in \mathfrak{A}(K_1)$, by rule III, $\Phi_2 = [\bar{1} \setminus (\bar{1}, \bar{1}, \bar{2})]$ $\in \mathfrak{A}(K_2)$ and by rule IV, $\Phi_3 = [(\bar{1}, \bar{1}, \bar{2}) \setminus (\bar{1}, \bar{2}, \bar{3})] \in \mathfrak{A}(K_3), \cdots, \Phi_r = [(\overline{1,r-2}, \overline{r-1}) \setminus (\overline{1,r-1}, \bar{r})] \in \mathfrak{A}(K_r)$. Now if $r = 1$, then by rule V, $\Theta_1 = [\bar{1} \setminus \Psi] \in \mathfrak{A}(L_1)$. If $r > 1$, then by rule VI, $\Theta_r = [(\overline{1,r-1}, \bar{r}) \setminus \Psi] \in \mathfrak{A}(L_r)$. In both cases the sequence $\beta = \Phi_1, \cdots \Phi_r, \Theta_r$ is a proper sequence for $K_1 \cdots K_r L_r$ and cancels to Ψ. Q.E.D.

Proof of Lemma 2: We shall use the following properties of RCSs:

(i) A sequence α directly cancels to β if and only if α and β are of the form: $\alpha = \gamma, \Lambda_j, [\Lambda_j \setminus \Psi], \delta$ and $\beta = \gamma, \Psi, \delta$, where Λ_j is primitive. In other words, the left member of a *cancellation pair* is always primitive, and the

---

[3] We use bars in order to avoid double indices: $\bar{1}$ is like i_1, $\bar{2} = i_2$, etc.

right member is always non-primitive. Thus, no member of a given cancellation pair can participate in another cancellation pair.

(ii) If a sequence α cancels to δ and also to δ', where neither δ nor δ' can be cancelled any further, then $\delta = \delta'$. In other words, the result of maximal cancellation in RCS is unique and does not depend on the order of the intermediate cancellations.

We sketch the proof of (ii). It proceeds by induction on the length of α. Consider two sequences of direct cancellations leading from α to δ and δ':

$$\alpha \to \beta \to \cdots \to \delta \;\; ; \;\; \alpha \to \beta' \to \cdots \to \delta'.$$ (Here $\to$ denotes direct cancellation.)

β is shorter than α, hence if $\beta = \beta'$, it follows from the induction hypothesis that $\delta = \delta'$. Suppose now that $\beta \neq \beta'$. This is possible only if α contains two distinct cancellation pairs, I, and II, and I is cancelled to obtain β while II is cancelled to obtain β'. It is easily seen that we must cancel II (resp. I) at some stage of the cancellation from β to δ (resp. from β' to δ'), and we may as well cancel it in the second stage (without changing the final outcome). Thus we obtain the schema:

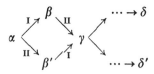

Since γ is shorter than α, we conclude that $\delta = \delta'$.

(iii) If α cancels to a single category Φ ($\alpha \neq \Phi$), then $\alpha = \Lambda, \cdots, \Psi$ where Λ is primitive, and $\Psi = [\Lambda \backslash \Phi]$ or $\Psi = [\Lambda \backslash [\Lambda' \backslash \Phi]]$.

We shall now prove Lemma 2 by induction on the length n of $D_1 \cdots D_n$. If $n = 1$, then $E = D$ and there is nothing to prove. Assume $n > 1$. By assumption, $\Phi_1, \cdots, \Phi_n$ cancels to Σ_E. Hence by property (i) above, Φ_1 is primitive (more precisely, in our case the category Φ is a natural number $\leqq m$) and Φ_n is of the form $[\Delta \backslash \Sigma_E]$, hence a right category. It follows that there are numbers s, t ($1 \leqq s + 1 < t \leqq n$), such that Φ_{s+1} is primitive, Φ_t is a right category and if $t - (s + 1) > 1$, Φ_i is left and non-primitive for $s + 1 < i < t$, i.e., $\Phi_i = [\Delta_i \backslash \Theta_i]$ where Θ_i and Δ_i are primitive, and $\Theta_i \in Q$. Hence, the partial sequence $\Phi_{s+1}, \cdots, \Phi_t$ must *itself* cancel to a single category Ψ (for otherwise the whole sequence would not cancel). Consideration of the assignment rules shows that this is possible if *and only if*, for suitable natural numbers $\bar{1}, \bar{2}, \cdots, \bar{r}$, we have

(5) $\Phi_{s+1} = \bar{1}, \;\; \Phi_{s+2} = [\bar{1} \backslash (\bar{1}, \bar{1}, \bar{2})], \;\; \Phi_{s+3} = [(\bar{1}, \bar{1}, \bar{2}) \backslash (\bar{1}, \bar{2}, \bar{3})], \cdots,$

$$\Phi_t = [(\bar{1}, \overline{r-1}, \bar{r}) \backslash \Psi],$$

and Ψ is a left category of C_1. (In case $t-s=3$, Φ_{s+3} does not appear in (5), in case $t-s=2$, Φ_{s+2} does not appear in (5) and $\Phi_1 = \Phi_{s+2} = [\bar{1}\backslash\Psi]$ appears instead.)

It follows again from the assignment rules and (5) that

$$(6) \qquad \langle C_{\bar{1}}, A_{\bar{1}}B_{\bar{1}}, A_{\bar{1}}A_{\bar{2}}B_{\bar{2}}, \cdots, A_{\bar{1}}A_{\bar{2}} \cdots A_{\overline{r-1}}A_{\bar{r}}, A_{\bar{1}}A_{\bar{2}} \cdots A_{\overline{r-1}}A_{\bar{r}}B_{\bar{r}}\rangle$$

forms a tree of the system $\mathfrak{P}$, and also that $A_{\bar{1}}A_{\bar{2}} \cdots A_{\overline{r-1}}B_r = D_{s+1} \cdots D_t$. In particular we have

$$(7) \qquad\qquad C_1 \overset{*}{\Rightarrow} D_{s+1} \cdots D_t.$$

Now, since the sequence $\Phi_1, \cdots \Phi_s, \Psi, \Phi_{t+1}, \cdots \Phi_n$ is obtained by partial cancellation of $\Phi_1, \cdots, \Phi_n$, it follows from property (ii) above that it can be further cancelled, and its maximally cancelled form can only equal Σ_E. $\Phi_1, \cdots, \Phi_s, \Psi, \Phi_{t+1}, \cdots, \Phi_n$ corresponds to $D_1 \cdots D_s C_{\bar{1}} D_{t+1} \cdots D_n$ and its length is less than n, hence, by the induction hypotheses, $E \overset{*}{\Rightarrow} D_1 \cdots D_s C_1 D_{t+1} \cdots D_n$. Using (7) we obtain:

$$(8) \qquad\qquad E \overset{*}{\Rightarrow} D_1 \cdots D_t D_{t+1} \cdots D_n.$$

This concludes the proof of Theorem 2 for the special case where all the productions are of the form $C \rightarrow AB$. For the reduction of the general case to this special case, we need two simple lemmas (3 and 4).

Lemma 3: For every SPS $\mathfrak{P} = (V,P)$ there exists a SPS $\mathfrak{P}' = (V,P')$ such that:

(i) $\mathfrak{P}'$ does not contain productions of the form $X \rightarrow Y$;

(ii) for $l(x) \geqq 2$ (length of $x \geqq 2$), $X \overset{*}{\Rightarrow} x$ in $\mathfrak{P}'$ if and only if $X \overset{*}{\Rightarrow} x$ in $\mathfrak{P}$.

Proof: To obtain the new set of productions P' from the old one P, perform the following steps:

(i) Omit from P all the productions $A \rightarrow B$, thus obtaining P_1.

(ii) Whenever $A \overset{*}{\Rightarrow} B$ in $\mathfrak{P}$, and $B \rightarrow b \in P_1$, add the new production $A \rightarrow b$. The set of productions obtained after step (ii) is denoted by P_2.

(iii) If $C \rightarrow c \in P_2$, then whenever $c = u_0 C_1 u_1 C u_2, \cdots, C_k u_k$ (the u's may be empty), and $C_j \overset{*}{\Rightarrow} D_j$ in $\mathfrak{P}$ for $1 \leqq j \leqq k$, add the new production $C \rightarrow u_0 D_1 u_1 D_2 u_2 \cdots D_k u_k$.

The set of productions obtained after step (iii) is the desired P'; the verification of this fact is easy and is left to the reader.

Lemma 4: For every SPS $\mathfrak{P} = (V,P)$ there exists a SPS $\mathfrak{P}' = (V',P')$ such that $V \subset V'$ and

(i) if $x, y \in V^*$, then $x \overset{*}{\Rightarrow} y$ in $\mathfrak{P}'$ if and only if $x \overset{*}{\Rightarrow} y$ in $\mathfrak{P}$:

(ii) in every production $X \rightarrow x$ of P', $l(x) \leqq 2$.

Remark: A $\mathfrak{P}'$ fulfilling (i) alone is usually called a *conservative extension* of $\mathfrak{P}$.

Proof: Let $X \to Y_1 \cdots Y_n$ $(n > 2)$ be the j'th production of P. In its place we introduce the following $n-2$ productions into P':

$$X \to Y_1 B_1^j, \quad B_1^j \to Y_2 B_2^j, \cdots, B_{n-2}^j \to Y_{n-1} Y_n,$$

where the B_k^j are new symbols of V', and the sets $\{B_k^j\}$ for different j are disjoint. Obviously the new system $\mathfrak{P}'$ is a conservative extension of $\mathfrak{P}$ fulfilling (ii).

Proof of Theorem 2 (concluded): Let $\mathfrak{P}$ be a general SPS (V,P). By Lemmas 3 and 4 we can construct a SPS $\mathfrak{P}' = (V',P')$ such that $V \subset V'$, all the productions of $\mathfrak{P}'$ are of the form $C \to AB$, and $\mathfrak{P}'$ is a "quasi-conservative" extension of $\mathfrak{P}$, i.e., for $l(x) \geqq 2$, $X \overset{*}{\Rightarrow} x$ in $\mathfrak{P}'$ if and only if $X \overset{*}{\Rightarrow} x$ in $\mathfrak{P}$.

Now for $\mathfrak{P}'$ we have shown how to construct a RCS $\mathfrak{H}$ and an assignment function $\mathfrak{A}$, as asserted in the theorem. Since $V \subset V'$, the assertion of the theorem (or of Lemmas 1 and 2) remains true for (V,P) with the restriction $l(x) \geqq 2$.

To take care of the case $E \overset{*}{\Rightarrow} D$ in $\mathfrak{P}$ we add the additional

Assignment rule VII: If $E \overset{*}{\Rightarrow} D$ in $\mathfrak{P}$, $\Sigma_E \in \mathfrak{A}(D)$.

By this rule, Lemma 1 becomes true for the case $E \overset{*}{\Rightarrow} D$, too. The truth of Lemma 2 is not hampered by this additional rule, since in case $\delta = \Phi_1, \cdots, \Phi_m$ $(m \geqq 2)$ cancels to the single category Σ_E, the only place Σ_E can appear is in the "right" part of $\Psi_m(\Phi_m = [\Theta \backslash \Sigma_E])$. This means that Φ_m was assigned to some symbol according to rule V or VI, and not according to rule VII.

4.   SHORT REMARK ON ADEQUACY

SPGs and CGs are, of course, more adequate than FSGs to serve as grammars for natural languages. Still, the questions remain whether ordinary languages can be completely represented by SPGs and whether such a description, even if theoretically feasible, could at all be practically useful. Chomsky [34] is convinced that the answer to the second question is negative. On the other hand, he regards SPGs, or rather the phrase structure grammars in general, of which the SPGs form only a special kind, as adequate for determining what he, following Harris [64] (though in a somewhat different sense), calls the *kernel* of such languages, from which, by a different kind of operations, the so-called *transformations*, the sets of sentences of these languages are generated. One such transformation for instance, is the English passive transformation which transforms sentences of the form $NP_1 V_t NP_2$ (NP—noun phrase, V_t—transitive verb) into NP_2 *is* V-*en by* NP_1 [34: 43ff], a rule which does not have the form characteristic for general phrase structure grammars. This, however, does not exclude the possibility that for a given transformational grammar there should exist an equivalent phrase structure grammar.

On Formal Properties of Simple Phrase Structure Grammars* | 9

SECTION 0: INTRODUCTION

This chapter deals with mathematical problems concerning simple phrase structure grammars (SPGs, for short). The interest in these systems arose from linguistic considerations, as SPGs are regarded as formal models which are able to describe the syntactic structure of natural languages with good approximation. The problem to what degree SPGs are adequate to describe natural language grammars will not be dealt with here. However, a satisfactory answer to this adequacy problem requires, inter alia, a deep knowledge of the formal (mathematical) properties of the model. Chomsky himself, who introduced the SPGs as well as other formal grammar-models, has published several works on the formal properties of the models [40; 35; 36].

The problems studied in this chapter include: representations of SPGs, relations with other formal systems (in particular with finite automata), characterizations of the languages obtainable by SPGs, closure under Boolean operations and decision problems for various properties of SPGs.

In Section 6 we prove that several properties of SPGs are *recursively undecidable*. For the exact meaning of this notion we refer the reader to [47]. This book contains also a chapter (no. 6) on combinatorial systems, of which the SPGs are a rather special kind.

Among the more significant results of Section 6 we would like to mention Theorem 6.3.c establishing the undecidability of the problem whether a given SPG is equivalent to a finite automaton.

SECTION 1: NOTATION, TERMINOLOGY AND BASIC DEFINITIONS

Let V be a given set — the *vocabulary*. Elements of V will be called *symbols* and denoted by capital Latin letters — X, Y, Z etc. Finite sequences of symbols of V — including the empty sequence — will be called *strings* over V and denoted by small Latin letters — x, y, z etc. The empty string

---

* First appeared in **Zeitschrift für Phonetik, Sprachwissenschaft und Kommunikationsforschung**, vol. 14 (1961), pp. 143–172.

will be denoted by Λ. Sets of strings over V will be called *languages* over V and denoted by Latin capitals — generally L with subscripts. If $x \in L$, we say that x is *a sentence* of L. The set of all strings over V will be denoted by W_V. A symbol $X \in W_V$ will be identified with the string of length 1 composed of X alone, hence we take $V \subseteq W_V$. The length of the string x (i.e. the number of its symbol occurrences) will be denoted by $l(x)$.

Reflection: If $x = X_{i_1} X_{i_2} \cdots X_{i_{n-1}} X_{i_n}$, then the reflection of x is the string

$$x^* = X_{i_n} X_{i_{n-1}} \cdots X_{i_2} X_{i_1} \quad (\Lambda^* = \Lambda).$$

Concatenation: If $x = X_{i_1} \cdots X_{i_m}$, $y = X_{j_1} \cdots X_{j_n}$, then the concatenate of x and y is the string

$$x \cdot y = X_{i_1} \cdots X_{i_m} X_{j_1} \cdots X_{j_n} \quad (\Lambda \cdot x = x \cdot \Lambda = x).$$

(For $x \cdot y$ we shall usually write simply xy.)

Powers: $x^0 = \Lambda$, $x^1 = x$, and generally $x^n = x \cdot x^{n-1}$ $(n = 1, 2, \cdots)$.

Substrings: x is a substring of y $(x \subseteq y)$ if there are strings u and v (possibly empty), such that $y = uxv$. x is a *proper* substring of y $(x \subset y)$ if $x \subseteq y$ and $x \neq y$.

W_V is the free semi-group with identity — Λ — over the set of generators V, under the operation of concatenation.

Reflection, products and powers of languages: The reflection of a language L is the language $L^* = \{x^* \mid x \in L\}$. The product of two languages L_1 and L_2 is the language $L_1 \cdot L_2 = \{x \cdot y \mid x \in L_1, y \in L_2\}$. Powers of a language L are defined as follows:

$L^0 = \{\Lambda\}$, $L^1 = L$ and generally $L^n = L \cdot L^{n-1}$ $(n = 1, 2, \cdots)$. $\{x\} \cdot L$ and $L \cdot \{x\}$ will be abbreviated as xL and Lx, respectively.

Multiplication of languages is the ordinary multiplication of complexes in semi-group theory.

Closure of a language L: $cl(L) = \bigcup\limits_{n=0}^{\infty} L^n$.

$cl(L)$ is the semi-sub-group with identity of W_V generated by L.

Grammars: By a grammar we understand a finite system of rules determining a language. Grammars will be denoted by Gothic capitals. The language determined by $\mathfrak{A}$ will be denoted by $L(\mathfrak{A})$. If $L(\mathfrak{A}) = L(\mathfrak{B})$, then $\mathfrak{A}$ and $\mathfrak{B}$ are called *equivalent*.

If $\mathfrak{A}$ is a device generating the sentences of $L(\mathfrak{A})$, we call $\mathfrak{A}$ a *production grammar*. If $\mathfrak{A}$ is a device which recognizes, given a string x, whether $x \in L(\mathfrak{A})$ or not, it is called a *recognition grammar*. If $\mathfrak{A}$ is a recognition grammar and $x \in L(\mathfrak{A})$, we say that x is *accepted* by $\mathfrak{A}$.

In the sequel we assume the vocabulary V to be finite.

Definition 1.1. *a*: A *simple phrase structure system* (SPS) is an ordered couple (V, P), where V is a finite vocabulary, and P is a finite set of *productions* of the form

$$X \to x \quad (x \neq X, \ X \in V, \ x \in W_V, \text{ and possibly } x = \Lambda).$$

1.1.*b*: y *directly generates* z ($y \Rightarrow z$), if $y = uXv$, $z = uxv$, and $X \to x$ is a production of P.

1.1.*c*: y *generates* z ($y \overset{*}{\Rightarrow} z$), if there exists a sequence of strings $z_0, z_1, \cdots, z_r$ ($r \geqq 0$), such that $y = z_0$, $z_r = z$, and $z_{i-1} \Rightarrow z_i$ ($i = 1, \cdots, r$). (In case $r = 0$, we have $y = z_0 = z_r = z$, which corresponds to the relation $y \overset{*}{\Rightarrow} y$.) The sequence $z_0, \cdots, z_r$ will be called a *generation tree* of z from y. It is generally not uniquely determined by y and z.

Obviously, if $x \overset{*}{\Rightarrow} y$ and $y \overset{*}{\Rightarrow} z$, then $x \overset{*}{\Rightarrow} z$. Also, if $x_1 \overset{*}{\Rightarrow} y_1$, $x_2 \overset{*}{\Rightarrow} y_2, \cdots$, $x_n \overset{*}{\Rightarrow} y_n$, then $x_1 x_2 \cdots x_n \overset{*}{\Rightarrow} y_1 y_2 \cdots y_n$. Conversely, if $x \overset{*}{\Rightarrow} y$ and $x_1 = x_1 \cdots x_n$, then there are strings $y_1, \cdots, y_n$, such that $x_1 \overset{*}{\Rightarrow} y_i$ ($i = 1, \cdots, n$), and $y = y_1 \cdots y_n$. The last assertion can easily be verified by induction on the length of a generation tree of y from x.

Definition 1.2.*a*: A *simple phrase structure grammar* (SPG) is an ordered quadruple $\mathfrak{G} = (V, P, T, S)$, where (V, P) is a SPS (see Def. 1.1.a), T (the *terminal* vocabulary) is a subset of V, none of whose elements occur on the left side of a production of P, and S (the *initial* symbol) is a distinguished element of $V - T$. $V - T$ is called the *auxiliary* vocabulary.

1.2.*b*: x is a *sentence* of $\mathfrak{G}$, if x is a string over T (a *terminal string*), and $S \overset{*}{\Rightarrow} x$ (in the SPS (V, P)). $L(\mathfrak{G})$ is the set of all sentences of $\mathfrak{G}$:

$$L(\mathfrak{G}) = \{x \mid x \in W_T \ \& \ S \overset{*}{\Rightarrow} x\}.$$

1.2.*c*: A language L *is representable* by an SPG, or is a *simple phrase structure language* (SPL), if there exists an SPG $\mathfrak{G}$, such that $L = L(\mathfrak{G})$.

SECTION 2: REPRESENTATION OF FINITE AUTOMATA BY SPGs

In this section we show how to construct SPGs equivalent or otherwise closely related to one-tape and two-tape finite automata, as defined in [128]. The following definition is adopted from [128, Defs. 1, 2, 3].

Definition 2.1.*a*: A *finite automaton* (FA) is a system $\mathfrak{A} = (T, \Sigma, M, \sigma_0, \Phi)$ where T is a finite vocabulary, Σ is a finite set (the *internal states* of $\mathfrak{A}$), M is a function defined on the Cartesian product $\Sigma \times T$ with values in Σ

(the *transition table*), $\sigma_0 \in \Sigma$ (the *initial state*), and $\Phi \subseteq \Sigma$ (the set of *designated final states*).

M can be extended from $\Sigma \times T$ to $\Sigma \times W_T$ by a definition by recursion as follows:

$$M(\sigma, \Lambda) = \sigma, \text{ for } \sigma \in \Sigma;$$

$$M(\sigma, xX) = M(M(\sigma, x), X), \text{ for } \sigma \in \Sigma, \; x \in W_T, \; X \in T.$$

The extended function M has the following property:

$$M(\sigma, x \cdot y) = M(M(\sigma, x), y), \text{ for } \sigma \in \Sigma, \; x, y \in W_T.$$

This can easily be proved by induction on the length of y. $M(\sigma, x) = \tau$ means that if the automaton reads through the whole string x from left to right, symbol by symbol, beginning in state σ and changing states according to the transition table M, then it will end in state τ.

2.1.*b*: Let $x \in W_T$. x is *accepted* by $\mathfrak{A}$, if $M(\sigma_0, x) \in \Phi$.

$$L(\mathfrak{A}) = \{x \mid M(\sigma_0, x) \in \Phi\}.$$

2.1.*c*: A language L is *representable* by a FA, or is an FAL, if $L = L(\mathfrak{A})$ for some FA $\mathfrak{A}$.

The class of all FALs over a vocabulary T is closed under Boolean operations as well as under reflection, multiplication and formation of closure. It is the least class of languages over T containing the finite languages and closed under the formation of unions, products and closures of languages. For proofs, as well as for more information about FALs and their representations, see [128] and Chapter 7.

Theorem 2.1: Let $\mathfrak{A} = (T, \Sigma, M, \sigma_0, \Phi)$ be a FA.

a) It is possible to construct an SPG $\mathfrak{G}$ equivalent to $\mathfrak{A}$.

b) It is possible to construct an SPG $\mathfrak{G}'$, such that

$$L(\mathfrak{G}') = \{y \mid y = xEx^*, \; x \in L(\mathfrak{A})\},$$

where E is a fixed additional symbol.

Proof: a) Define $\mathfrak{G} = (V, P, T, \sigma_0)$, where $V = T \cup \Sigma$ (we may assume $\Sigma \cap T = \emptyset$), $P = \{\sigma \to X \cdot M(\sigma, X) \mid \sigma \in \Sigma, \; X \in T\} \cup \{\sigma \to \Lambda \mid \sigma \in \Phi\}$.

If $x \in W_V$, then $\sigma_0 \overset{*}{\Rightarrow} x$ in $\mathfrak{G}$ if and only if either $x = y\sigma$, where $y \in W_T$ and $\sigma = M(\sigma_0, y)$, or $x \in W_T$ and $M(\sigma_0, x) \in \Phi$. Hence, if $x \in W_T$, then $\sigma_0 \overset{*}{\Rightarrow} x$ in $\mathfrak{G}$ if and only if $M(\sigma_0, x) \in \Phi$, i.e., $L(\mathfrak{A}) = L(\mathfrak{G})$.

b) Define $\mathfrak{G}' = (V', P', T', \sigma_0)$, where $V' = T \cup \{E\} \cup \Sigma$ (we may assume that $T \cap \Sigma = \emptyset$ and that $E \notin \Sigma$), $T' = T \cup \{E\}$,

$$P = \{\sigma \to X \cdot M(\sigma, X) \cdot X \mid \sigma \in \Sigma, \; X \in T\} \cup \{\sigma \to E \mid \sigma \in \Phi\}.$$

$\sigma_0 \overset{*}{\Rightarrow} y$ in $\mathfrak{G}'$, if and only if either $y = x\sigma x^*$, where $x \in W_T$ and $\sigma = M(\sigma_0, x)$, or $y = xEx^*$, where $x \in W_T$ and $M(\sigma_0, x) \in \Phi$. Hence,

$$L(\mathfrak{G}') = \{y \mid y \in W_{T'} \,\&\, \sigma_0 \overset{*}{\Rightarrow} y\} = \{y \mid y = xEx^*, \ x \in L(\mathfrak{A})\}.$$

Remarks: a) In order to get an SPG $\mathfrak{G}''$, such that

$$L(\mathfrak{G}'') = \{y \mid y = xx^*, \ x \in L(\mathfrak{A})\}$$

without an auxiliary symbol E, define $\mathfrak{G}'' = \{V, P'', T, \sigma_0\}$, where $V = T \cup \Sigma$,

$$P'' = \{\sigma \to X \cdot M(\sigma, X) \cdot X \mid \sigma \in \Sigma, \ X \in T\} \cup \{\sigma \to \Lambda \mid \sigma \in \Phi\}.$$

b) If $\mathfrak{A} = \{T, \Sigma, M, \sigma_0, \Phi\}$ is a FA, $E \notin T$, and $L(\mathfrak{A})$ is infinite, then the language $L' = \{y \mid y = xEx^*, \ x \in L(\mathfrak{A})\}$ is not an FAL. This follows easily from [128: Lemma 8]. This remark, together with Th. 2.1.b, demonstrates the existence of SPGs which are not equivalent to any FA.

c) The following converse of Th. 2.1.a holds true: Let $\mathfrak{G} = (V, P, T, S)$ be an SPG, all of whose productions are of the form $A_i \to A_j X_k$, $A_i \to X_k$ or $A_i \to \Lambda$ (or of the form $A_i \to X_k A_j$, $A_i \to X_k$ or $A_i \to \Lambda$), where A_i, A_j, $A_k \in V - T$, $X_k \in T$. It is possible to construct a FA $\mathfrak{A}$ equivalent to $\mathfrak{G}$.

Method of proof: First construct a nondeterministic FA $\mathfrak{A}'$ (see [128: Defs. 9–10]) equivalent to $\mathfrak{G}$. Then construct a deterministic FA $\mathfrak{A}$ equivalent to $\mathfrak{A}'$, by [128: Def. 11 and Th. 11]. For a detailed proof of a similar result see Chapter 7, Section 3.

d) The following converse of Th. 2.1.b will be proved in Sec. 7, Th. 7.2: Let L be a language over a vocabulary T, and E a symbol not contained in T. Let $L' = \{y \mid y = xEx^*, \ x \in L\}$. If L' is an SPL, then L is an FAL.

The following definition is adopted from [128: Defs. 15–16]. Def. 16 has been slightly corrected. The intuitive motivation for this definition is given in [128: preceding Def. 15].

Definition 2.2.a: A *two-tape finite automaton* (TTA) is a system

$$\mathfrak{A}^2 = (T, E, \Sigma, M, \sigma_0, \Phi, \Sigma_1, \Sigma_2),$$

where $(T \cup \{E\}, \Sigma, M, \sigma_0, \Phi)$ is an ordinary FA, $E \notin T$, and the sets Σ_1, Σ_2 form a *partition* of Σ, i.e., $\Sigma_1 \cap \Sigma_2 = \emptyset$, $\Sigma_1 \cup \Sigma_2 = \Sigma$. E is an auxiliary symbol (the *end-marker*).

A TTA accepts or rejects ordered pairs of strings over T. The following notation will be useful for defining when a pair of strings is accepted.

Let $\sigma_0, \sigma_1, \cdots, \sigma_n$ be a sequence of internal states of a TTA

$$\mathfrak{A}^2 = (T, E, \Sigma, M, \sigma_0, \Phi, \Sigma_1, \Sigma_2).$$

A pair of *associated sequences* of integers $k_0, \cdots, k_n$; $l_0, \cdots, l_n$ is defined as follows:

1. k_i is 1 or 2 according as $\sigma_i \in \Sigma_1$ or $\sigma_i \in \Sigma_2$;
2. l_i is the number of indices $j \leq i$ such that $k_j = k_i$.

2.2.b: Let $\mathfrak{A}^2$ be a TTA, and (x_1, x_2) an ordered pair of strings over T. Let

$$(x_1 E, x_2 E) = (X_{1,1} X_{1\,2} \cdots X_{1,m}, X_{2,1} X_{2,2} \cdots X_{2,n}), \text{ i.e.,}$$

$$x_1 = X_{1,1} \cdots X_{1,m-1}, \ x_2 = X_{2\,1} \cdots X_{2,n-1}, \text{ and } X_{1,m} = X_{2,n} = E.$$

The pair (x_1, x_2) is *accepted* by $\mathfrak{A}^2$ if and only if there is a (unique) sequence of states $\sigma_0, \sigma_1, \ldots, \sigma_p$, and associated sequences of integers $k_0, \cdots, k_p$; $l_0, \cdots, l_p$, such that:

1. σ_0 is the initial state of $\mathfrak{A}^2$;
2. $\sigma_i = M(X_{k_i-1, l_i-1}, \sigma_{i-1})$ for $i = 1, \cdots, p$;
3. for $i = 0, 1, \cdots, p-1$, if $k_i = 1$, then $l_i \leq m$, and if $k_i = 2$, then $l_i \leq n$;
4. if $k_p = 1$, then $l_p = m + 1$, and if $k_p = 2$, then $l_p = n + 1$;
5. $\sigma_p \in \Phi$.

$L(\mathfrak{A}^2)$ is the set of all pairs of strings over T accepted by $\mathfrak{A}^2$.

The intuitive picture is as follows: the two strings $x_1 E$ and $x_2 E$ are printed on two tapes and fed into the machine. The machine begins to operate in the initial state σ_0. When it is in a state $\sigma \in \Sigma_i$, it reads on the i-th tape ($i = 1, 2$). The machine reads through both tapes from left to right, symbol after symbol, changing states according to the transition table M, and switching from one tape to another according to the partition (Σ_1, Σ_2) of the internal states. Finally, one of the strings is exhausted, and the machine scans on one of the tapes the first empty square following the symbol E. Then it stops, and the pair (x_1, x_2) is accepted if and only if the machine is in a designated final state $\sigma_p \in \Phi$. Thus it may happen that the machine accepts or rejects a pair (x_1, x_2) without having scanned all the symbols of x_1 or all those of x_2. The end-markers E enable the machine to notice the end of the strings x_1 and x_2 before getting off the printed tape.

Theorem 2.2: Let $\mathfrak{A}^2 = (T, E, \Sigma, M, \sigma_0, \Phi, \Sigma_1, \Sigma_2)$ be a TTA. It is possible to construct an SPG $\mathfrak{G}$ such that

$$L(\mathfrak{G}) = \{z \mid z = xEy^*, \ (x, y) \in L(\mathfrak{A}^2)\}.$$

In principle the construction is similar to those in the proof of Th. 2.1. But the construction and the proof of this theorem are longer and more difficult, due to the complications in the definition of acceptance of pairs (x, y) by $\mathfrak{A}^2$.

Proof.   Define $\mathfrak{G} = (V, P, T', \sigma_0)$ with $V = T \cup \{E\} \cup \Sigma \cup \Sigma' \cup \Sigma'' \cup \{\lambda\}$ where $\Sigma' = \{\sigma' \mid \sigma \in \Sigma\}$, $\Sigma'' = \{\sigma'' \mid \sigma \in \Sigma\}$ (we may assume that the sets T, $\{E\}$, Σ, Σ', Σ'' and $\{\lambda\}$ are mutually disjoint); $T' = T \cup \{E\}$; $P = \bigcup_{i=1}^{12} P_i$, and

$$
\begin{aligned}
P_1 &= \{\sigma \to X \cdot M(\sigma, X) \mid \sigma \in \Sigma_1, X \in T\}, \\
P_2 &= \{\sigma \to M(\sigma, X) \cdot X \mid \sigma \in \Sigma_2, X \in T\}, \\
P_3 &= \{\sigma \to E\tau'' \mid \sigma \in \Sigma_1, \tau = M(\sigma, E)\}, \\
P_4 &= \{\sigma \to \tau' E \mid \sigma \in \Sigma_2, \tau = M(\sigma, E)\}, \\
P_5 &= \{\tau' \to X\rho' \mid \tau \in \Sigma_1, X \in T, \; \rho = M(\tau, X)\}, \\
P_6 &= \{\tau'' \to \rho'' X \mid \tau \in \Sigma_2, X \in T, \; \rho = M(\tau, X)\}, \\
P_7 &= \{\tau'' \to \lambda \mid \tau \in \Sigma_1 \cap \Phi\}, \\
P_8 &= \{\tau' \to \lambda \mid \tau \in \Sigma_2 \cap \Phi\}, \\
P_9 &= \{\lambda \to X\lambda \mid X \in T\}, \\
P_{10} &= \{\lambda \to \Lambda\}, \\
P_{11} &= \{\tau' \to \Lambda \mid \tau \in \Sigma_1, M(\tau, E) \in \Phi\}, \\
P_{12} &= \{\tau'' \to \Lambda \mid \tau \in \Sigma_2, M(\tau, E) \in \Phi\}.
\end{aligned}
$$

The following diagram illustrates the order in which the twelve sets of productions P_i ($1 \leq i \leq 12$) can be applied.

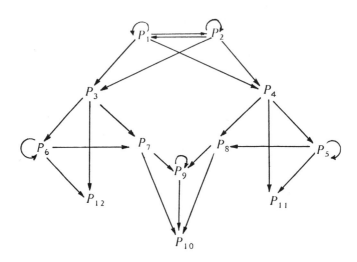

It may easily be verified that $\sigma_0 \overset{*}{\Rightarrow} z$ in $\mathfrak{G}$ if and only if either

1. $z = x\sigma y^*$, $x \in W_T$, $y \in W_T$ and σ is the state of the automaton $\mathfrak{A}^2$ after having scanned all the symbols of the pair (x, y), beginning in the initial state σ_0 (P_1, P_2); or

2. $z = xE\tau'' y^*$, $x \in W_T$, $y \in W_T$, and τ is the state of $\mathfrak{A}^2$ after having scanned all the symbols of the pair (xE, y), beginning in σ_0 (P_1, P_2, P_3, P_6), or

3. $z = x\tau'Ey^*$, $x \in W_T$, $y \in W_T$, and τ is the state of $\mathfrak{A}^2$ after having scanned all the symbols of the pair (x, yE), beginning in σ_0 (P_1, P_2, P_4, P_5); or

4. $z = xE\lambda y^*$, and $\mathfrak{A}^2$ accepts the pair (x, y) after having scanned the whole string xE and only a part of the string yE $(P_1, P_2, P_3, P_6, P_7, P_9)$; or

5. $z = x\lambda Ey^*$, and $\mathfrak{A}^2$ accepts the pair (x, y) after having scanned the whole string yE and only a part of the string xE $(P_1, P_2, P_4, P_5, P_8, P_9)$; or

6. $z = xEy^*$, and $\mathfrak{A}^2$ accepts the pair (x, y) after having scanned the whole string xE and only a part of the string yE $(P_1, P_2, P_3, P_6, P_7, P_9, P_{10})$; or

7. $z = xEy^*$, and $\mathfrak{A}^2$ accepts the pair (x, y) after having scanned the whole string yE and only a part of the string xE $(P_1, P_2, P_4, P_5, P_8, P_9, P_{10})$; or

8. $z = xEy^*$, and $\mathfrak{A}^2$ accepts the pair (x, y) after having scanned the whole string xE and the whole string yE $(P_1, P_2, P_3, P_6, P_{12}$, or $P_1, P_2, P_4, P_5, P_{11})$.

Since $T' = T \cup \{E\}$, we get:

$$L(\mathfrak{G}) = \{xEy^* \,|\, (x, y) \in L(\mathfrak{A}^2)\}.$$

Remark: Let $\mathfrak{A}^2 = (T, E, \Sigma, M, \sigma_0, \Phi, \Sigma_1, \Sigma_2)$ be a TTA and let

$$\mathfrak{A}^{2'} = (T, E, \Sigma, M, \sigma_0, \Sigma - \Phi, \Sigma_1, \Sigma_2).$$

Then $L(\mathfrak{A}^{2'}) = W_T \times W_T - L(\mathfrak{A}^2)$, where $W_T \times W_T$ is the set of all ordered pairs of strings over T. Hence, given a TTA $\mathfrak{A}^2$, we can construct an SPG $\mathfrak{G}'$, such that

$$L(\mathfrak{G}') = \{z \,|\, z = xEy^*, (x, y) \notin L(\mathfrak{A}^2)\}$$
$$= W_T \cdot E \cdot W_E - \{z \,|\, z = xEy^*, (x, y) \in L(\mathfrak{A}^2)\}.$$

It is also easy to construct an SPG $\overline{\mathfrak{G}}$, such that $L(\overline{\mathfrak{G}})$ is the set of all strings over $T \cup \{E\}$ containing either no E at all or more than one E, i.e.,

$$L(\overline{\mathfrak{G}}) = W_{T \cup \{E\}} - W_T \cdot E \cdot W_T.$$

(This set is even representable by a FA.) In Sec. 3, Th. 3.1.e, we shall see how to construct an SPG $\mathfrak{G}''$, such that $L(\mathfrak{G}'') = L(\mathfrak{G}') \cup L(\overline{\mathfrak{G}})$. But

$$L(\mathfrak{G}') \cup L(\overline{\mathfrak{G}}) = (W_T \cdot E \cdot W_T - \{z \,|\, z = xEy^*, (x, y) \in L(\mathfrak{A}^2)\})$$

$$\cup (W_{T \cup \{E\}} - W_T \cdot E \cdot W_T) = W_{T \cup \{E\}} - \{z \,|\, z = xEy^*, (x, y) \in L(\mathfrak{A}^2)\}.$$

Thus, given a TTA $\mathfrak{A}^2 = (T, E, \Sigma, M, \sigma_0, \Phi, \Sigma_1, \Sigma_2)$, we can construct an SPG $\mathfrak{G}''$, such that $L(\mathfrak{G}'') = W_{T \cup \{E\}} - \{z \,|\, z = xEy^*, (x, y) \in L(\mathfrak{A}^2)\}$.

SECTION 3: CLOSURE UNDER BOOLEAN AND OTHER OPERATIONS

Summary of results:

The class of SPLs is effectively closed under reflection, as well as under the formation of unions, products and closures of languages (Th. 3.1). ("Effectively closed under reflection" means that, given an SPG $\mathfrak{G}$, we can effectively construct an SPG $\mathfrak{G}^*$, such that $L(\mathfrak{G}^*) = L(\mathfrak{G})^*$, and similarly for the other operations.)

The class of SPLs over a vocabulary T containing at least two symbols is not closed under the formation of intersections, nor under complementation with respect to W_T (Th. 3.2).

The class of SPLs is effectively closed under a quite general kind of substitution (Th. 3.3).

Lemma 3.1: Let $\mathfrak{G} = (V, P, T, S)$ be an SPG, let $X \in V - T$ be an auxiliary symbol and let Y be a new symbol not contained in V. If we replace X by Y in V and in both sides of all productions of P, and if, in case $X = S$, we also replace S by Y in $\mathfrak{G}$, then we get an equivalent SPG. (In other words: renaming an auxiliary symbol of $\mathfrak{G}$ does not change $L(\mathfrak{G})$.)

The lemma can easily be verified by induction on the length of generation trees (see Def. 1.1.c, with $z_0 = S$).

Theorem 3.1:

a) Every finite language is an SPL.

b) If L is an SPL, so is L^*.

c) If L_1 and L_2 are SPLs, so is $L_1 \cdot L_2$.

d) If L is an SPL, so is $cl(L)$.

e) If L_1 and L_2 are SPLs, so is $L_1 \cup L_2$.

Moreover, (1) given a finite language $L = \{x_1, \cdots, x_n\}$, an SPG representing L can be effectively constructed;

(2) given an SPG representing an SPL L, we can effectively construct SPGs representing L^* and $cl(L)$, respectively;

(3) given two SPGs representing two SPLs L_1 and L_2, we can effectively construct SPGs representing $L_1 \cdot L_2$ and $L_1 \cup L_2$, respectively.

Proof: a) Let $L = \{x_1, \cdots, x_n\}$ be a finite language over a vocabulary T. Take a new symbol $S \notin T$ and define: $\mathfrak{G} = (V, T, P, S)$, where $V = T \cup \{S\}$ and $P = \{S \to x_1, \cdots, S \to x_n\}$. Obviously $L(\mathfrak{G}) = L = \{x_1, \cdots, x_n\}$.

b) Let $L = L(\mathfrak{G})$, $\mathfrak{G} = (V, P, T, S)$. Define: $\mathfrak{G}^* = (V, P^*, T, S)$, where $P^* = \{X \to x^* \mid X \to x \in P\}$. Obviously, $L(\mathfrak{G})^* = L^*$.

c) Let $L_i = L(\mathfrak{G}_i)$, $\mathfrak{G}_i = (V_i, P_i, T_i, S_i)$ $(i = 1, 2)$.

Without loss of generality, assume that $(V_1 - T_1) \cap V_2 = V_1 \cap (V_2 - T_2) = \emptyset$; otherwise, by Lemma 3.1, replace some of the symbols of $V_1 - T_1$ and $V_2 - T_2$ by new auxiliary symbols. Take a symbol $S \notin V_1 \cup V_2$, and define

$$\mathfrak{G} = (V, P, T, S),$$

where $V = V_1 \cup V_2 \cup \{S\}$, $P = P_1 \cup P_2 \cup \{S \to S_1 S_2\}$, $T = T_1 \cup T_2$. Obviously,

$$L(\mathfrak{G}) = L(\mathfrak{G}_1) \cdot L(\mathfrak{G}_2) = L_1 \cdot L_2.$$

d) Let $L = L(\mathfrak{G})$, $\mathfrak{G} = (V, P, T, S)$. Take a symbol $S_0 \notin V_1$ and define $\mathfrak{G}' = (V', P', T, S_0)$, where $V' = V \cup \{S_0\}$, $P' = P \cup \{S_0 \to SS_0, \ S_0 \to \Lambda\}$.

$$L(\mathfrak{G}') = cl(L(\mathfrak{G})) = cl(L),$$

as the reader will readily verify.

e) Let $L_i = L(\mathfrak{G}_i)$, $\mathfrak{G}_i = (V_i, P_i, T_i, S_i)$ $(i = 1, 2)$. As in c), assume that $(V_1 - T_1) \cap V_2 = V_1 \cap (V_2 - T_2) = \emptyset$. Take a symbol $S \notin V_1 \cup V_2$, and define $\mathfrak{G} = (V, P, T, S)$, where $V = V_1 \cup V_2 \cup \{S\}$, $P = P_1 \cup P_2 \cup \{S \to S_1, \ S \to S_2\}$, $T = T_1 \cup T_2$. Obviously, $L(\mathfrak{G}) = L(\mathfrak{G}_1) \cup L(\mathfrak{G}_2) = L_1 \cup L_2$.

Remark: The class of FALs is also effectively closed under reflection and multiplication, as well as under the formation of closures and unions [128: Ths. 4, 5, 6, 12, 13]. However, whereas the class of FALs over a vocabulary T is effectively closed also under intersection and complementation with respect to W_T [128: Ths. 5, 6], this is not the case for SPLs, as shown by the following

Theorem 3.2: Let T be a vocabulary containing more than one symbol.

a) The class of SPLs over T is not closed under formation of intersections.

b) The class of SPLs over T is not closed under complementation with respect to W_T.

Proof: a) Let $T = \{0, 1\}$, $L = \{0^n 10^n 10^k \mid n = 0, 1, 2, \cdots; \ k = 0, 1, 2, \cdots\}$. L is an SPL. In fact, define $\mathfrak{G} = (V, P, T, S)$, where $V = \{0, 1, S, A\}$, $T = \{0, 1\}$, $P = \{S \to S0, \ S \to A1, \ A \to 0A0, \ A \to 1\}$. Obviously, $L(\mathfrak{G}) = L$.

Now, $L^* = \{0^k 10^n 10^n \mid n = 0, 1, 2, \cdots; \ k = 0, 1, 2, \cdots\}$. L^* is an SPL, too, by Th. 3.1.b. $L \cap L^* = \{0^n 10^n 10^n \mid n = 0, 1, 2, \cdots\}$. In order to prove that $L \cap L^*$ is not an SPL, we use Th. 4.1 of Sec. 4. Indeed, if $L \cap L^*$ were an SPL, then by Th. 4.1 we would have for a sufficiently large n a decomposition: $0^n 10^n 10^n = xuwvy$, with $u \neq \Lambda$ or $v \neq \Lambda$, and $xu^2 wv^2 y \in L \cap L^*$, i.e., $xuuwvvy = 0^m 10^m 10^m$, for some $m > n$. The duplicated substrings u and v can contain only zeros, so that the effect of the duplication is to increase the length of one or two of the blocks 0^n in $0^n 10^n 10^n$, while one block remains unchanged. Hence $xuuwvvy$ cannot have the form $0^m 10^m 10^m$ with three equal blocks 0^m, contrary to the requirement that $xuuwvvy \in L \cap L^*$. Therefore $L \cap L^*$ is not an SPL, which proves a).

b) The class of SPLs over T is closed under union (Th. 3.1.e). Since

$$L_1 \cap L_2 = W_T - [(W_T - L_1) \cup (W_T - L_2)],$$

if the class of SPLs over T were closed under complementation with respect to W_T, then it would also be closed under intersection, contrary to a).

Example: Let

$$T = \{0, 1\}, \quad L = \{0^n 10^n 10^k \mid n = 0, 1, 2, \cdots; \ k = 0, 1, 2, \cdots\}.$$

We shall construct an SPG $\mathfrak{G}$ representing $W_T - (L \cap L^*)$.

Define: $\mathfrak{G} = (V, P, T, S)$, where $V = \{0, 1, S, S_0, S_1, S_2\}$, $T = \{0, 1\}$ and

$$P = \begin{cases}
1. \ S \rightarrow S_0 & 6. \ S_1 \rightarrow 0S_1 & 11. \ S \rightarrow S_0 1 S_2 0 S_0 \\
2. \ S \rightarrow S_0 1 S_0 & 7. \ S_1 \rightarrow 1S_1 & 12. \ S \rightarrow S_0 1 S_0 0 S_2 \\
3. \ S \rightarrow S_1 1 S_1 1 S_1 1 S_1 & 8. \ S_1 \rightarrow \Lambda & 13. \ S_2 \rightarrow 0 S_2 0 \\
4. \ S_0 \rightarrow 0 S_0 & 9. \ S \rightarrow S_0 0 S_2 1 S_0 & 14. \ S_2 \rightarrow 1 \\
5. \ S_0 \rightarrow \Lambda & 10. \ S \rightarrow S_2 0 S_0 1 S_0 &
\end{cases}$$

Productions no. 1, 2, 4 and 5 yield all strings over T with less than two occurrences of 1. Productions no. 3, 6, 7 and 8 yield all strings over T with more than two occurrences of 1. Productions no. 9–14 yield all strings of the form $0^k 10^l 10^m$, where $k \neq l$ or $l \neq m$. (9, 13, 14 yield $k > l$, 10, 13, 14 yield $k < l$, 11, 13, 14 yield $l < m$, and 12, 13, 14 yield $l > m$.)

Therefore $L(\mathfrak{G}) = W_T - (L \cap L^*)$. Thus, $W_T - (L \cap L^*)$ is an SPL, while $W_T - (W_T - (L \cap L^*)) = L \cap L^*$ is not an SPL, as proved in Th. 3.2.a. (If we omit from P productions no. 11 and 12, or productions no. 9 and 10, we get a representation of $W_T - L$, or $W_T - L^*$, respectively.)

Theorem 3.3: (Closure under substitution)

Let M be an SPL over a vocabulary U. Let a function ϕ assign to every symbol $X \in U$ an SPL $\phi(X) = L_X$ over a vocabulary T_X. Let L be the set of *all* strings over $\bigcup_{X \in U} T_X$ obtained from sentences $u \in M$ by substituting a sentence of L_X for each occurrence of X in u, i.e.:

$$L = \left\{ y_{X_1} \cdots y_{X_k} \ \middle| \ \begin{array}{l} X_i \in U \text{ and } y_{X_i} \in L_{X_i}, \text{ for } 1 \leq i \leq k, \\ 0 \leq k < \infty; \ X_1 \cdots X_k \in M \end{array} \right\}.$$

Then L is an SPL, and an SPG representing L can be effectively constructed from SPGs representing M and L_X $(X \in U)$.

Proof: Let $M = L(\mathfrak{G}_M)$, $\mathfrak{G}_M = (V_M, P_M, U, S_M)$, and let, for each $X \in U$:

$$L_X = L(\mathfrak{G}_X), \quad \mathfrak{G}_X = (V_X, P_X, T_X, S_X).$$

Assume, without loss of generality, that all the auxiliary vocabularies $V_M - U$ and $V_X - T_X$ $(X \in U)$, as well as $\bigcup_{X \in U} T_X$, are mutually exclusive; otherwise apply Lemma 3.1, as in the proof of Th. 3.1.b. (The terminal vocabularies T_X $(X \in U)$ may have elements in common. The vocabulary U itself will not appear explicitly in the SPG to be constructed, so that it may intersect the vocabularies V_X $(X \in U)$.)

Define: $\mathfrak{G} = (V, P, T, S)$, with $V = (V_M - U) \cup (\bigcup_{X \in U} V_X)$, $T = \bigcup_{X \in U} T_X$, and $P = P'_M \cap (\bigcup_{X \in U} P_X)$, where P'_M is obtained from P_M by substituting, in all productions, S_X—the initial symbol of $\mathfrak{G}_X$ — for every occurrence of $X \in U$.

Clearly, every sentence of L is generated by $\mathfrak{G}$: in order to generate $y_{X_1} \cdots y_{X_k}$, where $X_i \in U$, $y_{X_i} \in L_{X_i}$ $(1 \leq i \leq k)$ and $X_1 \cdots X_k \in M$, first generate $S_{X_1} \cdots S_{X_k}$ from S_M, applying P_M, then generate y_{X_i} from S_{X_i}, applying P_{X_i} $(1 \leq i \leq k)$.

Conversely, it is easily verified by induction on the length of generation trees in $\mathfrak{G}$, that for every $A \in V_M - U$, if $A \overset{*}{\Rightarrow} y$ by P and $y \in W_T$, then there is a decomposition $y = y_{X_1} \cdots y_{X_k}$, such that $X_i \in U$, $y_{X_i} \in L_{X_i}$ $(1 \leq i \leq k)$ and $A \overset{*}{\Rightarrow} X_1 \cdots X_k$ in $\mathfrak{G}_M$. By taking $A = S_M$, we see that every string over T generated by $\mathfrak{G}$ is a sentence of L. Therefore, $L(\mathfrak{G}) = L$.

In case the languages $L_X (X \in U)$ consist of single, possibly empty, strings, we get as a special case of Th. 3.3 the following

Corollary 3.1: Let T and T' be two vocabularies, and ϕ a function from T into $W_{T'}$. ϕ can be extended naturally to a function from W_T to to $W_{T'}$, by defining: if $x = X_1 \cdots X_k \in W_T$, then $\phi(x) = \phi(X_1) \cdots \phi(X_k)$.

If L is an SPL over T, then $\phi(L)$ is an SPL over T', and an SPG representing $\phi(L)$ can be effectively constructed from an SPG representing L.

Remark: Theorem 3.3 holds true if we replace throughout "SPL" by "FAL," and "SPG" by "FA".

Method of proof: a) First prove that if L is an FAL over a vocabulary T, and $X \in T$, then the language L' obtained from L by omitting all occurrences of the symbol X from all sentences of L is an FAL, and a FA representing L' can be effectively constructed from a FA representing L. This will be done most conveniently by first constructing a nondeterministic FA $\mathfrak{A}$ representing L', then reducing $\mathfrak{A}'$ to an equivalent deterministic FA $\mathfrak{A}''$, by [128: Def. 11 and Th. 11]. (A similar result is proved in [40].)

b) Let M be an FAL over U, and for each $X \in U$ let L_X be an FAL over T_X. Take new separating symbols A_X, one for each $X \in U$, all different and not contained in $\bigcup_{X \in U} T_X$. Given FAa representing M and L_X $(X \in U)$, construct a FA $\mathfrak{B}$ which will accept exactly all strings of the form

$$A_{X_1}y_{X_1}A_{X_1}A_{X_2}y_{X_2}A_{X_2} \cdots A_{X_k}y_{X_k}A_{X_k},$$

where $X_i \in U$, $y_{X_i} \in L_{X_i}$ $(1 \leq i \leq k)$, and $X_1 \cdots X_k \in M$.

c) By repeated application of a) construct from $\mathfrak{B}$ a FA $\mathfrak{A}$ which will accept exactly the strings obtained from strings of the form

$$A_{X_1}y_{X_1}A_{X_1}A_{X_2}y_{X_2}A_{X_2} \cdots A_{X_k}y_{X_k}A_{X_k}$$

$$(X_i \in U, \ y_{X_i} \in L_{X_i} \ (1 \leq i \leq k), \quad X_1 \cdots X_k \in M)$$

by omitting all occurrences of the separating symbols A_{X_1}. Clearly, $L(\mathfrak{A})$ is the language required in Th. 3.3.

In Section 8 we shall prove that the intersection of an SPL and an FAL is effectively an SPL.

SECTION 4:   SOME BASIC AUXILIARY PROPERTIES OF SPGs

Definition 4.1:   Let $\mathfrak{G} = (V, T, P, S)$ be an SPG.

a) $\mathfrak{G}$ is called a 1-SPG if, for every production $X \to x \in P$, $l(x) \geq 1$ (i.e., if P does not contain any production of the form $X \to \Lambda$).

b) $\mathfrak{G}$ is called a 2-SPG if, for every production $X \to x \in P$, $l(x) \geq 2$ (i.e. if P does not contain any production of the form $X \to \Lambda$ or $X \to Y$, with $Y \in V$).

The following two lemmata show how to reduce any SPG to an almost equivalent 1-SPG, and any 1-SPG to an almost equivalent 2-SPG. These reductions will be used later on. In the definition of SPGs given in Chapter 8, Section 2, all productions are required to be non-empty, i.e., of the form $X \to x$, $x \neq \Lambda$. Lemma 4.1 shows that the SPGs defined in Section 1 are completely equivalent to the SPGs defined in Chapter 8, with the possible exception of the empty string Λ.

Lemma 4.1:   Let $\mathfrak{G} = (V, P, T, S)$ be an SPG. It can be effectively decided whether $\Lambda \in L(\mathfrak{G})$, and a 1-SPG $\mathfrak{G}'$ can be constructed such that

$$L(\mathfrak{G}') = L(\mathfrak{G}) - \{\Lambda\}.$$

Proof: 1. We define an ascending chain of subsets of V:

$$V_1 = \{X \mid X \in V \ \& \ X \to \Lambda \in P\}$$

$$V_{k+1} = V_k \cup \{X \mid X \in V \ \& \ (\exists x)\,[x \in W_{V_k} \ \& \ X \to x \in P]\} \qquad (k = 1, 2, \cdots),$$

i.e., V_{k+1} contains V_k and all symbols which directly generate strings over V_k.

Obviously, $V_k \subseteq V_{k+1}$ for all k, and if for some k, $V_k = V_{k+1}$, then $V_k = V_l$, for all $l > k$, so that the chain remains constant after n steps at most, where n is the number of symbols in V. If $X \in V_n$, then $X \overset{*}{\Rightarrow} \Lambda$. Conversely, if $X \overset{*}{\Rightarrow} \Lambda$ then $X \in V_k$ for some k, and therefore $X \in V_n$. $\Lambda \in L(\mathfrak{G})$ iff $S \overset{*}{\Rightarrow} \Lambda$, i.e., iff $S \in V_n$.

2. Let $\mathfrak{G}' = (V, P', T, S)$, where P' is defined as follows: $X \to x \in P'$ iff $x \neq \Lambda$ and there is a production $X \to y \in P$, such that x is obtained from y by omission of some (possibly none) occurrences of symbols contained in V_n.

Obviously, if $X \overset{*}{\Rightarrow} x$ in $\mathfrak{G}'$, then $X \overset{*}{\Rightarrow} x$ in $\mathfrak{G}$, because the effect of every production of P' can be obtained by applying a finite number of productions of P. Conversely, if $X \overset{*}{\Rightarrow} x$ in $\mathfrak{G}$ and $x \neq \Lambda$, then $X \overset{*}{\Rightarrow} x$ in $\mathfrak{G}'$. This can easily be proved by induction on the lengths of the generation trees in $\mathfrak{G}$.

In particular, $S \overset{*}{\Rightarrow} x$ in $\mathfrak{G}'$ iff $x \neq \Lambda$ and $S \overset{*}{\Rightarrow} x$ in $\mathfrak{G}$. Therefore,

$$L(\mathfrak{G}') = L(\mathfrak{G}) - \{\Lambda\}.$$

Lemma 4.2: Let $\mathfrak{G} = (V, P, T, S)$ be a 1-SPG. For all $X \in T$ it can be effectively decided whether $X \in L(\mathfrak{G})$, and a 2-SPG $\mathfrak{G}'$ can be constructed, such that $L(\mathfrak{G}') = L(\mathfrak{G}) - T$ (i.e., $x \in L(\mathfrak{G}')$ iff $x \in L(\mathfrak{G})$ and $l(x) \geq 2$).

Proof: 1. We define ascending chains of subsets of V: For each $X \in V$,

$$V_1(X) = \{X\},$$

$$V_{k+1}(X) = V_k(X) \cup \{Y \mid Y \in V \,\&\, (\exists Z)[Z \in V_k(X) \,\&\, Z \to Y \in P]\} \,(k = 1, 2, \cdots),$$

i.e., $V_{k+1}(X)$ contains besides $V_k(X)$ all symbols which are directly generated by symbols of $V_k(X)$.

By an argument similar to that used in the proof of lemma 4.1 we have:

$$V_1(X) \subseteq V_2(X) \subseteq \cdots \subseteq V_n(X) = V_{n+1}(X) = V_{n+2}(X) = \cdots,$$

where n is the number of symbols of V.

$\mathfrak{G}$ is, by assumption, a 1-SPG, so that P contains no length-decreasing productions of the form $X \to \Lambda$. Therefore $Y \in V_n(X)$ iff $X \overset{*}{\Rightarrow} Y$. $X \in L(\mathfrak{G})$ iff $S \overset{*}{\Rightarrow} X$ and $X \in T$, i.e., iff $X \in T \cap V_n(S)$.

2. Let

$$P' = \{X \to x \mid l(x) \geq 2 \,\&\, (\exists Y)[Y \in V_n(X) \,\&\, Y \to x \in P]\}.$$

Define P'' as follows:

$X \to Y_1 \cdots Y_r \in P''$, iff there is a production $X \to X_1 \cdots X_r \in P'$, such that $Y_j \in V_n(X_j)$ for $1 \leq j \leq r$. Let $\mathfrak{G}' = (V, P'', T, S)$.

Obviously, if $X \overset{*}{\Rightarrow} x$ in $\mathfrak{G}'$, then $X \overset{*}{\Rightarrow} x$ in $\mathfrak{G}$. Conversely, if $X \overset{*}{\Rightarrow} x$ in $\mathfrak{G}$ and $l(x) \geqq 2$, then $X \overset{*}{\Rightarrow} x$ in $\mathfrak{G}'$. This can easily be proved by induction on the lengths of the generation trees in $\mathfrak{G}$.

In particular, $S \overset{*}{\Rightarrow} x$ in $\mathfrak{G}'$ iff $l(x) \geqq 2$ and $S \overset{*}{\Rightarrow} x$ in $\mathfrak{G}$. Therefore,

$$L(\mathfrak{G}') = L(\mathfrak{G}) - T.$$

Theorem 4.1:   Let $\mathfrak{G} = (V, P, T, S)$ be a 2-SPG. It is possible to determine two natural numbers p and q such that every sentence z of $L(\mathfrak{G})$ with $l(z) > p$ admits a decomposition of the form $z = xuwvy$, where $u \neq \Lambda$ or $v \neq \Lambda$, $l(uwv) \leqq q$, and all the strings

$$z_k = xu^k w v^k y \in L(\mathfrak{G}) \qquad (k = 1, 2, 3, \cdots).$$

Proof: The proof relies on a graphic representation of generation trees. By a *tree* we mean a "branching pattern" with a special notation of nodes. The following graphs are examples of trees:

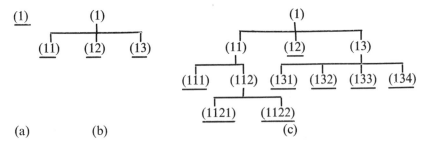

(a)   (b)   (c)

In general, taking in a given tree a *terminal node* (in the examples, the underlined nodes are terminal) which is denoted by the multi-index (α), we obtain a new tree by adding to the old one the "branch"

$$(\alpha)$$

$$(\alpha 1) \qquad (\alpha 2) \qquad \cdots \ (\alpha k).$$

Each one of the modes $(\alpha 1)$, $(\alpha 2)$, $\cdots$, (αk) is called *consecutive* to (α). A $\mathfrak{G}$-*tree* is obtained from a tree by attaching a symbol of V to each node of the tree, so that when A is attached to (α), B_j to (αj) $(1 \leqq j \leqq k)$, and these (αj) are all the consecutive nodes of (α), then $A \to B_1 B_2 \cdots B_k \in P$.

Note that a tree does not always yield a $\mathfrak{G}$-tree by a suitable attachment of symbols. For instance: in all the $\mathfrak{G}$-trees the components of the multi-indices cannot be greater than the length of the longest production in P.

The node (1) is the vertex of the tree, and the *vertex-symbol* of a $\mathfrak{G}$-tree is the symbol attached to the vertex. The *final string* of a $\mathfrak{G}$-tree is the string obtained by arranging the symbols attached to the terminal nodes in the lexicographic order of the multi-indices. (E.g., the order of the terminal nodes in the tree (c) is: (111), (1121), (1122), (12), (131), (132), (133), (134).)

A *path* in a tree is a sequence of consecutive nodes starting with the vertex and terminating in a terminal node. (E.g., (1), (11), (112), (1121) is a path in (c).) The sequence of symbols attached to the nodes of a path gives a 𝔊-path. Note that every terminal node determines a unique path.

Each node (α) in a tree determines, in a natural manner, a unique *subtree* of the given tree. This subtree contains (α) (as its vertex), the consecutive nodes of (α), the consecutive nodes of these nodes, and so on. (Properly speaking, a subtree is not a tree, but becomes a tree when we rename the node (α) by (1) and the other nodes correspondingly.) In a similar manner, a node in a 𝔊-tree determines a *𝔊-subtree*. The final string of a 𝔊-subtree is a substring of the final string of the 𝔊-tree.

Now it is easily verified that the vertex-symbol of a 𝔊-tree generates the final string (in the sense of Def. 1.1.c). Conversely, if $A \overset{*}{\Rightarrow} x$ in 𝔊, then a 𝔊-tree with vertex-symbol A and final string x can be constructed. This justifies the assertion that 𝔊-trees are graphic representations of generations in 𝔊.

After introducing the above notions, the actual proof of the theorem runs as follows: Let n be the number of symbols in V, and consider the 𝔊-trees in which all the paths are of length n at most. The number of all such 𝔊-trees is obviously finite and the lengths of their final strings are bounded. Call this bound p (p can easily be estimated). Every sentence z of $L(𝔊)$ with $l(z) > p$ is then the final string of a 𝔊-tree with vertex-symbol S, which contains a path longer than n. Let $A_1, A_2, \cdots, A_r$ ($r > n$) be a longest 𝔊-path in that 𝔊-tree. In the sequence $A_{r-n}, \cdots, A_r$, at least one symbol must occur twice. Suppose $A_i = A_j = W$ ($r - n \leq i < j \leq r$). Consider the 𝔊-subtree whose vertex-symbol is $W = A_i$ (i.e., the 𝔊-subtree determined by the node to which $W = A_i$ is attached). Since $W = A_j$ is attached to one of its nodes, the generation corresponding to this 𝔊-subtree has the form:

$$W \overset{*}{\Rightarrow} u'Wv' \overset{*}{\Rightarrow} uwv,$$

where, since we deal with a 2-SPG, u' or v' (and so u or v) $\neq \Lambda$. Here uwv is the final string of the 𝔊-subtree, hence it is a substring of z, the final string of the original 𝔊-tree. This means that z can be decomposed into the form $z = xuwvy$.

Now the generations $W \overset{*}{\Rightarrow} u'Wv'$, $u' \overset{*}{\Rightarrow} u$, $v' \overset{*}{\Rightarrow} v$ can be repeated k times. We obtain $W \overset{*}{\Rightarrow} (u')^k W(v')^k \overset{*}{\Rightarrow} u^k wv^k$, and from the original 𝔊-tree we obtain $S \overset{*}{\Rightarrow} xu^k wv^k y \in L(𝔊)$ ($k = 1, 2, 3, \cdots$).

Finally note that $A_{r-n}, \cdots, A_r$ is a longest path of the $\mathfrak{G}$-subtree — hence the length of all its paths is $\leq n + 1$; thus, with a suitable bound q, we have for its final string: $l(uwv) \leq q$.

The theorem just proved (combined with Lemma 4.2) is very useful in showing that various languages are *not* SPLs, and was already used in the proof of Theorem 3.2.

SECTION 5:   SOLVABLE DECISION PROBLEMS

In this section we shall exhibit decision procedures for two basic properties of SPGs, namely the emptiness and the infiniteness of $L(\mathfrak{G})$, as well as for the basic generation relations of strings in an SPG.

One way of obtaining decision procedures is to consider the graphic representation of generation trees, which was already used in proving Theorem 4.1. This way yields sometimes more economic procedures. However, we preferred the method of ascending chains of sets (of strings or of symbols), which allows for a more uniform and rigorous presentation. This last method was already used in the proofs of Lemmata 4.1 and 4.2.

In general, it is more convenient first to present decision procedures for 1-SPGs or even 2-SPGs, and afterwards use Lemmata 4.1 and 4.2 in order to reduce an arbitrary SPG to one of these special kinds of SPGs.

Theorem 5.1:   Let $\mathfrak{G} = (V, P, T, S)$ be a 1-SPG. For $A \in V$ and $x \in W_V$, the following relations are decidable:

a) $A \overset{*}{\Rightarrow} x$

b) $(\exists u)\,(\exists v)\,(A \overset{*}{\Rightarrow} uxv)$

c) $(\exists u)(A \overset{*}{\Rightarrow} ux)$ and, similarly, $(\exists v)\,(A \overset{*}{\Rightarrow} xv)$

d) $(\exists u)\,(\exists v)\,(u \neq \Lambda,\ v \neq \Lambda\ \&\ A \overset{*}{\Rightarrow} uxv)$

e) $(\exists u)\,(u \neq \Lambda\ \&\ A \overset{*}{\Rightarrow} ux)$ and, similarly, $(\exists v)\,(v \neq \Lambda\ \&\ A \overset{*}{\Rightarrow} xv)$.

Proof.   We prove b) first. Suppose that V contains n symbols and let $l(x) = m$. We construct inductively the following sets of strings:

$$A_m^1 = \{z \mid l(z) \leq m\ \&\ (\exists u)(\exists v)(A \Rightarrow uzv)\}$$
$$A_m^k = \{z \mid l(z) \leq m\ \&\ [z \in A_m^{k-1} \lor (\exists u)(\exists v)(\exists y)(y \in A_m^{k-1}\ \&\ y \Rightarrow uzv)]\}.$$

The relation $R(x, y) = (\exists u)(\exists v)(y \Rightarrow uxv)$, on which the definition of the A_m^k is based, is clearly decidable, since $\Rightarrow$ denotes *direct* generation. Thus the sets $A_m^1, A_m^2, A_m^3, \cdots$, can be effectively constructed one after the other. By definition we have $A_m^{k-1} \subseteq A_m^k$. Also, $A_m^{k-1} = A_m^k$ implies $A_m^k = A_m^{k+1}$. Indeed, a z with $l(z) \leq m$ belongs to A_m^{k+1} if $z \in A_m^k$ or $y \in A_m^k$ and $y \Rightarrow uzv$, for suitable y, u, and v. By assumption, y already belongs to A_m^{k-1}, hence, in any case, $z \in A_m^k$.

Thus the sequence of sets $A_m^1, A_m^2, \cdots$ strictly increases until an equality is obtained. But the total number of non-empty strings not longer than m is $\beta = \dfrac{n^{m+1} - 1}{n - 1} - 1$, hence the sequence must stop increasing when (or before) A_m^β is reached. In other words, $\lim\limits_{k \to \infty} A_m^k = A_m^\beta$.

Now it is readily seen that:

$$(\exists u)(\exists v)(A \overset{*}{\Rightarrow} uxv) \leftrightarrow [(A = x) \vee (\Lambda = x) \vee (\exists k)(x \in A_m^k)] \leftrightarrow [(A = x) \vee x \in A_m^\beta].$$

A decision procedure for b) would therefore be: Check whether $x = A$. If not, construct A_m^β and check whether $x \in A_m^\beta$.

The proofs of a) and c) are obtained analogously, by suitable modifications in the definition of A_m^k. As for d), note that d) holds if and only if

$$(\exists u)(\exists v)(A \overset{*}{\Rightarrow} uDxEv)$$

holds for at least one pair of symbols $D, E \in V$. A similar remark proves e).

Corollary: Let $\mathfrak{G}$ be a SPG. The property of sentencehood: $x \in L(\mathfrak{G})$ is decidable.

Proof: For a 1-SPG, $x \in L(\mathfrak{G})$ iff $S \overset{*}{\Rightarrow} x$ and $x \in W_T$, thus the corollary follows from part a) of the theorem. For an arbitrary SPG $\mathfrak{G}$, we construct by Lemma 4.1 a 1-SPG $\mathfrak{G}'$ which generates exactly the $x \in L(\mathfrak{G})$ with $l(x) \geqq 1$. Now $\Lambda \in L(\mathfrak{G})$ is decidable (again by Lemma 4.1) and a non-empty $x \in L(\mathfrak{G})$ iff $x \in L(\mathfrak{G}')$.

Next, we shall prove the solvability of the emptiness problem.

Theorem 5.2: Given an SPG $\mathfrak{G} = (V, P, T, S)$, we can effectively decide whether $L(\mathfrak{G})$ is empty.

Proof: Let:

$$T_0 = T, \quad T_j = T_{j-1} \cup \{X \in V \,|\, (\exists x)(x \in W_{T_{j-1}} \ \& \ X \Rightarrow x)\}.$$

Thus T_j includes T_{j-1} and contains also all the symbols that directly generate strings over T_{j-1}. Clearly, T_j can be effectively constructed from T_{j-1}; $T_{j-1} = T_j$ implies $T_j = T_{j+1}$. If $V - T$ contains r symbols, the ascending chain $T_0 \subseteq T_1 \subseteq T_2 \cdots$ strictly increases r steps at most, and we have

$$T_r = \lim\limits_{k \to \infty} T_k.$$

Since, clearly

$$(\exists x)[x \in L(\mathfrak{G})] \leftrightarrow (\exists x)[S \overset{*}{\Rightarrow} x \ \& \ x \in W_T] \leftrightarrow (\exists k)[S \in T_k] \leftrightarrow S \in T_r,$$

it follows that $L(\mathfrak{G})$ is empty iff $S \notin T_r$. This provides an effective procedure.

The constructions in the proofs of Theorems 5.1 and 5.2 enable us to present an SPG in a "reduced" form, in which superfluous symbols have been eliminated. We first define:

Definition 5.1: An SPG $\mathfrak{G} = (V, P, T, S)$ is called *reduced* if $L(\mathfrak{G}) = \emptyset$ and $V = \{S\}$, $P = T = \emptyset$; or in case $L(\mathfrak{G}) \neq \emptyset$, if the following two conditions are satisfied:

(i) for every $A \in V$, there are strings u and v such that $S \overset{*}{\Rightarrow} uAv$;

(ii) for every $A \in V - T$, there is a string $t \in W_T$ such that $A \overset{*}{\Rightarrow} t$.

Condition (i) means that every symbol of V actually occurs in some generation from S. Condition (ii) means that every auxiliary symbol generates a terminal string.

Lemma 5.1:   Let $\mathfrak{G} = (V, T, P, S)$ be an SPG. It is possible to construct a reduced SPG $\overline{\mathfrak{G}}$ equivalent to $\mathfrak{G}$, such that in $\overline{\mathfrak{G}} = (\overline{V}, \overline{P}, \overline{T}, S)$

$$\overline{V} \subseteq V, \quad \overline{P} \subseteq P, \quad \overline{T} \subseteq T.$$

Proof: If $L(\mathfrak{G}) = \emptyset$ (this is decidable, by Th. 5.2), take $\overline{V} = \{S\}$, $\overline{P} = \overline{T} = \emptyset$. If $L(\mathfrak{G}) \neq \emptyset$, we obtain $\overline{\mathfrak{G}}$ in two steps. First we delete from V the symbols which do not generate terminal strings, i.e., the symbols not contained in the set T_r constructed in the proof of Th. 5.2. We denote by P' the set of productions of P which contain only symbols of T_r. Then $\mathfrak{G}' = (T_r, P', T, S)$ is clearly equivalent to $\mathfrak{G}$. $\mathfrak{G}'$ fulfils condition (ii), since $T_r \ni A \overset{*}{\Rightarrow} t$ in $\mathfrak{G}$ implies that all the symbols in the generation tree from A to t belong to T_r, hence $A \overset{*}{\Rightarrow} t$ in $\mathfrak{G}'$.

Next we delete from T_r the symbols which are not generated from S in $\mathfrak{G}'$ (i.e., by the productions of P'). These are the symbols not contained in the set S^n constructed in the proof of Theorem 5.1. (Note that here $\lim_{k \to \infty} S_1^k = S_1^n$ where n is the number of symbols in T_r).

Now, if $\overline{V} = S_1^n$ (note that $S_1^n \subseteq T_r \subseteq V$), $\overline{T} = \overline{V} \cap T$ and $\overline{P}$ is the set of productions of P' which contain only symbols of $\overline{V}$, then $\overline{\mathfrak{G}} = (\overline{V}, \overline{P}, \overline{T}, S)$ is the required SPG. Indeed $\overline{\mathfrak{G}}$ is equivalent to $\mathfrak{G}'$, hence also to $\mathfrak{G}$, and it is easily verified that it fulfils condition (i). Regarding condition (ii), note that $S \overset{*}{\Rightarrow} \cdots A \cdots$ in $\mathfrak{G}'$ and $A \overset{*}{\Rightarrow} t$ in $\mathfrak{G}'$ imply that all the symbols in the generation tree from A to t also belong to $S_1^n = \overline{V}$. Hence $A \overset{*}{\Rightarrow} t$ in $\overline{\mathfrak{G}}$. Q.E.D.

Definition 5.2:   Let $\mathfrak{G} = (V, T, P, S)$ be an SPG, and let V contain n symbols. A symbol $A \in V$ is called an *embedding symbol* if $A \in A_1^n$. $\mathfrak{G}$ is called an *embedding* SPG, if some symbol $A \in V$ is embedding.

In other words, A is embedding iff there exists a non-trivial generation $A \overset{*}{\Rightarrow} uAv$. Obviously the property of being embedding is effectively decidable, for both symbols and SPGs.

Theorem 5.3: (i) Let $\mathfrak{G}$ be a reduced 2-SPG. $L(\mathfrak{G})$ is infinite iff $\mathfrak{G}$ is embedding. (This does not hold true if $\mathfrak{G}$ is not reduced or is not a 2-SPG.) (ii) Given an SPG $\mathfrak{G}$, we can effectively decide whether $L(\mathfrak{G})$ is infinite.

Proof: (i) If $\mathfrak{G}$ is an embedding 2-SPG, we have $A \overset{*}{\Rightarrow} uAv$, for a suitable A, with u or $v \neq \Lambda$. If $\mathfrak{G}$ is also reduced, we have $S \overset{*}{\Rightarrow} xAy$, for every A and for suitable x and y. Combining these generations, we have:

$$S \overset{*}{\Rightarrow} xAy \overset{*}{\Rightarrow} xuAvy \overset{*}{\Rightarrow} xu^2Av^2y \Rightarrow \cdots \overset{*}{\Rightarrow} xu^kAv^ky \overset{*}{\Rightarrow} \cdots$$

Using again the fact that $\mathfrak{G}$ is reduced, we have:

$$x \overset{*}{\Rightarrow} x', \; y \overset{*}{\Rightarrow} y' \; u \overset{*}{\Rightarrow} u', \; v \overset{*}{\Rightarrow} v', \; A \overset{*}{\Rightarrow} a,$$

where x', y', u', v' and a are suitable strings over T. Hence

$$S \overset{*}{\Rightarrow} x'(u')^k a(v')^k y',$$

and the right-hand side is a string over T, i.e., it belongs to $L(\mathfrak{G})$, for every $k = 1, 2, 3, \cdots$. We have thus proved that $L(\mathfrak{G})$ is infinite.

Conversely, if none of the symbols of V is embedding, only a finite number of strings are generated from S. (This can also be shown by considering the $\mathfrak{G}$-trees appearing in the proof of Theorem 4.1. For non-embedding $\mathfrak{G}$, the paths of $\mathfrak{G}$-trees are of length $\leq n$, hence the number of different $\mathfrak{G}$-trees, and a fortiori the number of final strings in $\mathfrak{G}$-trees, is finite.) In particular, $L(\mathfrak{G})$ is finite. Note that this converse holds also for any SPG.

(ii) For a 2-SPG, part (ii) follows from (i) and the remark that embedding is a decidable property. For an arbitrary SPG $\mathfrak{G}$, we construct, by Lemmata 4.1, 4.2 and 5.1, a reduced 2-SPG $\overline{\mathfrak{G}}$ which is equivalent to $\mathfrak{G}$, except for a finite number of strings of length ≤ 1. Hence, the infiniteness of $L(\mathfrak{G})$ is equivalent to that of $L(\overline{\mathfrak{G}})$, and therefore decidable.

SECTION 6: UNDECIDABLE PROPERTIES OF SPGs

In this section we prove certain properties of SPGs and relations between SPGs to be effectively *undecidable* (Theorems 6.1, 6.2 and 6.3). We proceed by reducing a known unsolvable decision problem to the decision problems of those properties and relations. This unsolvable problem is the following one, known as

Post's correspondence problem:

Let $(a_1, \cdots, a_n)$, $(b_1, \cdots, b_n)$ be two n-tuples of non-empty strings over a vocabulary V. Does there exist a sequence of indices $i_1, \cdots, i_k$, where $k \geq 1$ and $1 \leq i_j \leq n$ for $j = 1, \cdots, k$, such that $a_{i_1} \cdots a_{i_k} = b_{i_1} \cdots b_{i_k}$?

Post [122] proved that this correspondence problem is not effectively solvable, provided that V contains more than one symbol. Since we shall make constant use of Post's correspondence problem and his result, we introduce the following abbreviatory notation.

Definition 6.1:   Let (a, b) be a pair of n-tuples of nonempty strings over $\{0, 1\}$, $a = (a_1, \cdots, a_n)$, $b = (b_1, \cdots, b_n)$, $n \geq 1$. If there exists a sequence $i_1, \cdots, i_k$ of indices, where $k \geq 1$ and $1 \leq i_j \leq n$ for $j = 1, \cdots, k$, such that $a_{i_1} \cdots a_{i_k} = b_{i_1} \cdots b_{i_k}$, then we write $\mathscr{P}(a, b) = 1$; if there exists no such sequence, we write $\mathscr{P}(a, b) = 0$.

Theorem 6.1:   The following decision problems are effectively unsolvable:

Given two SPGs $\mathfrak{G}_1$ and $\mathfrak{G}_2$,
a) is $L(\mathfrak{G}_1) \cap L(\mathfrak{G}_2)$ empty?
b) is $L(\mathfrak{G}_1) \cap L(\mathfrak{G}_2)$ finite?
c) is $L(\mathfrak{G}_1) \cap L(\mathfrak{G}_2)$ an FAL?
d) is $L(\mathfrak{G}_1) \cap L(\mathfrak{G}_2)$ an SPL?

Moreover, these problems are unsolvable even in the special case that $\mathfrak{G}_1$ and $\mathfrak{G}_2$ have a common terminal vocabulary T which contains two symbols only, and they remain unsolvable for $\mathfrak{G}_1$, even if $\mathfrak{G}_2$ is held fixed to be a certain SPG $\overline{\mathfrak{G}}_s$ defined below.

Theorem 6.2:   The following decision problems are effectively unsolvable:

Given an SPG $\mathfrak{G}$ with a terminal vocabulary T,
a) is $W_T - L(\mathfrak{G})$ empty?
b) is $W_T - L(\mathfrak{G})$ finite?
c) is $W_T - L(\mathfrak{G})$ an FAL?
d) is $W_T - L(\mathfrak{G})$ an SPL?

These problems are unsolvable even if T is restricted to contain two symbols only.

Theorem 6.3:   The following decision problems are effectively unsolvable:

a) (Inclusion) Given two SPGs $\mathfrak{G}_1$ and $\mathfrak{G}_2$, is $L(\mathfrak{G}_1) \subseteq L(\mathfrak{G}_2)$?

This problem remains unsolvable for $\mathfrak{G}_2$, if $\mathfrak{G}_1$ is held fixed to be a certain SPG $\mathfrak{G}_W$ defined below, and remains unsolvable for $\mathfrak{G}_1$, if $\mathfrak{G}_2$ is held fixed to be a certain SPG $\overline{\mathfrak{G}}_s'$ defined below.

b) (Equivalence) Given two SPGs $\mathfrak{G}_1$ and $\mathfrak{G}_2$, is $L(\mathfrak{G}_1) = L(\mathfrak{G}_2)$?

This problem remains unsolvable for $\mathfrak{G}_1$, if $\mathfrak{G}_2$ is held fixed to be a certain SPG $\mathfrak{G}_W$ defined below.

c)   Given an SPG $\mathfrak{G}$, is $L(\mathfrak{G})$ an FAL?
d)   Given an SPG $\mathfrak{G}$ and a FA $\mathfrak{A}$, is $L(\mathfrak{G}) = L(\mathfrak{A})$?

This problem remains unsolvable for $\mathfrak{G}$, if $\mathfrak{A}$ is held fixed to be a certain FA $\mathfrak{G}_W$ defined below.

These four problems are unsolvable even in the special case that the terminal vocabularies of $\mathfrak{G}_1$, $\mathfrak{G}_2$ and $\mathfrak{G}$ and the vocabulary of $\mathfrak{A}$ contain each two symbols only.

The assertions of Theorem 6.3 will be derived as corollaries from Theorems 6.1 and 6.2. The proof of Theorem 6.3 will be given after the proofs of Theorems 6.1 and 6.2.

The reduction of Post's correspondence problem to the decision problems mentioned in Theorems 6.1 and 6.2 will require several auxiliary definitions and lemmata. Lemmata 6.1, 6.3, and 6.6 will be used in the proofs of both Theorems 6.1 and 6.2. Lemmata 6.2, 6.4 and 6.5 are needed for the proof of Theorem 6.2 only.

If we are contented to prove Theorems 6.1, 6.2 and 6.3 only for terminal vocabularies T containing more than two symbols, then we can dispense with Def. 6.5 and Lemma 6.5, and replace Lemma 6.6 by a simplified variant thereof (see Remark b) following the proof of Lemma 6.6).

The construction given here (Defs. 6.2, 6.3 and 6.4) is closely related to that used in [128: Theorem 18] for proving the unsolvability of the empty-intersection problem for TTAa.

Definition 6.2: Let $\xi = (x_1, \cdots, x_n)$ be an n-tuple of strings. Define:

$$L(\xi) = \{10^{i_k} \cdots 10^{i_1} E x_{i_1} \cdots x_{i_k} \mid k \geq 1, 1 \leq i_v \leq n \text{ for } v = 1, \cdots, k\}$$

where 0^i, we recall, is the string $0 \cdots 0$ consisting of i zeros).

If we look upon the string 10^i as a code for the natural number i and denote it by $\hat{\imath}$, then we have:

$$L(\xi) = \{\hat{\imath}_k \cdots \hat{\imath}_1 E x_{i_1} \cdots x_{i_k} \mid k \geq 1, \ 1 \leq i_v \leq n, \text{ for } v = 1, \cdots, k\}.$$

Definition 6.3: Let (a, b) be a pair of n-tuples of nonempty strings over $\{0, 1\}$, $a = (a_1, \cdots, a_n)$, $b = (b_1, \cdots, b_n)$. Define:

$$L(a, b) = L(a) \cdot E \cdot L(b)^*, \text{ i.e.,}$$

$$L(a, b) = \left\{ 10^{i_k} \cdots 10^{i_1} E a_{i_1} \cdots a_{i_k} E b_{j_l}^* \cdots b_{j_1}^* E 0^{j_l} 1 \cdots 0^{j_1} 1 \right.$$

$$\left. \begin{array}{l} k \geq 1, \ l \geq 1, \\ 1 \leq i_v \leq n \text{ for } v = 1, \cdots, k \\ 1 \leq j_v \leq n \text{ for } v = 1, \cdots, l \end{array} \right\}$$

(where x^*, we recall, is the reflection of x).

Lemma 6.1: $L(a,b)$ is an SPL, represented by the SPG:

$$\mathfrak{G}(a,b) = (V, P(a,b), T, S),$$

where

$$V = \{S, A, B, 0, 1, E\}, \ T = \{0, 1, E\}$$

$$P(a,b) = \left\{ \begin{array}{l} S \rightarrow AEB, \\ A \rightarrow 10^i A a_i, A \rightarrow 10^i E a_i \quad (i = 1, \cdots, n) \\ B \rightarrow b_j^* B 0^j 1, \ B \rightarrow b_j^* E 0^j 1 \ (j = 1, \cdots, n) \end{array} \right\}$$

Proof: Obvious.

Lemma 6.2: $W_T - L(a, b)$ is an SPL, represented by the SPG $\mathfrak{G}'(a,b) = (V', P'(a,b), T, S)$, where

$$V' = \{S, S_1, S_2, A, B, 0, 1, E\}, \qquad T = \{0, 1, E\},$$

$$P'(a,b) = P_1 \cup P_2 \cup P_3 \cup P_4 \cup P_5 \cup P_6 \cup P_7(n) \cup P_8(a) \cup P_9(b),$$

and $P_1 = \{S_1 \rightarrow \Lambda, \ S_1 \rightarrow 0, \ S_1 \rightarrow 1, S_1 \rightarrow 0 S_1, \ S_1 \rightarrow 1 S_1\},$

$\quad\ P_2 = \{S_2 \rightarrow \Lambda, S_2 \rightarrow 0, S_2 \rightarrow 1, S_2 \rightarrow E, S_2 \rightarrow 0 S_2, S_2 \rightarrow 1 S_2, S_2 \rightarrow E S_2\},$

$\quad\ P_3 = \{S \rightarrow S_1, \ S \rightarrow S_1 E S_1, \ S \rightarrow S_1 E S_1 E S_1\},$

$\quad\ P_4 = \{S \rightarrow S_2 E S_2 E S_2 E S_2 E S_2\},$

$\quad\ P_5 = \{S \rightarrow E S_2, \ S \rightarrow S_2 E, \ S \rightarrow S_2 E E S_2, \ S \rightarrow 0 S_2, \ S \rightarrow S_2 0\},$

$\quad\ P_6 = \{S \rightarrow S_1 1 E S_2, \ S \rightarrow S_2 E 1 S_1, \ S \rightarrow S_1 1 1 S_1 E S_2, \ S \rightarrow S_2 E S_1 1 1 S_1\},$

$P_7(n) = \{S \rightarrow S_1 0^{n+1} S_1 E S_2, \ S \rightarrow S_2 E S_1 0^{n+1} S_1\}$

(where n, we recall, is the length of the sequences a and b),

$$P_8(a) = \left\{ \begin{array}{l} S \rightarrow AES_2, \ A \rightarrow 10^i A a_i \ (i = 1, \cdots, n), \\ A \rightarrow ES_1 0, \ A \rightarrow ES_1 1, \ A \rightarrow 1 S_1 E, \\ A \rightarrow 10^i E \bar{a}_i, \ A \rightarrow 10^i 1 S_1 E \bar{a}_i \ (i = 1, \cdots, n), \\ A \rightarrow 10^i E S_1 \bar{\bar{a}}_i, \ A \rightarrow 10^i 1 S_1 E \bar{\bar{a}}_i \ (i = 1, \cdots, n), \\ \text{where } \bar{a}_i \text{ runs through all strings of } W_{\{0,1\}}, \text{ such that} \\ 1 \leq l(\bar{a}_i) < l(a_i), \text{ and } \bar{\bar{a}}_i \text{ runs through all strings of} \\ W_{\{0,1\}} \text{ such that } l(\bar{\bar{a}}_1) = l(a_1), \text{ except } a_i \text{ itself.} \end{array} \right\}$$

$$P_9(b) = \left\{ \begin{array}{l} S \rightarrow S_2 E B, \ B \rightarrow b_j^* B 0^j 1 \ \ (j = 1, \cdots, n), \\ B \rightarrow 0 S_1 E, \ B \rightarrow 1 S_1 E, \ B \rightarrow ES_1 1, \\ B \rightarrow \bar{b}_j^* E 0^j 1, \ B \rightarrow \bar{b}_j^* ES_1 10^j 1 \ (j = 1, \cdots, n), \\ B \rightarrow \bar{\bar{b}}_j^* S_1 0^j E 1, \ B \rightarrow \bar{\bar{b}}_j^* S_1 ES_1 10^j 1 \ (j = 1, \cdots, n), \\ \text{where } \bar{b}_j^* \text{ runs through all strings of } W_{\{0,1\}}, \text{ such that} \\ 1 \leq l(\bar{b}_j^*) < l(b_j), \text{ and } \bar{\bar{b}}_j^* \text{ runs through all strings of} \\ W_{\{0,1\}}, \text{ such that } l(\bar{\bar{b}}_j) = l(b_j^*), \text{ except } b_j^* \text{ itself.} \end{array} \right\}$$

Proof: From S_1 we get by P_1 every string over $\{0,1\}$. From S_2 we get by P_2 every string over T. By $P_1 \cup P_3$ we get all strings over T containing less than $3E$'s. By $P_2 \cup P_4$ we get all strings over T containing more than $3E$'s. By $P_2 \cup P_5$ we get all strings over T beginning or ending with E or 0, or containing two consecutive E's. By $P_1 \cup P_2 \cup P_6$ we get all strings over T with two consecutive 1's before the first E or after the last E, or with a 1 immediately preceding the first E or immediately following the last E. By $P_1 \cup P_2 \cup P_7(n)$ we get all strings over T with more than n consecutive zeros before the first E or after the last E.

Up to now we have obtained by $P_1 \cup P_2 \cup P_3 \cup P_4 \cup P_5 \cup P_6 \cup P_7(n)$ all strings over T, except those of the form

$$(1) \qquad 10^{i_k} \cdots 10^{i_1} ExEyE0^{j_1}1 \cdots 0^{j_1}1,$$

where $x \neq \Lambda$, $y \neq \Lambda$, $x \in W_{\{0,1\}}$, $y \in W_{\{0,1\}}$, $k \geq 1$, $l \geq 1$, $1 \leq i_v \leq n$ for $v = 1, \cdots, k$, and $1 \leq j_v \leq n$ for $v = 1, \cdots, l$.

$P_1 \cup P_2 \cup P_8(a)$ generates, among others, all strings of the form (1) for which $x \neq a_{i_1} \cdots a_{i_k}$. $P_1 \cup P_2 \cup P_9(b)$ generates, among others, all strings of the form (1) for which $y^* \neq b_{j_1} \cdots b_{j_l}$.

Thus, every string of $W_T - L(a,b)$ can be generated from S by $P'(a,b)$, and it is easily verified that no string over T generated by $P'(a,b)$ from S belongs to $L(a,b)$.

Hence, $L(\mathfrak{G}'(a,b)) = W_T - L(a,b)$.

Definition 6.4:

$$L_s = \{w_1 E w_2 E w_2^* E w_1^* \mid w_1 \in W_{\{0,1\}}, w_2 \in W_{\{0,1\}}\}.$$

Lemma 6.3: L_s is an SPL, represented by the SPG:

$$\mathfrak{G}_s = (V_s, P_s, T, S),$$

where

$$V_s = \{S, U, 0, 1, E\}, \qquad T = \{0, 1, E\},$$

$$P_s = \left\{ \begin{array}{l} S \to 0S0, \ S \to 1S1, \ S \to EUE, \\ U \to 0U0, \ U \to 1U1, \ U \to E \end{array} \right\}.$$

Proof: Obvious.

Lemma 6.4: $W_T - L_s$ is an SPL, represented by the SPG:

$$\mathfrak{G}' = (V_s', P_s', T, S),$$

where

$$V_s' = \{S, S_1, S_2, Q, R, 0, 1, E\}, \qquad T = \{0, 1, E\},$$

$$P_s' = P_1 \cup P_2 \cup P_3 \cup P_4 \cup P_{10} \cup P_{11}.$$

Here, P_1, P_2, P_3 and P_4 are those defined in Lemma 6.2 and

$$P_{10} = \begin{cases} S \to Q, & Q \to 0Q0, & Q \to 1Q1, \\ Q \to 0S_1ES_1ES_1E, & Q \to 1S_1ES_1ES_1E, \\ Q \to ES_1ES_1ES_10, & Q \to ES_1ES_1ES_11, \\ Q \to 0S_1ES_1ES_1ES_11, & Q \to 1S_1ES_1ES_1ES_10 \end{cases},$$

$$P_{11} = \begin{cases} S \to S_1ERES_1, & R \to 0R0, & R \to 1R1, \\ R \to 0S_1E, & R \to 1S_1E, & R \to ES_10, & R \to ES_11, \\ R \to 0S_1ES_11, & R \to 1S_1ES_10 \end{cases}.$$

Proof: By $P_1 \cup P_2 \cup P_3 \cup P_4$ we get all strings over T containing more than, or less than 3 E's (see Lemma 4.2). By $P_1 \cup P_{10}$ we get all strings of the form $w_1 E w_2 E w_3 E w_4$, where $w_i \in W_{\{0,1\}}$ $(i = 1,2,3,4)$ and $w_4 \neq w_1^*$. By $P_1 \cup P_{11}$ we get all strings of that form, where $w_3 \neq w_2^*$.

Remark: By Defs. 6.3 and 6.4 we have:

$$L(a,b) \cap L_s = \left\{ 10^{i_k} \cdots 10^{i_1} E a_{i_1} \cdots a_{i_k} E b_{i_1}^* \cdots b_{i_k}^* E O^{i_1} 1 \cdots 0^{i_k} 1 \right.$$

$$\left. k \geq 1; \ 1 \leq i_v \leq n \text{ for } v = 1, \cdots, k; \ a_{i_1} \cdots a_{i_k} = b_{i_1} \cdots b_{i_k} \right\}$$

(since $b_{i_k}^* \cdots b_{i_1}^* = (b_{i_1} \cdots b_{i_k})^*$). Hence, by Def. 6.1, $\mathscr{P}(a,b) = 0$ implies $L(a,b) \cap L_s = \emptyset$. If $\mathscr{P}(a,b) = 1$ then $L(a,b) \cap L_s$ is infinite, since

$$a_{i_1} \cdots a_{i_k} = b_{i_1} \cdots b_{i_k}$$

implies $(a_{i_1} \cdots a_{i_k})^m = (b_{i_1} \cdots b_{i_k})^m$ for $m = 1,2,3,\cdots$. Moreover, we shall show that when $\mathscr{P}(a,b) = 1$, $L(a,b) \cap L_s$ is not an SPL. But in order to prove our theorems also for SPGs with *two* terminal symbols only, we shall first appropriately recode the vocabulary of $L(a,b)$ and L_s.

Definition 6.5: Let $\phi : W_{\{0,1,E\}} \to W_{\{0,1\}}$ be the following mapping:

$$\phi(0) = 101, \quad \phi(1) = 1001, \quad \phi(E) = 10001,$$

and for any string $X_1 \cdots X_m$ over $\{0,1,E\}$:

$$\phi(X_1 \cdots X_m) = \phi(X_1) \cdots \phi(X_m) \text{ (and } \phi(\Lambda) = \Lambda).$$

Notations: $\bar{0} = \phi(0)$, $\bar{1} = \phi(1)$, $\bar{E} = \phi(E)$, and for any string x over $\{0,1,E\}$: $\bar{x} = \phi(x)$. $\bar{L}_s = \phi(L_s)$, $\bar{L}(a,b) = \phi(L(a,b))$, $\bar{W} = \phi(W_{\{0,1,E\}})$, $L' = W_{\{0,1\}} - \bar{W}$.

It can easily be verified that the mapping ϕ is one-to-one. Therefore we have, for any languages L, L_1, L_2 over $\{0,1,E\}$: $\phi(L_1 \cap L_2) = \phi(L_1) \cap \phi(L_2)$; $\phi(W_{\{0,1,E\}} - L) = \phi(W_{\{0,1,E\}}) - \phi(L) = \bar{W} - \phi(L) = W_{\{0,1\}} - (L' - \phi(L)) = W_{\{0,1\}} - (L' \cup \phi(L))$.

Lemma 6.5: L' is an SPL, represented by the SPG:

$$\mathfrak{G}' = (V_1, P', T', S),$$

where

$$V_1 = \{S, S_1, 0, 1\}, \quad T' = \{0, 1\},$$

$$P' = \begin{cases} S &\to 0S_1, \ S \to S_1 0, \ S \to 11S_1, \ S \to S_1 11, \\ S &\to S_1 010 S_1 \ S \to S_1 111 S_1, \\ S &\to S_1 0000 S_1, \\ S_1 &\to 0S_1, \ S_1 \to 1S_1, \ S_1 \to \Lambda \end{cases}.$$

Proof: L' consists of all strings over $\{0,1\}$ which start or terminate with 0 or with 11, or which contain a substring of the form 010 or 111 or 0000. These are exactly the strings over $\{0,1\}$ generated by $\mathfrak{G}'$.

Lemma 6.6: Let (a, b) be the same as in Def. 6.1, and let $\mathscr{P}(a,b) = 1$. Then $\bar{L}(a,b) \cap \bar{L}_s$ is not an SPL.

Proof: The mapping ϕ is one-to-one. Therefore

$$\bar{L}(a,b) \cap \bar{L}_s = \phi(L(a,b)) \cap \phi(L_s) = \phi(L(a,b) \cap L_s).$$

Since $\mathscr{P}(a,b) = 1$, $L(a,b) \cap L_s$ is infinite (see Remark preceding Def. 6.5), and therefore $\bar{L}(a,b) \cap \bar{L}_s$ is infinite too, and the lengths of its sentences are not bounded.

Every sentence $\bar{z} \in \bar{L}(a,b) \cap \bar{L}_s$ admits a unique decomposition of the form $\bar{z} = cE\bar{d}\bar{E}d^* \bar{E}\bar{c}^*$, where

$$\bar{c} = \bar{1}\bar{0}^{\,i_k} \cdots \bar{1}\bar{0}^{\,i_1} \ (k \geq 1, \quad 1 \leq i_v \leq n \text{ for } v = 1, \cdots, k),$$

and $d = \bar{a}_{i_1} \cdots \bar{a}_{i_k} = \bar{b}_{i_1} \cdots \bar{b}_{i_k}$. The strings $\bar{c}$ and d do not contain $\bar{E}$ as a substring ($\bar{E} = 10001$). Clearly, the substring $\bar{c}$ uniquely determines the whole string $\bar{z}$.

If the sentence $\bar{z}$ is long, then the number k must be large, since the lengths of the strings $\bar{a}_i$, $\bar{b}_i$, $\bar{1}\bar{0}^i$ $(1 \leq i \leq n)$ are bounded, and then d must be long, too, because the strings $\bar{a}_i$, b_i $(1 \leq i \leq n)$ are non-empty.

Assume that $\bar{L}(a,b) \cap \bar{L}_s$ is an SPL. Then we have, by Theorem 4.1, two numbers p and q, such that every sentence $\bar{z} \in \bar{L}(a,b) \cap \bar{L}_s$, with $l(\bar{z}) \geq p$, admits a decomposition $\bar{z} = xuwvy$ with $l(u) + l(v) \geq 1$, $l(uwv) \leq q$, such that $xu^m wv^m y \in \bar{L}(a,b) \cap \bar{L}_s$ for $m = 1,2,3,\cdots$.

Take a sentence $\bar{z} = \bar{c}\bar{E}\bar{d}\bar{E}d^*\bar{E}\bar{c}^* \in \bar{L}(a,b) \cap \bar{L}_s$, such that

$$l(\bar{z}) \geq p, \quad l(d) \geq q.$$

(This is possible by the remark on the length of $\bar{z}$ and d.) Compare the two decompositions:

(2) $$\bar{z} = \bar{c}\bar{E}\bar{d}\bar{E}d^* \bar{E}\bar{c}^* = xuwvy.$$

$$l(\bar{E}) = l(10001) = 5, \quad l(\bar{c}^*) = l(\bar{c}), \quad l(d^*) = l(d) \geq q, \quad l(uwv) \leq q.$$

Therefore:

$$l(\bar{z}) = 2 \cdot l(\bar{c}) + 2 \cdot l(\bar{d}) + 15 = l(x) + l(uwv) + l(y),$$

$$l(x) + l(y) = 2 \cdot l(\bar{c}) + 2 \cdot l(\bar{d}) + 15 - l(uwv) \geq 2 \cdot l(\bar{c}) + 15.$$

Hence

$$l(x) \geq l(\bar{c}) + 5 \quad \text{or} \quad l(y) \geq l(\bar{c}) + 5.$$

Let

$$xuuwvvy = \bar{z}_2 = \bar{c}_2 \bar{E} d_2 \bar{E} d_2{}^* \bar{E} \bar{c}_2{}^* \in L(a, b) \cap \bar{L}_s.$$

If $l(x) \geq l(\bar{c}) + 5$, then $\bar{c}\bar{E}$ is an initial segment of x (see (2)), and therefore $\bar{c}_2 = \bar{c}$ ($\bar{c}_2$ is the substring of $\bar{z}_2$ preceding the first occurrence of a substring $\bar{E}$ in $\bar{z}_2$), which implies $\bar{z}_2 = \bar{z}$, since the first quarter $\bar{c}$ uniquely determines the whole string $\bar{z}$. Similarly, if $l(y) \geq l(\bar{c}) + 5$, then $\bar{E}\bar{c}^*$ is a confinal segment of y (see (2)), and therefore $\bar{c}_2{}^* = \bar{c}^*$ ($\bar{c}_2{}^*$ is the substring of $\bar{z}_2$ following the last occurrence of a substring $\bar{E}$ in $\bar{z}_2$), which again implies $\bar{c}_2 = \bar{c}$ and $\bar{z}_2 = \bar{z}$.

But $\bar{z}_2$ cannot equal $\bar{z}$, since

$$l(\bar{z}_2) = l(\bar{z}) + l(u) + l(v) > l(\bar{z}) \quad (l(u) + l(v) \geq 1).$$

Thus the assumption that $\bar{L}(a, b) \cap \bar{L}_s$ is an SPL leads to a contradiction Hence, if $\mathscr{P}(a, b) = 1$, then $\bar{L}(a, b) \cap \bar{L}_s$ is not an SPL.

Remarks: a) The proof of Lemma 6.6 shows that in case $\mathscr{P}(a, b) = 1$, $\bar{L}(a, b) \cap \bar{L}_s$ is not only different from any SPL, but does not even *contain* an infinite SPL.

b) If we were contented to prove Theorems 6.1, 6.2 and 6.3 only for terminal vocabularies T containing more than two symbols, then the "translation" ϕ would be superfluous and it would suffice to prove that $L(a, b) \cap L_s$ is not an SPL (for $\mathscr{P}(a, b) = 1$), which is somewhat easier than Lemma 6.6.

Proof of Theorem 6.1: Given a pair (a, b) of n-tuples of non-empty strings over $\{0, 1\}$, construct $\mathfrak{G}(a, b)$ as in Lemma 6.1, and $\mathfrak{G}_s$ as in Lemma 6.3. $L(\mathfrak{G}(a, b)) = L(a, b)$, $L(\mathfrak{G}_s) = L_s$. By Corollary 3.1 to Theorem 3.3 construct an SPG $\bar{\mathfrak{G}}(a, b)$, such that $L(\bar{\mathfrak{G}}(a, b)) = \phi(L(a, b)) = \bar{L}(a, b)$, and an SPG $\bar{\mathfrak{G}}_s$, such that $L(\bar{\mathfrak{G}}_s) = \phi(L_s) = \bar{L}_s$.

If $\mathscr{P}(a, b) = 1$, then, by Lemma 6.5, $\bar{L}(a, b) \cap \bar{L}_s = L(\bar{\mathfrak{G}}(a, b)) \cap L(\bar{\mathfrak{G}}_s)$ is not an SPL, and therefore, by Theorem 2.1, is not an FAL, and is certainly neither empty not finite. But if $\mathscr{P}(a, b) = 0$, then, by the Remark preceding Def. 6.5, $\bar{L}(a, b) \cap \bar{L}_s = L(\bar{\mathfrak{G}}(a, b)) \cap L(\bar{\mathfrak{G}}_s)$ is empty, and therefore certainly finite, and is representable by an FA and by an SPG.

Thus, if any one of the four problems a, b, c, d of Theorem 6.1 were effectively solvable, then we would have a decision procedure for Post's correspondence problem, which is impossible, by [122].

Proof of Theorem 6.2: Given a pair (a, b) of n-tuples of non-empty strings over $\{0, 1\}$, construct $\mathfrak{G}'(a, b)$, as in Lemma 6.2, and $\mathfrak{G}'_s$ as in Lemma 6.4. $L(\mathfrak{G}'(a, b)) = W_{\{0,1,E\}} - L(a, b)$, $L(\mathfrak{G}'_s) = W_{\{0,1,E\}} - L_s$. By Corollary 3.1 to Theorem 3.3 construct an SPG $\bar{\mathfrak{G}}'(a, b)$, such that

$$L(\bar{\mathfrak{G}}'(a, b)) = \phi(W_{\{0,1,E\}} - L(a, b)) = \bar{W} - \bar{L}(a, b)$$

$(\bar{W} = \phi(W_{\{0\ 1,E\}})$ and ϕ is one-to-one), and an SPG $\bar{\mathfrak{G}}_{s,}$, such that

$$L(\bar{\mathfrak{G}}'_s) = \phi(W_{\{0,1,E\}} - L_s) = \bar{W} - \bar{L}_s.$$

Since

$$\bar{L}(a, b) \cap \bar{L}_s \subseteq \bar{W} \subseteq W_{\{0,1\}}$$

we have:

$$W_{\{0,1\}} - \bar{L}(a,b) \cap \bar{L}_s = (W_{\{0,1\}} - \bar{W}) \cup (\bar{W} - \bar{L}(a,b)) \cup (\bar{W} - \bar{L}_s).$$

By Lemma 6.5, construct an SPG $\mathfrak{G}'$, such that $L(\mathfrak{G}') = L' = W_{\{0,1\}} - \bar{W}$. Finally, construct from $\mathfrak{G}', \bar{\mathfrak{G}}'(a, b)$ and $\mathfrak{G}^{\varepsilon}_s$ an SPG $\bar{\mathfrak{G}}''(a, b)$, such that

$$L(\bar{\mathfrak{G}}(a,b)) = L(\mathfrak{G}') \cup L(\bar{\mathfrak{G}}'(a,b)) \cup L(\bar{\mathfrak{G}}'_s) =$$

$$= (W_{\{0,1\}} - \bar{W}) \cup (\bar{W} - \bar{L}(a,b)) \cup (\bar{W} - \bar{L}_s) = W_{\{0,1\}} - \bar{L}(a,b) \cap \bar{L}_s$$

(by a double application of Theorem 3.1.e).

Now,

$$W_T - L(\bar{\mathfrak{G}}''(a,b)) = W_{\{0,1\}} - (W_{\{0,1\}} - \bar{L}(a,b) \cap \bar{L}_s) = \bar{L}(a,b) \cap \bar{L}_s.$$

Therefore, as in Theorem 6.1, the answers to the four questions a, b, c, d of Theorem 6.2 are positive for $\mathfrak{G} = \bar{\mathfrak{G}}''(a, b)$ if $\mathscr{P}(a, b) = 0$, and are negative if $\mathscr{P}(a, b) = 1$. Thus a decision procedure for any of the four problems a, b, c, d of Theorem 6.2 would yield a decision procedure for Post's correspondence problem. Hence, no such decision procedure exists.

Proof of Theorem 6.3: a.1) Let $\mathfrak{G}_W = (V_W, P_W, T, S)$, where

$$V_W = \{0, 1, S\}, \quad T = \{0, 1\}, \quad P_W = \{S \to S0,\ S \to S1,\ S \to \Lambda\}.$$

$L(\mathfrak{G}_W) = W_{\{0,1\}}$. Now, for any SPG $\mathfrak{G}_2$ with a terminal vocabulary $T = \{0, 1\}$, $W_{\{0,1\}} = L(\mathfrak{G}_W) \subseteq L(\mathfrak{G}_2)$ iff $L(\mathfrak{G}_2) = W_{\{0,1\}}$, i.e., iff $W_T - L(\mathfrak{G}_2) = \emptyset$, and the problem whether $W_T - L(\mathfrak{G}_2)$ is empty is effectively unsolvable for $\mathfrak{G}_2$, by Theorem 6.2.a.

a.2) Let $\bar{\mathfrak{G}}_s$ be the SPG constructed in the proof of Theorem 6.2, such that $L(\bar{\mathfrak{G}}'_s) = \bar{W} - \bar{L}_s$. Let $\bar{\mathfrak{G}}(a, b)$ be the SPG constructed in the proof of Theorem 6.1, such that

$$\bar{L}(\bar{\mathfrak{G}}(a, b)) = \bar{L}(a, b), \quad \bar{L}(a, b) = \phi(L(a, b)) \subseteq \bar{W} = \phi(W_{\{0,1,E\}}).$$

If $\mathscr{P}(a,b) = 0$, then $\bar{L}(a,b) \cap \bar{L}_s = \emptyset$ so that

$$L(\bar{\mathfrak{G}}(a,b)) = \bar{L}(a,b) \subseteq W - \bar{L}_s = L(\overline{\mathfrak{G}'_s}).$$

If $\mathscr{P}(a,b) = 1$, then $\bar{L}(a,b)) \cap \bar{L}_s$ is nonempty, so that

$$L(\bar{\mathfrak{G}}(a,b)) = \bar{L}(a,b) \nsubseteq W - \bar{L}_s = L(\overline{\mathfrak{G}'_s}).$$

The effective unsolvability of Post's correspondence problem thus implies the effective unsolvability of the problem whether, for any given pair (a,b) of n-tuples of non-empty strings over $\{0,1\}$, $L(\bar{\mathfrak{G}}(a,b)) \subseteq L(\overline{\mathfrak{G}'_s})$, and a fortiori the effective unsolvability of the problem whether, for any given SPG $\mathfrak{G}_1$ with a terminal vocabulary $T = \{0,1\}$, $L(\mathfrak{G}_1) \subseteq L(\overline{\mathfrak{G}'_s})$.

  b) Let $\mathfrak{G}_W$ be the SPG constructed in a.1), such that $L(\mathfrak{G}_W) = W_{\{0\ 1\}}$. Now, for any SPG $\mathfrak{G}_1$ with a terminal vocabulary $T = \{0,1\}$, $L(\mathfrak{G}_1) = L(\mathfrak{G}_W) = W_{\{0.1\}}$ iff $W_T - L(\mathfrak{G}_1) = \emptyset$, and the problem whether $W_T - L(\mathfrak{G}_1)$ is empty is effectively unsolvable for $\mathfrak{G}_1$, by Theorem 6.2a.

  c) The class of FALs over a vocabulary T is closed under complementation with respect to W_T. Therefore $L(\mathfrak{G})$ is an FAL iff $W_T - L(\mathfrak{G})$ is an FAL, where T is the terminal vocabulary of the SPG $\mathfrak{G}$. The problem whether $W_T - L(\mathfrak{G})$ is an FAL is effectively unsolvable, by Theorem 6.2c.

  d) Let $\mathfrak{A}_W = (T, \Sigma, M, \sigma_0, \Phi)$, where

$$T = \{0,1\}, \Sigma = \Phi = \{\sigma_0\}, M(\sigma_0, 0) = M(\sigma_0, 1) = \sigma_0. \ L(\mathfrak{A}_W) = W_{\{0.1\}}.$$

For any SPG $\mathfrak{G}$ with a terminal vocabulary $T = \{0,1\}, L(\mathfrak{G}) = L(\mathfrak{A}_W) = W_{\{0,1\}}$ iff $W_T - L(\mathfrak{G}) = \emptyset$, and the problem whether $W_T - L(\mathfrak{G})$ is empty is unsolvable for $\mathfrak{G}$, by Theorem 6.2a.

  Remarks: a) Theorems 6.1, 6.2 and 6.3 may be proved also for SPGs with terminal vocabularies T containing n symbols, for any $n \geqq 3$. This may be done, for example, by letting the terminal vocabulary T of the SPGs $\mathfrak{G}(a,b)$, $\mathfrak{G}'(a,b)$, $\mathfrak{G}_s$ and $\mathfrak{G}'_s$ (Lemmata 6.1, 6.2, 6.3 and 6.4, respectively) be $T = \{E, 0, 1, 2, \cdots, n - 2\}$, and changing $\mathfrak{G}'(a,b)$ and $\mathfrak{G}'_s$ such that they represent $W_T - L(a,b)$ and $W_T - L_s$, respectively, with the new vocabulary T. Then the "translation" ϕ (Def. 6.5) becomes superfluous, and the proof proceeds as in Lemma 6.6, except that $L(a,b) \cap L_s$ (instead of $\bar{L}(a,b) \cap \bar{L}_s$) is shown not to be an SPL, if $\mathscr{P}(a,b) = 1$.

  b) There is a simpler proof of Theorem 6.1a,b,c, and Theorem 6.2a,b,c. Given a pair (a,b) of n-tuples of non-empty strings over $\{0,1\}$, construct SPGs $\mathfrak{G}(a)$ and $\mathfrak{G}(b)$ representing the languages $L(a)$ and $L(b)$ (see Def. 6.2). If $\mathscr{P}(a,b) = 0$, then $L(a) \cap L(b) = \emptyset$. If $\mathscr{P}(a,b) = 1$, then $L(a) \cap L(b)$ is infinite and is not representable by a FA, as is easily proved by [128: Lemma 8].

This simplified proof of Theorem 6.1 a, b, c via $L(a)$ and $L(b)$ is almost identical with the proof of the effective unsolvability of the empty intersection problem for TTAa, given in [128: Theorem 18]. This proof, however, would not have yielded the effective unsolvability for $\mathfrak{G}_2$ of problems a, b, c of Theorem 6.1 with $\mathfrak{G}_1$ fixed, which we obtained here by using $L(a, b)$ and L_s. Theorem 6.1 d cannot be proved in this way, since $L(a) \cap L(b)$ may be an SPL even when $\mathcal{P}(a, b) = 1$.

In order to prove Theorem 6.2 a, b, c, construct SPGs $\mathfrak{G}'(a)$ and $\mathfrak{G}'(b)$ representing $W_T - L(a)$ and $W_T - L(b)$ $(T = \{0, 1, E\})$, and an SPG $\mathfrak{G}'(a)(b)$ representing $(W_T - L(a)) \cup (W_T - L(b)) = W_T - L(a) \cap L(b)$. Now,

$$W_T - L(\mathfrak{G}'(a)(b)) = W_T - (W_T - L(a) \cap L(b)) = L(a) \cap (b),$$

which language is empty if $\mathcal{P}(a, b) = 0$, and not representable by a FA if $\mathcal{P}(a, b) = 1$.

In order to get the results for SPGs with a terminal vocabulary containing two symbols only, use the mapping $\phi : W_{\{0,1,E\}} \to W_{\{0,1\}}$ given in Def. 6.5. Note that

$$W_{\{0,1\}} - \phi(L(a) \cap L(b)) = (W_{\{0\;1\}} - \bar{W}) \cup (\bar{W} - \phi(L(a) \cap L(b)))$$

$$= L' \cup \phi(W_{\{0,1,E\}} - L(a) \cap L(b)).$$

L' is represented by the SPG $\mathfrak{G}'$ constructed in Lemma 6.5, and an SPG representing $W_{\{0,1\}} - \phi(L(a) \cap L(b))$ can be effectively constructed from $\mathfrak{G}'$ and $\mathfrak{G}'(a)(b)$.

Similarly, we could also have proved Theorem 6.3 by the method mentioned here, except for that part of Theorem 6.3 a in which $\mathfrak{G}_2$ is assumed to be fixed, which part is based on Theorem 6.1 a with fixed $\mathfrak{G}_2$.

SECTION 7: SOME RELATIONS BETWEEN SPGS AND FINITE AUTOMATA

Lemma 7.1: Let $\mathfrak{G} = (V, P, T, S)$ be a 1-SPG. If all the productions of P have the form $A \to tB$ or $A \to t$, where $\Lambda \neq t \in W_T$, then $L(\mathfrak{G})$ is an FAL. The same result holds if all the productions of P have the dual form $A \to Bt$ or $A \to t$.

Proof: The case $l(t) = 1$ in every production was already dealt with (Remark following Th. 2.1). The general case is easily reduced to it: replace each production $A \to T_1 \cdots T_k B$ by

$$A \to T_1 B_1, \; B_1 \to T_2 B_2, \cdots, B_{k-1} \to T_k B,$$

where all B_j are distinct and new.

Definition 7.1:   A symbol A of an SPG is called *self-embedding* (s.e.) if the condition:

$$(\exists u)(\exists v)(u \neq \Lambda \ \& \ v \neq \Lambda \ \& \ A \overset{*}{\Rightarrow} uAv)$$

holds for A. An SPG is called *self-embedding* (s.e.) if it contains a s.e. symbol. (Compare Def. 5.2.)

By Th. 5.1d, the property of being s.e., for a symbol as well as for an SPG, is effectively decidable.

Theorem 7.1:   A non-s.e. SPG is equivalent to a FA.

Remarks: a) The theorem is due to Chomsky [35; 36]. It provides an effective sufficient condition for an SPG to be equivalent to a FA. However, we know that an effective *criterion* (necessary and sufficient condition) does not exist (Th. 6.3c).

b)   For an actual examination of SPGs, the theorem can be stated in a more useful form: a 1-SPG, whose reduced form is non-s.e., is equivalent to a FA. Indeed, an SPG may contain superfluous s.e. symbols which are eliminated in its reduced form.

c)   The proof given below is Chomsky's second proof [36] which, except for slight modifications, was also obtained independently by us.

Proof: By Lemmata 4.1, 4.2 and 5.1, we pass to a reduced 2-SPG $\mathfrak{G} = (V, P, T, S)$ which is equivalent to the original SPG except for strings of length ≤ 1. $\mathfrak{G}$ is also non-s.e., and it suffices to prove that $L(\mathfrak{G})$ is an FAL.

Let $A_1 = S$, $A_2, \cdots, A_k$ be the auxiliary symbols of $\mathfrak{G}$, i.e., the symbols of $V - T$. $\mathfrak{G}$ being reduced, we have

(1) $$A_1 \overset{*}{\Rightarrow} u_i A_i v_i \text{ with } l(u_i v_i) \geq 1 \quad (i = 2, 3, \cdots, k).$$

We first prove the theorem in a special case:

Case I: Suppose that we have:

(2 $$A_i \Rightarrow w_i A_1 z_i, \text{ with } l(w_i z_i) \geq 1 \quad (i = 1, 2, \cdots, k).$$

In this case, all the A_i are embedding symbols. Since A_1 is non-s.e., the embeddings of A_1 are either all of them left: $A_1 \overset{*}{\Rightarrow} A_1 a \ (a \neq \Lambda)$, or all of of them right: $A_1 \overset{*}{\Rightarrow} a A_1$. We claim that if A_1 admits left embeddings, then all the productions of P have the form $A_i \to t A_j$ or $A_i \to t$, $t \in W_T$. Indeed suppose that $A_i \to x A_j y$, $y \neq \Lambda$, belongs to P. Then by (1) and (2) we obtain:

$$A_i \to x A_j y \overset{*}{\Rightarrow} x w_j A_1 z_j y \overset{*}{\Rightarrow} x w_j a A_1 z_j y \overset{*}{\Rightarrow} x w_j a u_i A_i v_i z_j y.$$

Since $a \neq \Lambda$, $y \neq \Lambda$, this contradicts the assumption that A_i is non-s.e.

In the same way, if A_1 admits right embeddings only, then the productions are all of the form $A_i \rightarrow A_j t$ or $A_i \rightarrow t$. In both cases we obtain by Lemma 1 that $L(\mathfrak{G})$ is an FAL.

In the general case, we shall proceed by induction on k. If $k = 1$, then S is the only auxiliary symbol and all the productions have the form $S \rightarrow tS$, $S \rightarrow t$ or the dual form $S \rightarrow St$, $S \rightarrow t$, $t \in W_T$. Again by Lemma 1, $L(\mathfrak{G})$ is an FAL.

We assume now that the theorem holds true for SPGs with less than k auxiliary symbols. We may also assume that we do not have Case I, i.e., that the negation of (2) holds:

(3)   For some j, $1 \leq j \leq k$, $\sim(\exists w)(\exists z)(A_j \overset{*}{\Rightarrow} wA_1 z)$.

Suppose first that $j > 1$ in (3). Let $\mathfrak{G}'$ be the SPG which differs from $\mathfrak{G}$ only in that A_j and each production $A_j \rightarrow a$ are deleted and that in the other productions A_j is everywhere replaced by a new terminal symbol D. This $\mathfrak{G}'$ is a non-s.e. SPG which contains $k - 1$ auxiliaries, hence by the induction hypothesis $L(\mathfrak{G}')$ is an FAL. The same is true for the language

$$K = \{x \,|\, x \in W_T \,\&\, A_j \overset{*}{\Rightarrow} x \text{ in } L(\mathfrak{G})\},$$

since K is determined by the SPG $(V - \{S\}, P_1, T, A_j)$ where P_1 is obtained from P by deleting all the productions containing S. (Here $S = A_1$ is superfluous because of (3).) Now a string z belongs to $L(\mathfrak{G})$ just in case it is obtained from some string x of $L(\mathfrak{G}')$ by a substitution of arbitrary strings of K in all the occurrences of D in x. Hence the fact that $L(\mathfrak{G})$ is an FAL follows from the Remark following Th. 3.3.

Finally we take the case $j = 1$ in (3). Let $a_1, \cdots, a_r$ be all the strings such that $A_1 \rightarrow a_i$. Let $H_i = \{x \in W_T \,|\, a_i \overset{*}{\Rightarrow} x\}$. Clearly $L(\mathfrak{G}) = \overset{r}{\underset{i=1}{\cup}} H_i$. Let $a_1 = B_1 \cdots B_n$ and let $K_m = \{x \in W_T \,|\, B_m \overset{*}{\Rightarrow} x\}$, then H_1 equals the product $K_1 \cdot K_2 \cdot \cdots \cdot K_n$. The other H_i are given by similar products. K_m is determined by the SPG $(V - \{S\}, P_1, T, B_m)$ which contains $k - 1$ auxiliaries, hence each K_m is an FAL. Thus $L(\mathfrak{G})$ is obtained from FALs by products and unions and is therefore an FAL itself. (See Section 2.)

This concludes the proof of the theorem.

Theorem 7.2: Let L be an SPL over the vocabulary $T \cup \{H\}$ ($H \notin T$), fulfilling the conditions:
(i) Every sentence of L has the form xHy, where $x, y \in W_T$ and $l(xy) \geq 1$;
(ii) for a given x, the number of y such that $xHy \in L$ is finite, and for a given y, the number of x such that $xHy \in L$ is finite.

Then the sets $M = \{x \,|\, (\exists y)(xHy \in L)\}$ and $N = \{y \,|\, (\exists x)(xHy \in L)\}$ are FALs.

Proof: Suppose L is represented by the reduced 2-SPG $\mathfrak{G} = (V, P, T \cup \{H\}, S)$. Let $R = \{A \in V \,|\, (\exists u)(\exists v)(A \stackrel{*}{\Rightarrow} uHv)\}$, and let $Q = V - R$. The set R contains H and every symbol from which an "H-string" can be generated. Clearly $S \in R$.

Consider any "maximal" generation chain (a chain which cannot be continued) starting from S: $S \stackrel{*}{\Rightarrow} a_1 \stackrel{*}{\Rightarrow} a_2 \stackrel{*}{\Rightarrow} \cdots \stackrel{*}{\Rightarrow} a_k$. Since $\mathfrak{G}$ is reduced, a_k is a sentence of L. Therefore, each string a_i in such a chain contains exactly one *occurrence* of a symbol of R. For if $a_i = \cdots A \cdots B \cdots$, where $A, B \in R (A = B$ not excluded), we would obtain

$$S \stackrel{*}{\Rightarrow} a_i \stackrel{*}{\Rightarrow} \cdots A \cdots B \cdots \stackrel{*}{\Rightarrow} \cdots H \cdots H \cdots \in L,$$

which is impossible. (It should be constantly remembered that in a reduced SPG any non-terminal string generates a terminal string.)

It follows that in our reduced SPG all the productions of P are of the form:

> (1) $A \to uBv$, where $A, B \in R$ and $u, v \in W_Q$,
>
> or $C \to d$, where $C \in Q$ and $d \in W_Q$.

Now, by using condition (ii), we obtain that no symbol of Q is embedding. For if $C \in Q$ were embedding, i.e., if there were d and e such that $C \stackrel{*}{\Rightarrow} dCe$, with $l(de) \geq 1$, we would have:

$$S \stackrel{*}{\Rightarrow} \cdots C \cdots Ht \text{ or } S \stackrel{*}{\Rightarrow} tH \cdots C \cdots, \text{ with } t \in W_T.$$

Since C is embedding, we would obtain an infinite number of strings $x \in W_T$ with $xHt \in L$, or an infinite number of $y \in W_T$ with $tHy \in L$, contradicting condition (ii).

Therefore each string over Q generates only a finite number of terminal strings, and we do not change the language if we replace the productions $A \to uBv$, $C \to d$ (see (1)) by the productions $A \to u_i Bv_j$, $C \to d_k$, where u_i, v_j and d_k run over all the terminal strings generated by u, v and d, respectively.

Consider now the SPG $(V, P_1, T \cup \{H\}, S)$ whose productions are $A \to u_i B$ and $C \to d_k$ (i.e. we replace each of the productions $A \to u_i Bv_j$ by $A \to u_i B$). This SPG fulfils the requirement of Lemma 1, hence it determines an FAL. It is immediately verified that this FAL consists of all the strings xH for which there exists a y with $xHy \in L$. Omitting the symbol H, we obtain that $M = \{x \,|\, (\exists y)(xHy \in L)\}$ is an FAL. In a similar manner we obtain that N is an FAL.

Example: Let L be a *mirror language*, i.e., all its strings have the form xHx^*. Our theorem yields: If L is an SPL, *then* $M = \{x \mid xHx^* \in L\}$ is an FAL. The converse is easy and was proved (Th. 2.1. b). We could use this fact, in place of Theorem 4.1, in order to show that various languages are not SPLs. For instance, $\{0^n 10^n H 0^n 10^n\}$ ($n = 1, 2, 3 \cdots$) is not an SPL, though it can easily be shown to be an intersection of two SPLs.

SECTION 8: THE INTERSECTION OF SPGs AND FAa

In this last section we prove the following

Theorem 8.1: Let $\mathfrak{G}$ be an SPG, $\mathfrak{A}$ a FA. It is possible to construct an SPG $\overline{\mathfrak{G}}$ such that $L(\overline{\mathfrak{G}}) = L(\mathfrak{G}) \cap L(\mathfrak{A})$.

Proof: First note that it suffices to deal with 1-SPGs. Secondly, if $\mathfrak{A}$ is a FA with r final states, then $L(\mathfrak{A})$ is a union $\bigcup_{i=1}^{r} L(\mathfrak{A}_i)$, where each $\mathfrak{A}_i$ has a single final state. Thus

$$L(\mathfrak{G}) \cap L(\mathfrak{A}) = \bigcup_{i=1}^{r} [L(\mathfrak{G}) \cap L(\mathfrak{A}_i)].$$

Hence it suffices to prove the theorem for FAa with a single final state. Let therefore $\mathfrak{G} = (V, P, T, S)$ be a 1-SPG, and let

$$\mathfrak{A} = (T, \Sigma, M, \sigma_0, \{\sigma_f\})$$

be a FA with σ_f as a single final state.

Construction: We construct the 1-SPG $\overline{\mathfrak{G}} = (\overline{V}, \overline{P}, \overline{T}, \overline{S})$ where:
1. $\overline{V} = (\Sigma \times V \times \Sigma) \cup T$, (i.e., $\overline{V}$ contains T and all the triplets (σ, A, τ) where $\sigma \in \Sigma$, $A \in V$, $\tau \in \Sigma$),
2. $\overline{S} = (\sigma_0, S, \sigma_f)$,
3. $\overline{P}$ contains the following productions:
(i) if $X \rightarrow A_1 \cdots A_k \in P$, then
$(\sigma, X, \tau) \rightarrow (\sigma, A_1, \tau_1)(\tau_1, A_2, \tau_2) \cdots (\tau_{k-2}, A_{k-1}, \tau_{k-1})(\tau_{k-1}, A_k, \tau) \in \overline{P}$,
for every $\sigma, \tau, \tau_1, \cdots, \tau_{k-1} \in \Sigma$;
(ii) if $X \in T$ and $M(\sigma, X) = \tau$, then $(\sigma, X, \tau) \rightarrow X$.

Lemma 8.1: If $x \in L(\mathfrak{G}) \cap L(\mathfrak{A})$, then $x \in L(\overline{\mathfrak{G}})$.

Proof: Let $x = A_1 \cdots A_k$. $x \in L(\mathfrak{A})$ implies the existence of a sequence $\sigma_0, \cdots, \sigma_k = \sigma_f$ such that $\sigma_i = M(\sigma_{i-1}, A_i)$, $i = 1, \cdots, k$. $x \in L(\mathfrak{G})$ implies $S \overset{*}{\Rightarrow} A_1 \cdots A_k$ in $\mathfrak{G}$. From the production of 3(i) it follows that

$$\overline{S} = (\sigma_0, S, \sigma_f) \overset{*}{\Rightarrow} (\sigma_0, A_1, \sigma_1)(\sigma_1, A_2, \sigma_2) \cdots (\sigma_{k-1}, A_k, \sigma_f)$$

in $\overline{\mathfrak{G}}$. (The last assertion, for *any* sequence $\sigma_0, \sigma_1, \cdots, \sigma_{k-1}, \sigma_f$ is easily verified.) Since $\sigma_i = M(\sigma_{i-1}, A_i)$, we obtain from 3(ii) that $(\sigma_{i-1}, A_i, \sigma_i) \to A_i$, for $i = 1, \cdots, k$. Hence we finally obtain $\bar{S} \overset{*}{\Rightarrow} A_1 \cdots A_k$ in $\overline{\mathfrak{G}}$.

Lemma 8.2: If $x \in L(\overline{\mathfrak{G}})$, then $x \in L(\mathfrak{G}) \cap L(\mathfrak{A})$.

Proof: We have $\bar{S} = (\sigma_0, S, \sigma_f) \overset{*}{\Rightarrow} x = A_1 \cdots A_k$ in $\overline{\mathfrak{G}}$. Clearly each $A_i \in T$ is generated from some (σ, A_i, τ) by one of the productions of 3(ii). Before using these productions, i.e., before the passage to the terminals, we necessarily had

(I) $\bar{S} = (\sigma_0, S, \sigma_f) \overset{*}{\Rightarrow} (\sigma_0, A_1, \sigma_1)(\sigma_1, A_2, \sigma_2) \cdots (\sigma_{k-1}, A_k, \sigma_f).$

(Every string generated from (σ_0, S, σ_f), which does not contain terminal symbols, is composed of triplets, such that the first triplet begins with σ_0, the last triplet ends with σ_f, and the last element of each triplet equals the first one of its successor—this is easily proved by induction.)

A consideration of the productions of $\overline{\mathfrak{G}}$ shows that relation (I) holds in $\overline{\mathfrak{G}}$ only if $S \overset{*}{\Rightarrow} A_1 \cdots A_k$ in $\mathfrak{G}$. Thus $A_1 \cdots A_k = x \in L(\mathfrak{G})$. Since the A_i were generated from $(\sigma_{i-1}, A_i, \sigma_i,)$ by application of 3(ii), we have also

$$\sigma_i = M(\sigma_{i-1}, A_i)$$

which proves that $A_1 \cdots A_k \in L(\mathfrak{A})$. Lemmata 8.1 and 8.2 together yield $L(\overline{\mathfrak{G}}) = L(\mathfrak{G}) \cap L(\mathfrak{A})$. This concludes the proof of Theorem 8.1.

As a simple application we note the following: If we delete a finite set of strings from an SPL, the resulting language is still an SPL. Indeed, it is obtained as the intersection of the original SPL with the complement of the finite set.

PART III
Machine Translation

The State of Machine Translation in 1951*

10

One of the interesting examples of the influence which a newly invented tool may exert in opening up fresh lines in theoretical research and in advancing new techniques for the solution of old problems is provided by the rise of electronic computers. They were originally designed to solve certain mathematical problems quicker than the human brain could but it soon turned out that their components, in which elementary logical and computational operations could be carried out at extremely high speed, might well be recombined to yield similar results in noncomputational fields.

When electronic computers were still in their infancy, in 1945, the question was raised whether a computer-like machine could not be designed that would automatically translate from one language to another. The story of this idea is told by the man who apparently conceived it first, Dr. Warren Weaver, Director of the Natural Sciences Division of the Rockefeller Foundation, in a memorandum of July 15, 1949 [148]. This memorandum aroused considerable interest, followed by some active research. Some of the first steps towards a solution of the problem of mechanical translation are described in another memorandum by Dr. Weaver, dated March 6, 1951.

The present chapter summarizes the results achieved up to the end of 1951. They involve a clearer understanding of the aims of machine translation, of various possible divisions of labor between man and machine in a translation partnership, and of the preliminary steps that have to be taken before the final solution of the problem can be found. Some of these steps seem to have independent value and especially the task of providing for an operational syntax [131] is a challenge that should appeal to structurally-minded linguists and give a new twist to their investigations.

AIMS

Interest in machine translation (MT) may arise through sheer intellectual curiosity concerning a problem whose solution, perhaps even attempted

---

*First appeared in **American Documentation**, vol. 2 (1951), pp. 229–237.

solutions, will in all probability provide valuable insights into the functioning of linguistic communication. Interest may also arise from many practical standpoints. One of these is the urgency of having foreign language publications, mainly in the fields of science, finance, diplomacy, translated with high accuracy and reasonable speed: the scarcity of expert bilinguals is causing a log jam in scientific translation which is costing research an amount that can hardly be estimated but might well run into millions of dollars yearly, due to the fact that important scientific methods and results are not made available in time or perhaps not at all to research workers. Another is the need of high-speed, though perhaps low-accuracy, scanning through the huge printed output [of actual or potential enemies] in newspapers, journals, propaganda leaflets, etc. These two aims are only partly overlapping, but a good method of achieving one of them would probably be of great help in attacking the other, since we apparently have here another case of a well-known situation where accuracy may be traded for speed, and vice versa.

PURE MT

It seems obvious that fully automatic MT, i.e., one without human intervention between putting the foreign text into the reading organ of the mechanical translator and reading off its output, is achievable only at the price of inaccuracy, if only for the reason that no method is feasible, for the time being, by which the machine would eliminate *semantical ambiguities*. Such an achievement would require either a knowledge of the relative frequencies of all word digrams (sequences of two words), trigrams, etc., or a knowledge of equivalent conditional frequencies of the foreign language (FL) on the part of the machine, a knowledge that is not even at the disposal of the human linguist (which is not at all astonishing in view of the fact that the number of digrams alone, say in German with more than a million words in actual use, will probably run into the billions); or else it would presuppose a "learning" organ, the construction of which is still in its rudimentary stage.

This fact, that high-accuracy, fully automatic MT is not achievable in the foreseeable future, has discouraged many thinkers from whom an interest in MT as a socially important, noncomputational application of digital computer-like machines might have been expected; it has discouraged them to such a degree that they have failed to see that, with a lowering of the target, there appear less ambitious aims the achievement of which is still theoretically and practically valuable.

Whether or not the inaccuracy involved in fully automatic MT will be so great as to make the "translation" completely worthless, as would be the case if a trained interpreter of the machine's output were unable to find out even roughly what the passage in question was about, will depend on the two languages involved and on the specific ways by which the completeness and the uniqueness of the translation is achieved. Only extensive experiments will be able to show whether there is any future along this line. Preliminary studies in this direction have been made by a Rand Corporation group, but the results achieved so far do not seem to be decisive.

MIXED MT

For those targets in which high accuracy is a *conditio sine qua non*, pure MT has to be given up in favor of a mixed MT, i.e., a translation process in which a human brain intervenes. There the question arises: Which parts of the process should be given to the human partner? In principle, there are a large number of ways in which a machine and a human brain may collaborate. The following considerations are pertinent: First, the more the human partner does, the less complex the machine will have to be; second, the human partner will have to be placed either at the beginning of the translation process or the end, perhaps at both, but preferably not somewhere in the midst of it, according to a well-known principle of electronic computer handling; third, and perhaps most important, since the major bottleneck in translation lies in the scarcity of expert translators, the human partner should be required to know only one of the languages concerned, either the FL or the target language (TL). Even a tripartite partnership between two humans and one machine, where one human knows each language and the machine performs the transformation, might still have considerable practical value, though its theoretical importance might now be trivial. Even collaboration by a bilingual translator would not necessarily trivialize the task, provided this bilingual partner were required to put only a small fraction of the time he would have had to use to work for a completely autonomous translation, for example if a bilingual chemist together with a number of unilingual associates could use the time he would need for an autonomous translation of one Russian chemical paper for the translation of fifty important Russian papers, there seems to be no doubt as to the practicality of such a procedure.

Let us use the term *pre-editor* for the human partner who has to know the FL, *post-editor* for the man who knows the TL, *bilingual editor* for the man who knows both. The tasks to be performed by a pre-editor and by a post-editor are not symmetrical, contrary to what might be supposed at first sight. It would seem natural to have the pre-editor deal with the elimination of *morphological* and *syntactical ambiguities* and with the rearrangement of the FL text in accordance with a standard order in the TL following a set of instructions available to him in his own language. The main business of the post-editor would be elimination of semantical ambiguities, in addition, of course, to stylistic smoothing.

MT WITH A POST-EDITOR

It appears that a post-editor is indispensable for elimination of semantical ambiguities, so let us see first how, without a pre-editor, the post-editor will perform his task, then investigate how a machine could deal with the preliminary elimination of grammatical ambiguities and rearrangement of word order. The post-editor, relying upon the machine alone, faces a formidable looking obstacle. Consider the relatively simple task, of translation from German to English. Take a typical German sentence of 25 words. Assuming that the average number of translations offered for each German lexical unit in an ordinary German-English dictionary is only two (and this is probably a very conservative estimate), then corresponding to the German sentence there will be a set of many tens of millions of English sentences. (For sentences of 60-word length, we would have quadrillions of correlates.) Is it conceivable that a human brain, even that of an expert, would be able to pick the pertinent correlate out of this astronomical number of offerings in a reasonable time? It is understandable that this situation should have discouraged workers in the field of MT from continuing work along this line. This is exactly what happened, for instance, to Prof. Erwin Reifler from the Far Eastern and Russian Institute of the University of Washington, according to oral information. After having begun his investigations in MT by considering the case of a post-editor, he shifted to the case of a pre-editor, out of despair in the ability of the post-editor to solve this apparently super-human task.

The author, however, has been able to show experimentally that the post-editor's task is not super-human but, on the contrary, rather easy, if one assumes that a machine has eliminated all the grammatical ambiguities and part or all of the so-called "idioms," and has rearranged the text in the TL word order. A sample output of a hypothetical German-English Mechanical Translator is given in the Appendix. The reader is invited to pick out of each column just one expression, to smoothen the resulting word sequence stylistically, and then to compare his English sentence with one produced by someone else as a translation of the German original given in the Appendix. Another test would be to retranslate the English sentence into German and compare this product with the original.

The extremely interesting results achieved by Abraham Kaplan in a study made for the Rand Corporation [74] partially explain the human editor's success. This study was explicity intended to be an auxiliary tool for rapid processing of foreign language material. Though it seems that the direct impact of this study on MT is not great, its indirect importance is high. For our purposes, let just one result be mentioned: The amount of ambiguity in meaning of a certain word within a given sentence is reduced, on the average, to something very near its minimal value through inspection of a context consisting of two neighboring words to the left and two to the right. The present author's interpretation of this result is that the ambiguity is not so much reduced by cumulative effect as by the occurrence of some one particular word which has a great chance of appearing in the given context. This means that in order to pick one word out of a column in the above-mentioned example, only one other column in the near neighborhood of the first column has to be inspected, and this is certainly an easier task than a choice of one out of billions.

If one takes into account the fact that the post-editor will receive instructions, in his own language, for handling certain strange-looking combinations, that certain words with many possible translations might reoccur in the passage quite frequently in this same meaning so that time-consuming decisions will not have to be repeated, and so on, it should be clear that the burden on the post-editor will not be too heavy. He should be able to produce out of the raw output of this hypothetical machine a readable translation in a fraction of the time it would take a bilingual expert to produce a translation with the conventional procedure. If the machine can produce its part in a time span comparable with that of the conventional human translator, the machine post-editor partnership may well be able to compete in time and accuracy with an all-human translator. And even if the cost of a mixed translation should turn out to be higher, one should take into account, first, that there are certain practical situations where the cost-factor is secondary and, second, that the operation cost per man-hour is likely to rise in the future whereas the operation cost of the machine will, in all probability, be reduced as soon as such machines are produced on the assembly line and new inventions, such as the transistor, are efficiently incorporated.

In order to eliminate grammatical ambiguities and to rearrange the words of the FL sentence in accordance with the standard order of the TL, the machine will have to perform a syntactical analysis of the FL sentence. This may be more complicated than at first appears. In the case where the FL and the TL do not have the same syntactical structure, the task of the machine is more than recognition and elimination of ambiguities — note that ambiguities with respect to the TL need not at all be so considered by the native speaker of the FL. The task of the machine for languages of different syntactical structures would be that of a transformation of the original sentence that would keep its semantical contents intact and would

enable identification of parts that belong to syntactical categories of the TL·
For lack of space no detailed explanation of this process can be given here'
but it appears that the minimum operations will be the following:

1. *Mechanical analysis* of each *word* in the FL into the *stem (lexical unit)*
and *morphological category*. Since linguistic terminology is not unique, let
us exemplify the required type of analysis, taking German as the FL. The
German 'ging' will have to be analyzed into 'gehen' (past, singular, 1st or
3rd person), the German 'lieben' into 1) 'lieben' (infinitive), 2) 'lieben' (present,
plural, 1st or 3rd person), 3) 'lieb' (adjective, plural) 4) 'lieb' (adjective,
singular, genitive, dative or accusative-masculine). The analysis of 'lieben'
is not complete and is even partly incorrect, but it is not necessary here to
go into all the linguistic complexities.

2. *Mechanical identification* of small syntactical units within the given
sentence on the basis of the morphological categories to which its words
belong and, for most languages, their order.

3. *Transformation* of the given sentence into another that is logically
equivalent to it, and *rearrangement* of the parts of the transformed sentence
in accordance with some standard order of the TL.

The performance of these operations will encounter not only great
practical difficulties, especially for operation 1, but will also require certain
theoretical preparations, on a linguistic and logical level, of a kind that so
far has been dealt with only more or less incidentally. To carry out operation
2, an *operational* (or *instructional* or *analytic* or *sequential*) *syntax* for the
given FL will have to be prepared that will enable the machine (or, a human
translator who does not know the FL) to identify the small syntactical units
into which this sentence has to be broken up. This identification will be
achieved by operating according to a definite sequential program on the set
of sequences of the morphological categories to which the words of a given
sentence might belong.

A considerable body of descriptive data about the languages of the world
has been amassed in recent years, but so far no operational syntax of any
natural language exists with a sizeable degree of completeness, and the
necessity of providing such a syntax has apparently not been recognized by
linguists. To give an analogy: Just as even the most extensive knowledge
of all imaginable properties of all chemical substances will not materially
assist a student of chemistry in developing a method of analyzing a given
mixture of unknown chemical substances, so even the most elaborate
description of the properties of all morphological units of a given language
will not enable a student of linguistics to find, in a reasonable time, a method
of analyzing a given sentence-specimen of this language. Chemists have had
to write, in addition to their general textbooks, special books instructing

students on how to proceed in a fixed sequential order (an order which sometimes depends on the outcome of the preceding step) in his attempted analysis of a given mixture. Likewise special books will have to be written containing sequential instructions for linguistic analysis, i.e., an *operational syntax*.

An important step in this direction has been taken by Professor Victor A. Oswald, Jr. and Stuart L. Fletcher, Jr. [112] in an investigation made explicitly with MT in mind, under the auspices of the Institute for Numerical Analysis of the National Bureau of Standards at Los Angeles. In their paper, there are very valuable suggestions and proposals and various routines are developed for elimination of morphological ambiguities, such as occur in the analysis of 'lieben' mentioned above, and of syntactical ambiguities, as in the determination of whether the phrase 'die Menge' functions as the subject or as the direct object in a given sentence. Oswald and Fletcher are fully aware of the incompleteness of these proposals, but apparently were not sufficiently aware of the necessity of combining the different routines investigated into *one* sequential system. Such awareness has been shown by C.V. Pollard [118] who has developed a set of 11 rules to be followed in a certain sequence by his students of German. These 11 rules are sufficient, according to his claims, to assure satisfactory translation from German into English in almost all cases. Pollard's system presupposes, however, that morphological ambiguities are somehow overcome (an assumption that is not unreasonable for intelligent human translators); and he relies often and heavily, though not always consciously, on the fact that his students can and will use semantical shortcuts, a procedure that obviously does not stand at the disposal of a machine. It seems, however, that by making these tacit assumptions explicit and by incorporating the required additional rules into Pollard's system, an advance towards an operational syntax of German can be made.

To be sure, the problem still remains of finding a sequential system of rules that will be reasonably effective and enable the machine to finish the analysis of an average sentence in a few seconds at most.

At the end of their paper, Oswald and Fletcher point out that they postponed the accomplishment of a complete mechanical syntactical analysis until certain other problems (connected with our operation 1) have been solved. This seems rather unfortunate. It is not clear why there should exist a functional dependence of an operational syntax on counts of the relative frequencies of members of certain syntactical categories within large samples. Important as these investigations might be in themselves, their value for MT is very slight and their influence on the construction of operational syntaxes is almost nil.

One motive for this preoccupation with frequency counts lies in the fact that our operation 1 requires, at least under certain assumptions, a huge storage organ of a not-too-large access time. For the complete German language, the number of words actually or potentially in use today is probably between one and two million. It is indeed true that no system exists at the moment in which such a large memory can be scanned in a short time within reasonable limits of expenditure for equipment; yet the time span that can be allocated for comparing a word stored in a electronic register with the corresponding key-word in the storage organ has to be measured in tenths of seconds, at most. This state of affairs seems to have discouraged the UCLA group from continuing their investigations into operational syntax and induced them to look for ways of reducing the required storage capacity by a considerable factor. They apparently hoped that insights into the relative frequencies of the syntactical categories will somehow enable such reductions.

Now it is true and well-known that a large part of every discourse of sufficient length will consist of repetitions of not too many words belonging to the most frequently occurring words of the given language. A storage of 10,000 suitably chosen words would certainly enable a German-English mechanical translator to identify and translate more than 90 percent of the words appearing in any average text. One might now be led to conclude that such a translation would be satisfactory insofar as an intelligent editor should be able to interpolate the remaining 10 percent or less. There can, however, be little doubt that this widely-held view is false. And this for the following reason: The remaining few percent of words will be of rare occurrence, some of them probably extremely infrequent. For this very reason, they will be least predictable and highly loaded with information. Their interpolation would at the best be very difficult and time-consuming and sometimes, probably in the most decisive places, not possible at all. The result is that so long as the machine, and not a pre-editor, is required to perform the syntactical analysis and no human bilingual expert is available to take care of the infrequent "remainder," the problem of constructing huge storage-organs has to be faced and solved.

Before we go on to discuss this fact, let us remark that the cheapest and theoretically simplest (so simple as to be almost trivial) solution of the MT from, say, German to English will be in using both pre- and post-editors and, in addition, a bilingual expert to deal with the "remainder." The instructions for the pre-editor would, in this case, be, in all probability, so simple that by using existing machinery a translation could be provided that would not take, altogether, more time nor cost any more money than the translation produced by a good bilingual expert, and it would be of considerable practical importance insofar as the bilingual expert would have to spend on this type of translation only a fraction of the time he would have had to spend on a completely autonomous translation. It might therefore turn out that, for this method of translation, namely that making restricted use of bilingual expert plus pre- and post-editors, the UCLA frequency counts will prove to have some practical value, insofar as they might point to certain constructions in the FL that occur so infrequently that one should not complicate the machine in order to deal with them but should leave them to the bilingual editor.

To return to the storage problem, there is no reason to assume that it will not be solved satisfactorily. Many possibilities present themselves, from simple gravitational non-scanning devices, to magnetic, electronic, or photo-electric devices, or any combination of such, scanning or semi-scanning. Further experimentation in this direction for use in fields quite independent of translation is under way with results expected in the near future.

Under the assumption that the storage problem has been solved, the possibility of providing the machine with the results of a complete morphological analysis arises. It should be remembered, however, that there is in principle no reason for the machine's not being able to perform this analysis by itself. This is the method which will have to be used if sufficient storage is not available.

MT WITH A PRE-EDITOR

Prof. Reifler [131], as already mentioned, has occupied himself mainly with MT involving a pre-editor only. He discusses at great length various possibilities of actually eliminating grammatical ambiguities and rearranging by the pre-editor. Besides a discussion of such devices as addition of diacritical marks to the original test, vowel-signs in Hebrew and Arabic where books and scientific papers are usually printed without them, artificlai stress-signs to distinguish, in English, between 'cónvíct' and 'convict', etc., he also has some interesting though somewhat speculative and not too specific remarks on using a universal artificial system of morphological and syntactical categories. The gravest problem for this method is obviously the elimination of semantical ambiguities. Reifler envisages, for this purpose, a "mechanized dictionary," i.e., a device that will give the pre-editor, for every word in the FL, a set of interpretations in the FL that will stand in bi-unique correspondence to the translations usually given in some ordinary bilingual dictionary. When the pre-editor sees, for instance, that the German word 'Hahn' is used in a certain context referring to a weapon, he would tag this occurrence of 'Hahn' by the numeral '2' if the following set of "associations" is put before him:

Hahn   1.(Tier)...   2.(Gewehr)...   3.(Wasser)...

corresponding to the entries in a German-English dictionary

Hahn: 1. cock   2. hammer   3. faucet

It is hard to foresee whether this method can be made to work quickly and efficiently, but if it can, the pre-editor can take upon himself a larger part of the whole translation process than can be put on the shoulders of a post-editor, with a corresponding reduction in the complexity of the machine.

Reifler makes a clear distinction between *general* MT, where translation from any language into any other language is considered, and *specific* translation where only two languages are treated. Obviously, certain methods that depend heavily on the close syntactical relation of two languages will be useless for general MT. This latter problem is, therefore, of a higher order of complexity.

UNIVERSAL GRAMMAR

Whereas specific MT will, in all probability, continue to be mainly an application of trial-and-error investigations, general MT will require establishment of a *universal*, or at least *general grammar*, perhaps even the construction of a whole artificial exchange-language. Prior attempts in this direction have failed completely and brought the whole topic of a *characteristica universalis* or even a *grammatica universalis* into disrepute. The usual combination of metaphysical preconceptions, Aristotelian logic, and complete innocence of any knowledge with respect to the so-called exotic languages is not a very promising mixture. Empirical open-mindedness, mathematical logic, and modern structural linguistics may perhaps prove to be a better one. There is good reason to believe that a combination of the methods developed by K. Ajdukiewicz [1] with those developed by Zellig S. Harris [62] may lead to the beginnings of a universal system of syntactical categories. Other contributions have been made by Rudolf Carnap [24], Hans Reichenbach [130], and the author (Chapter 1). Professor Stuart C. Dodd's system [48] is highly interesting and has been experimentally tested but is not yet in its final form.

The construction of a universal grammar is, at the best, a long-term project, and specific MT should by no means be postponed until its succesful accomplishment.

Somewhat less ambitious are investigations into so-called *transfer-grammars*, i.e., systems in which the grammar of one language is stated in categories appropriate to some other language. This method, too, is old and now popular, but it is by no means clear that important achievements cannot be reached with a careful use of it. Preliminary results have been achieved by Harris and his pupils, but little, if anything, has been published.

MT BETWEEN RESTRICTED LANGUAGES

So far, only MT between complete natural languages has been treated. There are situations, where perhaps a restricted vocabulary or a restricted number of sentence-patterns, or perhaps both, are used or might be used.

This is true of "basic" languages such as Basic English, artificial international auxiliary languages such as Esperanto, Interlingua etc., and also with regard to the pilots' Q-code or the code used by meteorologists. These codes are so restricted that pilots and meteorologists are simply required to learn them as they are, but situations are conceivable in which the richness of information to be transmitted might be so great that a memorizing of the corresponding code should not be required of a pilot, for instance, whose responsibilities are already exceedingly arduous and complex. Some mechanical translation system from the pilots' native language into the international code and another system for translating from this code into the control tower operator's native language might be of great help.

In such cases, the units of translation need not be words since the number of all admitted larger syntactical units, even of all admitted sentences, might still be relatively small. Translation of whole sentences or of sentence-patterns might be an effective method here and is already in use, to a certain degree. The theoretical difficulties of such a type of MT are clearly less formidable and are included in the difficulties of ordinary MT so that no special treatment is necessary here.

More important, perhaps, might be the possibility of restricting, by voluntary convention, the richness of expression in writing abstracts of technical papers, for instance, to such a degree that sentence-pattern translation might easily and quickly be applied, perhaps not directly into any other language but first into some exchange language, natural or artificial.

HARDWARE PROBLEMS

Little thought has been given so far to the problem of the type of machine that should do the mechanical part of a translation; so long as the various alternative possibilities had not been explored to a sufficient degree, experimentation in the uses of computer-like machines was not warranted. It seems, however, that the stage has been reached where experimentation could be started. The main problem is whether general-purpose computers or special translation machines would, in the long run, be more satisfactory with regard to the speed-accuracy/cost ratio. The major operations to be carried out by the machine seem to be *comparison* and *identification, shifting and transferring, unconditional and conditional selection,* but not specifically arithmetical operations.

It seems that for reasons of cost MT will have to be undertaken on a large scale, if at all. It will be justified only if the equipment operates on a full-time basis. Reasons of economy also dictate that the equipment be as well adapted as possible to its special task. Computers in their present form are not ideally suited for MT. Nevertheless certain preliminary experimentation can be carried on with them.

SUMMARY

Practical interest in MT arose with the desire for very rapid, low accuracy, provisional translation of large amounts of general material in foreign languages, as well as for high accuracy translation, mainly of scientific material. On the other hand, engineers have been impressed by the possibilities inherent in various components of electric computers and are now looking for further practical applications in noncomputational fields of new combinations of these components. MT seems to them to be promising since its basic logical operations are of a kind already carried out in existing computers.

Active investigation in the use of MT for rapid mass-translation is going on in the Rand Corporation; research in the use of MT for high-accuracy translation is being done by the author at the Research Laboratory of Electronics of M.I.T.; and certain bordering problems are being investigated by a group at UCLA. Reifler's valuable contribution has been somewhat isolated, and no further research has been undertaken by him. No additional information on progress made by an English group centered around A. D. Booth and R. H. Richens could be obtained, but to all appearances no new important results have been achieved.

The author's own results, only a small part of which are incorporated in this interim report, will be published separately (Chapter 5).

The following tasks seem to be of great importance for their own sake and sufficiently independent of each other to permit their undertaking by separate groups:

1. The *compilation of a word-index* for each language, giving the (unique or multiple) analysis of each word into stem and morphological category.

2. The *construction of a permanent large-scale storage organ*, of medium or low access-time, for utilization of the word index.

3. The *construction of a mechanical bilingual stem-dictionary*. It seems rather obvious that radical departures from ordinary dictionaries will be necessary.

4. The *construction of an operational syntax* for each language, giving a complete sequential program for the analysis of every sentence.

5. *Experimentation on relative speed, accuracy, and cost* of translation by

pre-editor, post-editor, pre- and post-editors, part-time bilingual translators, etc.

6. *Construction of various universal grammars* and comparison of their efficiency in translation.

Though these tasks may be quite independent, MT must be based on the completion of most of them. Hence organization and synchronization are important and require the establishment of some coordinating organism, if real progress is to be made.

APPENDIX

Hand-simulated sample output of a German-English Mechanical Translator for sentence B below

if when whenever though	a	modern new fashionable	electron super microscope	be —— Pres.	judge estimate criticize interpret understand review —— Part. Past		
with regard to	its his her	optical	capacity efficiency ability to perform productive power	so thus then	the	question problem demand inquiry	
stand be become fit be upright Pres.	almost nearly	always ever	in the	foreground	till until up to	to	which what who	magnitude quantity size amount
down downward down here	small little short narrow	detail particular —— Plural	be —— Pres.	prepare produce manufacture exhibit present describe —— Part. Past	in	faithful true	form shape cut size usage mold frame

A. Original German Passage

Wenn ein modernes Elektronenübermikroskop hinsichtlich seiner optischen Leistungs-fähigkeit beurteilt wird, so steht fast immer die Frage im Vordergrund, bis zu welcher Grösse herab kleine Einzelheiten in getreuer Form dargestellt werden.

B. German Passage Rearranged for English Translation

Wenn ein modernes Elektronenübermikroskop wird beurteilt hinsichtlich seiner optischen Leistungsfähigkeit, so die Frage steht fast immer im Vordergrund, bis zu welcher Grösse herab kleine Einzelheiten werden dargestellt in getreuer Form.

Aims and Methods in Machine Translation*

11

During the first years of the research in MT, a considerable amount of progress was made which sufficed to convince many people, who originally were highly skeptical, that MT was not just a wild idea. It did more than that. It created among many of the workers actively engaged in this field the strong feeling that a working system is just around the corner. Though it is understandable that such an illusion should have been formed at the time, it was an illusion. It was created, among other causes, also by the fact that a large number of problems were rather readily solved, and that the output of machine-simulated "translations" of various texts from Russian, German or French into English were often of a form which an intelligent and expert reader could make good sense and use of. It was not sufficiently realized that the gap between such an output, for which only with difficulty the term "translation" could be used at all, and high quality translation proper, i.e., a translation of the quality produced by an experienced human translator, was still enormous, and that the problems solved until then were indeed many but just the simplest ones, whereas the "few" remaining problems were the harder ones—very hard indeed.

Many groups engaged in MT research regard fully automatic, high quality translation (FAHQT) as an aim towards which it is reasonable to work. Claims to the effect that FAHQT from Russian to English is attainable in the near future are often made. I could not be persuaded of their validity. On the contrary, I am quite ready to commit myself to concoct Russian sentences or, should this for some reason be regarded as unfair, to exhibit actually printed Russian sentences for which a perusal of the proposed translation program of any group that claims to be ready to offer in the near future a method of fully automatic translation, would result either

---

* First appeared as Sections 1.2 through 1.5 of *The present status of automatic translation of languages*, **Advances in Computers**, vol. 1 (F.L. Alt, ed.), Academic Press, New York, 1960, pp. 91–163 (slightly revised).

in gibberish or, what is even worse, in meaningful but wrong translations. I am so convinced of this because I believe to be in possession of an argument which amounts to an almost full-fledged demonstration of the unattainability of FAHQT, not only in the near future but altogether. This demonstration is given in Chapter 12.

Most groups, however, seem to have realized, sometimes very reluctantly, that FAHQT will not be attained in the near future. Two consequences can be drawn from this realization. One can go on working with FAHQT in mind, in the hope that the pursuit of this aim will yield interesting theoretical insights which will justify this endeavor, whether or not these insights will ever be exploited for some practical purpose. Or one gives up the ideal of FAHQT in favor of some less ambitious aim with a better chance of attainability in the near future. Both consequences are equally reasonable but should lead to rather different approaches. Lack of clarity in this respect, vague hopes that somehow or other both aims can be attained simultaneously and by the use of the same methods, must lead to confusion and result in waste of effort, time and money. Those who are interested in MT as a primarily practical device must realize that full automation of the translation process is incompatible with high quality. There are two possible directions in which a compromise could be struck; one could sacrifice quality or one could reduce the self-sufficiency of the machine output. There are very many situations where less than high quality machine output is satisfactory. There is no need to present examples. If, however, high quality is mandatory —and I do not think, for instance, that scientists are prepared to be satisfied with less than the present average standard of human translation, while many regard this standard as too low for their purposes—then the machine output will have to be post-edited, thereby turning, strictly speaking, machine translation into *machine aids to translation.*

COMMERCIAL PARTLY MECHANIZED, HIGH QUALITY TRANSLATION ATTAINABLE IN THE NEAR FUTURE

In the remainder of this survey, I shall deal exclusively with those situations where translation involved has to be of high quality. It should be easy to see how the conclusions at which I arrive have to be modified in order to deal with situations in which lesser quality is satisfactory.

As soon as the aim of MT is lowered to that of high quality translation by a *machine–post-editor partnership*, the decisive problem becomes to determine the region of optimality in the continuum of possible divisions of labor. It is clear that the exact position of this region will be a function of, among other things, the state of linguistic analysis to which the languages involved have been submitted. It may be safely assumed that, with machine-time/

efficiency becoming cheaper and human time becoming more expensive, continuous efforts will be made to push this region in the direction of reducing the human element. However, there is no good reason to assume that this region can be pushed to the end of the line, certainly not in the near future.

It seems that with the state of linguistic analysis achieved today, and with the kind of electronic computers already in existence or under construction, especially with the kind of large capacity, low cost and low-access-time internal memory devices that will be available within a few years, a point has been reached where commercial partly mechanized translation centers stand a serious chance of becoming a practical reality. However, various developments are still pending and certain decisions will have to be made.

First, a reliable and versatile mechanical print reader will have to become available. It has been estimated that the cost of retyping printed Russian material into a form and on a medium that could be processed by a machine would amount, under present conditions, to about one fourth of a cent per word. This estimate is probably too low, as the quality of the retyping has to be exceptionally high, in order to avoid printing mistakes which would perhaps be quite harmless for a human reader, but could be rather disastrous for machines which so far are totally unable to deal with misprints. The original text might therefore have to be key-punched by two operators, verified, etc., or else to be keypunched once, but at highly reduced speed. Indeed, whereas the above estimate is based on a rate of 20 Russian words per minute, another report gives the maximum rate of trained and experienced keypunch operators as half this number. In one place, it is estimated that an automatic print reader might be ten times cheaper than human retyping. The difference between one half of a cent per keypunched word and one twentieth of a cent per print-read word could make all the difference, as the present cost per word of human Russian-to-English translation in the United States is generally given as lying between one and three cents, apparently depending on the quality and urgency of the job, and perhaps also on the exact form of the output. The costs may be different, of course, for other language pairs and in other countries. An informative synopsis on the variation or rates of payment for scientific and technical translation is given in a recent UNESCO survey [143:103–110].

Secondly, a concerted effort will have to be made by a pretty large group in order to prepare the necessary dictionary or dictionaries in the most suitable form. That this is not such a straightforward affair as laymen are apt to think becomes clear in the work of the Harvard MT group [100] which developed an interesting semiautomatic method for preparing dictionaries.

Thirdly, a good amount of thinking accompanied by an equally large amount of experimenting will have to go into the determination of the location of the interval in the above-mentioned continuum within which the optimal point of the division of labor between machine and post-editor will have a good chance of being situated, as a function of the specific translation program and the specific qualities of the envisaged post-editor. Among other things, these would have to determine whether some minimal pre-editing, while requiring but very little knowledge of the source language by the pre-editor, could not be utilized in order to reduce the load of the machine by a considerable amount. At present, many of the experimental MT programs make use of such limited pre-editing. As one illustration of an operation that is in almost all cases so ridiculously simple for a human pre-editor that it could be almost instantaneously performed by a keypunch operator with only the barest knowledge of the source language, let me mention the distinction between the functioning of a point as a period, hence as one of the all-important markers of end-of-sentence, and its various other functions. Having the machine make this decision—a vital one, indeed so vital that it is one of the first operations, if not the first, in many translation programs that shun the use of pre-editing altogether—might be a complex and costly affair, throwing some doubts on the soundness of the case presented above in favor of a mechanical print reader. For the time being, at least, so long as keypunching is being used for the input, it is doubtless profitable to introduce as much elementary pre-editing as the keypunch operator can take into stride without considerably slowing down.

Fourthly, an old question which has not been treated so far with sufficient incisiveness, mostly because the ideal of FAHQT diverted the interests of the research workers into other, less practical directions, namely the question whether MT dictionaries should contain as their source-language entries all letter sequences that may occur between spaces, sometimes called *inflected forms*, or rather so-called *canonical forms* [110:134], or perhaps something in between like *canonical stems*, has to be decided one way or other before mass production of translations is taken up. This question is clearly highly dependent, among other things, upon the exact type of internal and external memory devices available, and it is therefore mandatory to have a reliable estimate of this dependence. It is obvious that the speed of the machine part of the translation, and thereby the cost of the total translation process, will depend to a high degree on the organization of the dictionaries used. Most workers in the field of MT seem to have rather definite, though divergent, opinions in this respect. However, I am not aware of any serious comparative studies, though the outcome of such studies most surely will have a considerable impact upon the economics of MT.

In general, the intention of reducing the post-editor's part has absorbed so much of the time and energy of most workers in MT, that there has not been sufficient discussion of the problem whether partially automatic translation, even with such a large amount of participation by the post-editor as would be required under present conditions, is not nevertheless a desirable and feasible achievement. I fully understand the feeling that such an achievement is not of very high intellectual caliber, that the real challenge has thereby not yet been taken up, but I do not think that those agencies for whom any reduction of the load imposed at the moment on the time of highly qualified expert translators is an important achievement, should necessarily wait with the installation of commercial man–machine translation outfits until the post-editor's part has become very small, whatever amount of satisfaction the MT research worker will get from such an achievement. It is gratifying to learn that this attitude coincides with that of the Harvard group and is probably now shared by many other groups in the USA, USSR, and England, though it would further the issue if clear-cut statements of policy could be obtained in this respect.

COMPROMISING IN THE WRONG DIRECTION

At this stage, it is probably proper to warn against a certain tendency which has been quite conspicuous in the approach of many MT groups. These groups, realizing that FAHQT is not really attainable in the near future so that a less ambitious aim is definitely indicated, had a tendency to compromise in the wrong direction for reasons which, though understandable, must nevertheless be combated and rejected. Their reasoning was something like the following: since we cannot have 100% automatic high quality translation, let us be satisfied with a machine output which is complete and unique, i.e., a smooth text of the kind you will get from a human translator (though perhaps not quite as polished and idiomatic), but which has a less than 100% chance of being correct. I shall use the expression "95%" for this purpose since it has become a kind of slogan in the trade, with the understanding that it should by no means be taken literally. Such an approach would be implemented by one of the two following procedures: the one procedure would require to print the most frequent target-language counterpart of a given source-language word whose ambiguity has not been resolved by the application of the syntactical and semantical routines, necessitating, among other things, large-scale statistical studies of the frequency of usage of the various target renderings of many, if not most, source-language words; the other would be ready to work with syntactical rules of analysis with a degree of validity of no more than 95%, so long as this degree is sufficient to insure uniqueness and smoothness of the translation. This approach seems wrong to me and even dangerous since the machine output of the corresponding program will be of low quality in a misleading and soothing disguise. Since so many sentences, "5%" of a given text, will have a good chance of being mistranslated by the machine, it is by no means clear whether the reader will always be able to detect these mistranslations, just because the machine output is so smooth and grammatical (so let us assume for the sake of the argument, though I doubt whether even this much can really be achieved at this stage of the game) that he might be able to find only few cues to warn him that something is wrong with it. It is not inconceivable that the machine translation would be so wrong at times as to lead its user to actions which he would not have taken when presented by a correct translation. (When I talk about "100%", I obviously have in mind not some heavenly ideal of perfection, but the product of an average qualified translator. I am aware that such a translator will on occasion make mistakes and that even machines of a general low quality output will avoid some of these mistakes. I am naturally comparing averages only.)

But there is really no need at all to compromise in the directon of reducing the reliability of the machine output. True enough, a smooth machine translation looks impressive, especially if the reader is unable to realize at first sight that this translation is faulty every so often, but this esthetically appealing feature should not blind us to the dangers inherent in this approach. It is much safer to compromise in the other direction. Let us be satisfied with a machine output which will every so often be neither unique nor smooth, which every so often will present the post-editor with a multiplicity of renderings among which he will have to take his choice, or with a text which, if it is unique, will not be grammatical. On the other hand, whenever the machine output is grammatical and unique it should be, to adopt a slogan current in the Harvard group, "fail-safe" (to about the same degree, to make this qualification for the last time, as the average qualified human translator's output is fail-safe). Let the machine by all means provide the post-editor with all possible help, present him with as many possible renderings as he can digest without becoming confused by the *embarras de richesse*—and here again we have quite a problem of finding an interval of optimality—but never let the machine make decisions by itself on purely frequential reasons even if these frequencies can be relied upon. If these frequency counts could be done cheaply—and I doubt very much whether this is feasible to such a high degree of reliability as would probably be required for our purposes—let this information too be given the post-editor, but by no means should practical MT wait until this information is obtained.

The only reasonable aim, then, for short-range research into MT seems to be that of finding some machine–post-editor partnership that would be commercially competitive with existing human translation, and then to try to improve the commercial effectiveness of this partnership by improving the programming in order to delegate to the machine more and more operations in the total translation process which it can perform more effectively than the human post-editor. These improvements will, of course, utilize not only developments in hardware, programming (especially automatic programming), and linguistic analysis, but also the experience gained by analyzing the machine output itself. Should it turn out that for the sake of competitiveness some use of a pre-editor, and perhaps even of a bilingual post-editor, would be at least temporarily required, then this fact should be accepted as such, in spite of the trivialization of the theoretical challenge of the MT problem which would be entailed by such a procedure.

A CRITIQUE OF THE OVERESTIMATION OF STATISTICS AND THE "EMPIRICAL APPROACH"

Let me warn in general against overestimating the impact of statistical information on the problem of MT and related questions. I believe that this overestimation is a remnant of the time, some ten years ago, when many people thought that the statistical theory of communication would solve many, if not all, of the problems of communication. Though it is often possible by a proper organization of the research effort to get a certain amount of statistical information at no great extra cost, it is my impression that much valuable time of MT workers has been spent on trying to obtain statistical information whose impact on MT is by no means evident. It is not true that every statistic on linguistic matters is automatically of importance for MT so that the gathering of any such statistics could be regarded as an integral part of MT research without any need for additional justification.

Gathering of statistics is regarded by many MT groups as being part of a more general methodological approach—the so-called "*empirical approach.*" This term has already caused a lot of confusion. I am using it here in the sense in which it is employed by the RAND group. This sense should become obvious from the following discussion. Adherents of this approach are distrustful of existing grammar books and dictionaries, and regard it as necessary to establish from scratch the grammatical rules by which the source-language text will be machine analyzed, through a human analysis of a large enough corpus of source-language material, constantly improving upon the formulation of these rules by constantly enlarging this corpus. With regard to dictionaries, a similar approach is often implemented and a dictionary compiled from translations performed by bilingual members of the group or by other human translators considered to be qualified by this group. This approach seems to me somewhat wasteful in practice and not sufficiently justified in theory. The underlying distrust seems to have been caused by the well-known fact that most existing grammars are of the normative type, hence often of no great help in the analysis of actual writing (and to an even higher degree, of actual speech), and that existing dictionaries are of such a nature that quite often none of the present target-language counterparts of a source-language word are satisfactory within certain contexts, especially with regard to terms used in recently developed scientific fields. However, even in view of these facts, I believe that the baby has far too often been thrown away with the bathwater. No justification has been given for the implicit belief of the "empiricists" that a grammar satisfactory for MT purposes will be compiled any quicker or more reliably by starting from scratch and "deriving" the rules of grammar from an analysis of a large corpus than by starting from some authoritative grammar and changing it, if necessary, in accordance with analysis of actual texts. The same holds *mutatis mutandis* with regard to the compilation of dictionaries. But grammars have in general not wholly been dreamt up, nor have dictionaries been compiled by some random process. Existing grammars and dictionaries are already based, though admittedly not wholly, upon actual texts of incomparably larger extension than those that serve as a basis for the new compilers. Russian is not Kwakiutl, and with all due regard to the methods and techniques of structural linguistics and to the insights which this science has given us in respect to some deficiencies of traditional grammars, I do not think that it follows from its teachings that all existing codifications of languages with a highly developed literature should be totally disregarded. Let me add, without going here into details for lack of space, that the empiricalness of the derivations of grammar rules from actual texts is rather doubtful as such. From certain general methodological considerations one might as well be led to the conclusion that these rules incorporate a lot of subjective and highly biased and untested assumptions such that their degree of validity might very well, on the average, be lower than that of the well-established, often-tested and critically examined grammars, in spite of their normativity.

A Demonstration of the Nonfeasibility of Fully Automatic High Quality Translation*

12

One of the reasons why we do not have as yet any translation centers, not even in the planning stage, in which electronic computers, general or special purpose, are used to automate certain parts of the translation process, in spite of the fact that such centers would fulfil a vital function in saving a considerable amount of qualified human translator time per document translated, and thereby facilitate more, quicker and, after some time, cheaper translation, is the reluctance of many MT workers to recognize that the idea of inventing a method for fully automatic high quality translation (FAHQT) is just a dream which will not come true in the foreseeable future. By not realizing the practical futility of this aim, whatever its motivational importance for certain types of basic research, they have misled themselves and the agencies which sponsored their research into not being satisfied with a partly automated translation system whose principles are well understood today, and instead to wait for the real thing which was believed, and made to believe, to be just around the corner.

During the last years I have repeatedly tried to point out the illusory character of the FAHQT ideal even in respect to mechanical determination of the syntactical structure of a given source-language sentence. Here I shall show that there exist extremely simple sentences in English—and the same holds, I am sure, for any other natural language—which, within certain linguistic contexts, would be uniquely (up to plain synonymy) and unambiguously translated into any other language by anyone with a sufficient knowledge of the two languages involved, though I know of no program that would enable a machine to come up with this unique rendering unless by a completely arbitrary and *ad hoc* procedure whose futility would show itself in the next example.

A sentence of this kind is the following:

---

* First appeared as Appendix III to *The present status of automatic translation of languages*, **Advances in Computers,** vol. I (F. L. Alt, ed.), Academic Press, New York 1960, pp. 158–163.

The box was in the pen.

The linguistic context from which this sentence is taken is, say, the following:

Little John was looking for his toy box. Finally he found it.
The box was in the pen. John was very happy.

Assume, for simplicity's sake, that *pen* in English has only the following two meanings (1) a certain writing utensil, (2) an enclosure where small children can play. I now claim that no existing or imaginable program will enable an electronic computer to determine that the word *pen* in the given sentence within the given context has the second of the above meanings, whereas every reader with a sufficient knowledge of English will do this "automatically." Incidentally, we realize that the issue is not one that concerns translation proper, i.e., the transition from one language to another, but a preliminary stage of this process, viz., the determination of the specific meaning in context of a word which, in isolation, is semantically ambiguous (relative to a given target-language, if one wants to guard oneself against the conceivable though extremely unlikely case that the target-language contains a word denoting both the same writing utensil and an enclosure where children can play).

It is an old prejudice, but nevertheless a prejudice, that taking into consideration a sufficiently large linguistic environment as such will suffice to reduce the semantical ambiguity of a given word. Let me quote from the memorandum which Warren Weaver sent on July 15, 1949 [148] to some two hundred of his acquaintances and which became one of the prime movers of MT research in general and directly initiated the well-known researches of Reifler and Kaplan [131;74]: "... if ... one can see not only the central word in question, but also say N words on either side, then if N is large enough one can *unambiguously* [my italics] decide the meaning of the central word. The formal truth of this statement becomes clear when one mentions that the middle word of a whole article or a whole book is unambiguous if one has read the whole article or book, providing of course that the article or book is sufficiently well written to communicate at all [148:21]". Weaver then goes on to pose the practical question: "What minimum value of N will, at least in a tolerable fraction of cases, lead to the correct choice of meaning for the central word," a question which was, we recall, so successfully answered by Kaplan. But Weaver's seemingly lucid argument is riddled with a fateful fallacy: the argument is doubtless valid (fortified, as it is, by the escape clause beginning with "providing") but only for *intelligent* readers, for whom the article or book was written to begin with. Weaver himself thought at that time that the argument is valid also for an electronic computer, though he did not say so explicitly in the quoted passage, and on the contrary, used the word "one"; that this is so will be clear to anyone who reads with care the whole section headed "Meaning and Context." In this fallacious transfer Weaver has been followed by almost every author on MT problems, including many Russian ones.

Now, what exactly is going on here? Why is it that a machine with a memory capacity sufficient to deal with a whole paragraph at a time, and a syntactico-semantic program that goes, if necessary, beyond the boundaries of single sentences up to a whole paragraph (and, for the sake of the argument, up to a whole book)—something which has so far not gotten beyond the barest and vaguest outlines—is still powerless to determine the meaning of *pen* in our sample sentence within the given paragraph? The explanation is extremely simple, and it is nothing short of amazing that, to my knowledge, this point has never been made before, in the context of MT, though it must surely have been made many times in other contexts. What makes an intelligent human reader grasp this meaning so unhesitatingly is in addition to all the other features that have been discussed by MT workers (Dostert [49], e.g., lists no less than seven of what he calls areas of meaning determination, none of which, however, takes care of our simple example), his *knowledge* that the relative sizes of pens, in the sense of writing implements, toy boxes, and pens, in the sense of playpens, are such that when someone writes under ordinary circumstances and in something like the given context, "The box was in the pen," he almost certainly refers to a playpen and most certainly not to a writing pen. (The occurrence of this sentence in the mentioned paragraph tends to increase the confidence of the reader that the circumstances are ordinary, though the whole paragraph could, of course, still have formed part of a larger fairy tale, or of some dream story, etc.) This knowledge is not at the disposal of the electronic computer and none of the dictionaries or programs for the elimination of polysemy puts this knowledge at its disposal.

Whenever I offered this argument to one of my colleagues working on MT, his first reaction was: "But why not envisage a system which will put this knowledge at the disposal of the translation machine?" Understandable at this reaction is, it is very easy to show its futility. What such a suggestion amounts to, if taken seriously, is the requirement that a translation machine should not only be supplied with a dictionary but also with a universal encyclopedia. This is surely utterly chimerical and hardly deserves any further discussion. Since, however, the idea of a machine with encyclopedic knowledge has popped up also on other occasions, let me add a few words on this topic. The number of facts we human beings know is, in a certain very pregnant sense, infinite. Knowing, for instance, that at a certain moment there are exactly eight chairs in a certain room, we also know that there are more than five chairs, less than 9, 10, 11, 12, and so on *ad infinitum*, chairs in that room. We know all these additional facts by inferences which we are able to perform, at least in this particular case, instantaneously, and it is clear that they are not, in any serious sense, stored in our memory. Though one could envisage that a machine would be capable of performing the same inferences, there exists so far no serious proposal for a scheme that would make a machine perform such inferences in the same or similar circumstances under which an intelligent human being would perform them. Though a lot of thought should surely be given to the problems which could only be touched lightly here, it would very definitely mean putting the horse before the cart if practical MT would have to wait for their solution. These problems are clearly many orders of magnitude more difficult than the problem of establishing practical machine aids to translation. I believe that it is of decisive importance to get a clear view of this whole issue and hope that my remarks will contribute to its clarification.

I have no idea how often sentences of the mentioned kind, whose ambiguity is resolvable only on the basis of extra-linguistic knowledge which cannot be presumed to be at the disposal of a computer, occur on the average in the various types of documents in whose translation one might be interested. I am quite ready to assume that they would occur rather infrequently in certain scientific texts. I am ready to admit that none might occur on a whole page or even in some whole article. But so long as they will occur *sometimes*, a translation outfit that will claim that its output is of a quality comparable to that of a qualified human translator will have to use a post-editor, and this not only for polishing up purposes, contrary to what even so acute and impartial an observer as Warren Weaver was still hoping for in 1955 [89:vii].

Having shown, I hope, that FAHQT is out of the question for the foreseeable future because of the existence of a large number of sentences the determination of whose meaning, unambiguous for a human reader, is beyond the reach of machines, let me now discuss this issue of reduction of semantical ambiguity a little further. There exist in the main two methods of reducing semantical ambiguity. One is the use of idioglossaries, the other is the already mentioned method of utilizing the immediate linguistic environment of the word which is ambiguous in isolation. Though some doubts have been raised on occasion as to the validity of the first of these methods, I do not know of any serious attempt to put its validity to test.

At this point I would only like to stress the vital necessity of performing such tests before an MT method based upon the utilization of idioglossaries is claimed to yield high quality translations, even in collaboration with a post-editor. It is just the great effectiveness of the use of idioglossaries in general which is apt to yield disastrously wrong translations on occasion without giving the post-editor even a chance to correct these mistakes. It is just because a certain Russian word in a chemical paper will *almost always* have a certain specific English rendering that the danger is so great that in those exceptional cases where this word, for some reason or other, will have a different meaning, this exception will not be taken into account, yielding a meaningful but wrong translation.

In regard to the second method, the situation is even worse, and has lately become even more confused through the use of certain slogan terms like "thesaurus" in this connection. (Notice, e.g., that the very same— fictitious!—thesaurus approach for English-to-French translation that would correctly render *pen* by "plume" in the sentence *The pen was in the ink-stand* would incorrectly render *pen* by "plume" in the sentence *The inkstand was in the pen*.) It is undoubtedly true that consideration of the immediate linguistic neighborhood of a given ambiguous word is a very powerful method, but it is again necessary to realize its limitations. I am referring no longer to those limitations which I pointed out through the use of my sample sentence, but rather to the fact that many MT workers seem to underestimate the importance of those cases of reduction of polysemy which cannot be obtained by looking at the immediate neighborhood, and even more so about the fact that partial successes in this direction have led many people to underestimate the depth of the remaining gap. Let me state rather dogmatically that there exists at this moment no method of reducing the polysemy of the, say, twenty words of an average Russian sentence in a scientific article below a remainder of, I would estimate, at least five or six words with multiple English renderings, which would not seriously endanger the quality of the machine output. It is looking at the quantities involved which creates a distorted picture with many people. Many tend to believe that by reducing the number of initially possible renderings of a twenty word Russian sentence from a few tens of thousands (which is the approximate number resulting from the assumption that each of the twenty Russian words has two renderings on the average, while seven or eight of them have only one rendering) to some eighty (which would be the number of renderings on the assumption that sixteen words are uniquely rendered and four have three renderings apiece, forgetting now about all the other aspects such as change of word order, etc.) the main bulk of this kind of work has been achieved, the remainder requiring only some slight additional effort. We have before us another case of what, in a superficially different but intrinsically very similar situation, has been called the "80% fallacy" [19]. The remaining 20% will require not one quarter of the effort spent for the first 80%, but many, many times this effort, with a few percent remaining beyond the reach of every conceivable effort.

The Future of Machine Translation* | 13

Translation is an activity that requires, in general, a good amount of intelligence, in addition, of course, to good knowledge of both languages involved, the source and the target language. With the advent of electronic digital computers, the question how seriously the term "intelligence" has to be taken in this context attained particular importance. By 1946, these computers had already proved their uncanny ability to carry out long and complex computations at enormous speed and great accuracy and thereby to perform tasks which had until then been considered to be the privilege of human intelligence. It was then that people began looking around in earnest for other activities requiring intelligence as candidates for automation and happened to hit upon translation as one such likely candidate.

It was, of course, quickly realized that there existed big differences between computation and translation. Whereas perfect algorithms were available for the performance of the elementary arithmetical operations, of which every computable function is composed, so that only meticulous programming and craftmanslike construction were required in order to ensure (almost) faultless computation by a computer that was able to perform these operations and was equipped with a large enough memory, no such algorithms were in existence for translation. Moreover, whereas the notion of a "correct" computation is unproblematic—leaving aside certain philosophical reservations which are irrelevant in our context—and, whenever approximations due to round-offs or other reasons are indicated, the degree of approximation is perfectly well determined, the notion of a "good" translation is ridden with problems and no serious criterion for the comparison of degrees of adequateness of translations is in view.

When, in 1951, I got myself interested in the automation of translation, I tried at first to find out what psychologists knew about human translation, only to discover to my dismay that very little was known that was not purely anecdotal or speculative. Machine simulation of human translating

* First appeared in **Freeing the Mind**, Articles and Letters from the Times Literary Supplement during March–June, 1962, pp. 32–37.

having consequently been discarded as one possible approach, a "let's-see-how-far-we-can-get" attitude was generally adopted. Almost from the start there was a differentiation between those who thought that fully automatic and good quality translation was a reasonable goal to aim at and those who regarded such a goal as utopian, at least for the foreseeable future, and preferred to work towards a man-machine partnership in translation, with the machine doing the routine chores and the man making the "intelligent" decisions. At that time, however, this difference was based more on intuitive judgement (and temperament) than on rational deliberation, since no analysis of the translation process into "routine" and "intelligence-requiring" had yet been performed.

In the beginning, MT made great strides forward. By 1952, it turned out that the hand-simulated output of certain machine programs for Russian-to-English translation of scientific and technological material, based on nothing more sophisticated than a (simulated) mechanical dictionary in which each Russian word had one or more (or none, on occasion) English words or short phrases as its counterparts, was generally of such a quality that an English reader, expert in the appropriate field and with a good amount of effort and time, could make sense, and most of the time good sense, of it. In addition, the mechanical determination of syntactic structure made good progress, too, promising a further increase in the quality of the machine output and thereby a further reduction of the interpretative effort required of the reader.

Thousands of other major and minor problems found their solution. One quickly learnt how to deal with idioms, how to economize in the size of the dictionary, a step which was a practical necessity due to the then relatively small size of the rapid-access machine memories, how to optimize dictionary look-up, and so on.

Two years later a highly publicized demonstration was staged in the United States which, though proving nothing to the small group of experts, certainly had the effect of drawing MT into the public limelight and turning it into a battlefield of international prestige. Whereas until then MT had been studied only in the United States and England, immediately thereafter Soviet Russia moved into the field with such a concentrated effort that it became, within a couple of years, the leading country of MT. Other countries quickly followed suit, and today MT research groups exist in most European countries, as well as in the United States, Mexico, Japan, China and Israel. More countries will doubtless join in the near future.

There are three journals which are exclusively dedicated to MT, and many others willingly accept papers on this topic. Many national and international conferences gathered to deal with MT, starting with the 1952 conference at the Massachusetts Institute of Technology, which I had the privilege of organizing and which was "international" owing to the presence of a lone British participant, and coming to its climax so far with a conference held at Teddington, Middlesex, in the autumn of 1961. I could easily go on and bolster the success story of MT with statistics about the amount of man-years and money spent on MT research in 1960 compared with, say, 1950. But let me spare the reader this.

In spite of all this rapid development, there are some who feel that MT has reached an impasse from which it is not likely to emerge without a radical change in the whole approach. It seems now quite certain to some of us, a small but apparently growing minority, that with all the progress made in hardware, programming techniques and linguistic insight, the quality of fully autonomous mechanical translation, even when restricted to scientific or technological material, will never approach that of qualified human translators and that therefore MT will only under very exceptional circumstances be able to compete wih human translation.

This "pessimistic" evaluation is based upon various considerations, only one of which will be presented here, and even this, for obvious reasons, only very shortly and therefore dogmatically. Expert human translators use their *background knowledge*, mostly subconsciously, in order to resolve syntactical and semantical ambiguities which machines will have either to leave unresolved or resolve by some "mechanical" rule which will ever so often result in a wrong translation. The perhaps simplest illustration of a syntactical ambiguity which is unresolvable by a machine except by arbitrary or ad hoc rules is provided by a sentence, say, ". . . slow neutrons and protons . . .", whereas, in general though by no means always, the human expert reader will have no difficulty in resolving the ambiguity through utilization of his background knowledge, no counterpart of which could conceivably stand at the disposal of computers. Similarly, there are innumerable semantical ambiguities which nothing but plain, factual knowledge or considerations of truthfulness and consistency will resolve, all of which are beyond the reach of computers.

On the other hand, though the best present machine-produced "translations" of scientific material between languages with closely related syntaxes are "readable" in the sense that in many cases, though not in all, they convey to the expert reader approximately the same information as good human-produced translations, they do so only at the price of greatly increasing the load on the reader estimated in one report to require about four times as much time as a human translation, in addition to a greater intensity of mental strain which cannot easily be measured and often borders on frustration. This is, of course, utterly intolerable, in general. In practice, therefore, unless this factor can be greatly reduced—and the prospects for such a reduction are none too good, in view of the above-mentioned limitations—the machine output will have to be "post-edited", before submission of the finished product to the readers.

Though I would regard it as likely that, at least for certain language pairs, the quality of a translation product of the combined effort of an appropriately programmed computer and a suitably trained post-editor (whose knowledge of the source language need not be very extensive, this "saving" then being the whole crux of the matter) would by and large be commensurate with that of purely human translation, and on occasion even better since the rough machine output might bring to the post-editor's attention possibilities which a translator might overlook, no such combination is economically feasible today. Nor is it likely to become so in the near future unless much more thought is given to optimizing the workings of such a partnership rather than to the doubtless intellectually much more exciting endeavor of establishing fully automatic, high quality translation.

Not even the advent of print-reading machinery will substantially change the picture. A good part of the savings which direct machine encoding will produce, as against human key-punching, might well be lost due to the fact that a machine will be helpless before very bad type or elementary misprints (which even a dull key puncher could quickly be trained to correct while doing her typing) and not be able to indicate, as the key-puncher again could easily be made to do, which periods are full-stops, decimal points or abbreviation-indicators, &c., indications that would doubtless save the translation machine time and mistakes.

To sum this part up, I would say that there is no prospect whatsoever that the employment of electronic digital computers in the field of translation will lead to any revolutionary changes. A complete automation of the activity is wholly utopian, since the fact that books and papers are usually written for readers with a certain background knowledge and an ability for logical deduction and plausible reasoning cannot be over-ridden by even the cleverest utilization of all formal features of a discourse. The hopes to the contrary which many of us had a decade ago just turned out to be by and large unrealizable. The quicker this is understood, the better are the chances that more attention will be paid to finding efficient ways of improving the status of scientific and technological translation—I am not qualified to discuss literary translation—including judicious and modest use of *mechanical aids*.

Because of the great prestige value that has been attached to machine translation during the past decade, it is possible that both the United States and Soviet Russia, and perhaps also other countries, will attempt to impress the world with a demostration in which, say, a whole article in chemistry or electronics will be automatically translated from Russian into English (or vice versa), perhaps including a mechanical reading of the source text. Few newspaper readers, who will then doubtless be confronted with a reproduction of an original page and its "translation", will be in a position to evaluate the quality of the translation and might therefore be persuaded to regard this feat as another sputnik. They will be badly deceived.

Perhaps the following little (and admittedly very rough) computation could help to harden them against this propaganda effect: it takes a good human translator up to a couple of hours to produce a finished translation of a page from a Russian scientific article into English, and his fee would be, say, two British pounds. The demonstrating machine will produce her output in something like a minute and would have charged about the same amount, had the translation been done commercially. Now assume that one hundred scientists will want to read this page. Reading the human translation would take them, say, six minutes on the average, altogether ten scientist-hours for a cost of, say, ten pounds. Reading the machine's output will take, say, twelve minutes on the average (which is half of what the above-mentioned estimate would give!), hence altogether twenty scientist-hours, for a cost of twenty pounds. The saving of two hours human translation time would cause the waste of ten hours additional reading time and of ten pounds additional reading cost. Notice that even if the next computer generation will be able to produce an output in ten seconds and for one pound, this will make little difference so long as the quality of the output is not improved.

I have deliberately refrained from dealing with any of the countless speculations that create in the field of MT a science-fictional and sometimes lunatic fringe. At the best, as with regard to the speculations on the use of machines with learning and self-organizing abilities for translation purposes, they are premature; at the worst, they exhibit the free flight of fantasy at its wildest recklessness, and I would not have mentioned this point at all were it not that every so often I happen to meet otherwise serious and responsible scientists who have been taken in by these fantasies and gone overboard. But the borderline between imaginative creativity and reckless speculation is surely hard to draw, and no man, angel or machine, will ever develop an algorithm for drawing this line.

Four Lectures on Algebraic Linguistics and Machine Translation* | 14

First Lecture: THE ROLE OF GRAMMATICAL MODELS IN MACHINE TRANSLÁTION†

Linguistics, as every other empirical science, is a complex mixture of theory and observation. The precise nature of this mixture is still not too well understood, and in this respect the difference between linguistics and, say, physics is probably at most one of degree. The lack of methodological insight has often led to futile disputes between linguists and other scientists dealing with language, such as psychologists, logicians, or communication theoreticians, as well as among linguists themselves.

Recently, however, considerable progress has been made in the understanding of the function of theory in linguistics, as a result of which *theoretical linguistics* has come into full-fledged existence. Interestingly enough, the present customary name for this new subdiscipline is rather *mathematical linguistics*. This is slightly unfortunate: though the adjective 'mathematical' is quite all right if 'mathematics' is understood in the sense of 'theory of formal systems', which is indeed one of its many legitimate senses, it is misleading inasmuch as it is still associated, at least among the non-specialists, including the bulk of the linguists themselves, with numbers and quantitative treatment. That subdiscipline of linguistics, however, which deals with numbers and statistics should better be called *statistical linguistics* and rather carefully be kept apart from mathematical linguistics *qua* theoretical linguistics. Should one prefer to regard 'mathematical linguistics' as a term for a genus of which statistical linguistics is a species, then the other species should perhaps be named *algebraic linguistics*.

---

* A revised version of a series of lectures given in July, 1962, before a NATO Advanced Summer Institute on Automatic Translation of Languages in Venice, Italy.

† This lecture incorporates, with slight revisions, my paper, "Some recent results in theoretical linguistics," **Logic, Methodology and Philosophy of Science: Proceedings of the 1960 International Congress** (E. Nagel, P. Suppes, A. Tarski, eds.), Stanford University Press, 1962, pp. 551–557.

After this terminological aside which, I think, was not superfluous, let us briefly sketch the background and development of algebraic linguistics. In the hands of such authors as Harris [62] and Hockett [70] in the United States, Hjelmslev [68] and Uldall [142] in Europe, structural linguistics became more and more conscious of the chasm between theory and observation, and linguistic theory deliberately got an *algebraic* look. At the same time, Carnap [24] and the Polish logicians, especially Ajdukiewicz [1], developed the logical syntax of language which was, however, too much preoccupied with rules of deduction, and too little with rules of formation, to exert a great influence on current linguistics. Finally, Post [121] succeeded in formally assimilating rules of formation to rules of deduction, thereby paving the way for the application of the recently developed powerful theory of recursive functions, a branch of mathematical logic, to all ordinary languages viewed as combinatorial systems [47], while Curry [46] became more and more aware of the implications of combinatorial logic to theoretical linguistics. It is, though, perhaps not too surprising that the ideas of Post and Curry should be no better known to professional linguists than those of Carnap and Ajdukiewicz.

It seems that a major change in the peaceful but uninspiring coexistence of structural linguists and syntax-oriented logicians came along when the idea of *mechanizing the determination of syntactic structure* began to take hold of the imagination of various authors. Though this idea was originally but a natural outcome of the professional preoccupation of a handful of linguists and logicians, it made an almost sensational breakthrough in the early fifties when it became connected with, and a cornerstone of, automatic translation between natural languages. At one stroke, *structural linguistics had become useful.* Just as mathematical logic, regarded for years as the most abstract and abstruse scientific discipline, became overnight an essential tool for the designer and programmer of electronic digital computers, so structural linguistics, regarded for years as the most abstract and speculative branch of linguistics, is now considered by many a must for the designer of automatic translation routines. The impact of this development was at times revolutionary and dramatic. In Soviet Russia, for instance, structural linguistics had, before 1954, unfailingly been condemned as idealistic, bourgeois and formalistic. However, when the Russian government awakened from its dogmatic slumber to the tune of the Georgetown University demonstration of machine translation in January 1954, structural linguistics became within a few weeks a discipline of high prestige and priority. And just as mathematical logic had its special offspring to deal with digital computers, i.e., the *theory of automata*, so structural linguistics had its special offspring to deal with mechanical structure determination, i.e., *algebraic linguistics*, also called, when this application is particularly stressed, *computational linguistics* or *mechano-linguistics*. As a final surprise, it has recently turned out that these two disciplines, automata theory and algebraic linguistics, exhibit extremely close relationships which at times amount to practical identity.

To complete this historical sketch, Chomsky, influenced by, and in constant exchange of ideas with Harris, started his investigations into a new typology of linguistic structures. In a series of publications, of which the booklet **Syntactic Structures** [34] is the best known, but also the least technical, he defined and constantly refined a complex hierarchy of such structures, meant to serve as models for natural languages with varying degrees of adequacy. Though models for the treatment of linguistic structures were also developed by many other authors, Chomsky's publications exhibited a degree of rigor and testability which was unheard of before that in the linguistic literature and therefore quickly became for many a standard of comparison for other contributions.

I shall now turn to a presentation of the work of the Jerusalem group in linguistic model theory before I continue with the description and evaluation of some other contributions to this field.

In 1937, while working on a master's thesis on the logical antinomies, I came across Ajdukiewicz's work [1]. Fourteen years later, having become acquainted in the meantime with structural linguistics, and especially with the work of Harris [62], and instigated by my work at that time on machine translation, I realized the importance of Ajdukiewicz's approach for the mechanization of the determination of syntactic structure, and published an adaptation of Ajdukiewicz's ideas (Chapter 5).

The basic heuristic concept behind the type of grammar proposed in this paper, and later further developed by Lambek [82;83;84], myself (Chapter 6) and others, is the following: the grammar was meant to be a *recognition* (*identification* or *operational*) *grammar*, i.e., a device by which the syntactic structure, and in particular the sentencehood, of a given string of elements of a given language could be determined. This determination had to be formal, i.e., dependent exclusively on the shape and order of the elements, and preferably effective, i.e., leading after a finite number of steps to the decision as to the structure, or structures, of the given string. This aim was to be achieved by assuming that each of the finitely many elements of the given natural language had finitely many syntactic functions, by developing a suitable notation for these syntactical functions (or categories, as we became used to calling them, in the tradition of Aristotle, Husserl, and Leśniewski), and by designing an algorithm operating on this notation.

More specifically, the assumption was investigated that natural languages have what is known to linguists as a *contiguous immediate-constituent structure*, i.e., that every sentence can be parsed, according to finitely many rules, into two or more contiguous constituents, either of which is already a final constituent or else is itself parsible into two or more immediate constituents, etc. This parsing was not supposed to be necessarily unique. Syntactically ambiguous sentences allowed for two or more different parsings. Examples should not be necessary here.

The variation introduced by Ajdukiewicz into this conception of linguistic structure, well known in a crude form already to elementary school students, was to regard the combination of constituents into *constitutes* (or *syntagmata*) not a concatenation *inter pares* but rather as the result of the operation of one of the constituents (the *governor*, in some terminologies) upon the others (the *governed* or *dependent* units). The specific form which the approach took with Ajdukiewicz was to assign to each word (or other appropriate element) of a given natural language a finite number of *fundamental* and/or *operator categories* and to employ an extremely simple set of rules operating upon these categories, so-called "cancellation" rules.

Just for the sake of illustration, let me give here the definition of *bi-directional categorial grammar*, in a slight variation of the one presented in Chapter 8. We define it as an ordered quintuple $\langle V, C, \Sigma, R, \mathfrak{A} \rangle$, where V is a finite set of elements (the *vocabulary*), C is the closure of a finite set of *fundamental categories*, say $\psi_1, \ldots, \psi_n$, under the operations of right and left diagonalization (i.e., whenever α and β are categories, $[\alpha/\beta]$ and $[\alpha \backslash \beta]$ are categories), Σ is a distinguished category of C (the category of *sentences*), R is the set of the two *cancellation rules* $[\varphi_i/\varphi_j]$, $\varphi_j \to \varphi_i$, and $\varphi_i, [\varphi_i \backslash \varphi_j] \to \varphi_j$, and $\mathfrak{A}$ is a function from V to finite sets of C (the *assignment* function).

We say that a category sequence α *directly cancels* to β, if β results from α by one application of one of the cancellation rules, and that α *cancels* to β, if β results from α by finitely many applications of these rules (more exactly, if there exist category sequences $\gamma_1, \gamma_2, \ldots, \gamma_n$ such that $\alpha = \gamma_1$, $\beta = \gamma_n$, and γ_i directly cancels to γ_{i+1}, for $i = 1, \ldots, n-1$).

A string $x = A_1 \cdots A_k$ over V is defined to be a *sentence* if, and only if, at least one of the category sequences assigned to x by $\mathfrak{A}$ cancels to Σ. The set of all sentences is then the *language determined* (or *represented*) *by the given categorial grammar*. A language representable by such a grammar is a *categorial language*.

In addition to bidirectional categorial grammars we also dealt with *unidirectional categorial grammars*, employing either right or left diagonalization only for the formation of categories, and more specifically with what we called *restricted categorial grammars*, whose set of categories consists only of the (finitely many) fundamental categories ψ_i, and the operator categories $[\psi_i \backslash \psi_j]$ and $[\psi_i \backslash [\psi_j \backslash \psi_k]]$ (or, alternatively, $[\psi_i / \psi_j]$ and $[\psi_i / [\psi_j / \psi_k]]$).

One of the results obtained by Gaifman in 1959 was that *every language determinable by a bidirectional categorial grammar can also be determined by a unidirectional grammar and even by a restricted categorial grammar.*

A heuristically (though not essentially) different approach to the formalization of immediate-constituent grammars was taken by Chomsky, within the framework of his general typology. He looked upon a grammar as a device, or a system of rules, for *generating* (or *recursively enumerating*) the class of all sentences. In particular, a *context-free phrase structure grammar*, a CF grammar for short, may be defined, again in slight variation from Chomsky's original definition, as an ordered quadruple $\langle V, T, S, P \rangle$, where V is the (total) *vocabulary*, T (the *terminal* vocabulary) is a subset of V, S (the *initial* symbol) is a distinguished element of $V–T$ (the *auxiliary* vocabulary), and P is a finite set of *production rules* of the form $X \rightarrow x$, where $X \in V - T$ and x is a string over V.

We say that a string x *directly generates* y, if y results from x by one application of one of the production rules, and that x *generates* y, if y results from x by finitely many applications of these rules (more exactly, if there exist sequences of strings $z_1, z_2, ..., z_n$ such that $x = z_1$, $y = z_n$ and z_i directly generates z_{i+1}, for $i = 1, ..., n-1$).

A string over T is defined to be a *sentence* if it is generated by S. The set of all sentences is the *language determined* (or *represented*) *by the given CF grammar.*

My conjecture that the classes of CF languages and bidirectional categorial languages are identical—in other words, that for each CF language there exists a weakly equivalent bidirectional categorial language and vice versa—was proved in 1959 by Gaifman (Chapter 8). He proved, as a matter of fact, slightly more, namely that for each CF grammar there exists a weakly equivalent restricted categorial grammar and vice versa. The equivalent representation can in all cases be effectively obtained from the original representation.

This equivalence proof was preceded by another in which it was shown that the notion of a *finite state grammar*, FS grammar for short, occupying the lowest position in Chomsky's hierarchy of generation grammars, was equivalent to that of a *finite automaton*, in the sense of Rabin and Scott [128], which can be viewed as another kind of recognition device. The proof itself was rather straightforward and almost trivial, relying mainly on the equivalence of deterministic and non-deterministic finite automata, shown by Rabin and Scott (Chapter 7).

Chomsky had already shown that the FS languages formed a proper subclass of the CF languages. We have recently been able to prove (Chapter 9) that the problem whether a CF language is also representable by a FS grammar—a problem which has considerable linguistic importance—is recursively unsolvable. The method used was reduction to Post's correspondence problem, a famous problem in mathematical logic which was shown by Post [122] to be recursively unsolvable.

Among other results recently obtained, let me only mention the following: whereas FS languages are, in view of the equivalence of FS grammars to finite automata and well-known results of Kleene [78] and others, closed under various Boolean and other operations, *CF languages whose vocabulary contains at least two symbols are not closed under complementation and intersection*, though closed under various other operations. *The union of two CF languages is again a CF language*, and a representation can be effectively constructed from the given representation. *The intersection of a CF language and a FS language is a CF language.*

Undecidable are such problems as the equivalence problem between two CF grammars, the inclusion problem of languages represented by CF grammars, the problem of disjointedness of such languages, etc. In this connection, *interesting relationships have been shown to exist between CF grammars and two-tape finite automata*, as defined and treated by Rabin and Scott, for which the disjointedness problem of the sets of acceptable tapes is similarly unsolvable.

A particular proper subset of the CF languages, apparently of greater importance for the treatment of programming languages, such as ALGOL, than for natural languages, is the set of so-called *sequential languages*, studied in particular by Ginsburg [58;59] and Shamir [135]. I have no time for more than just this remark.

In a somewhat different approach, closely related to the classical notions of *government* and *syntagmata*, the notions of *dependency grammars* and *projective grammars* have been developed by Hays [67], Lecerf [85], and others, including some Russian authors, utilizing ideas most fully presented in Tesnière's posthumous book [141], and are thought to be of particular importance for machine translation. However, it has not been too difficult to guess, and has indeed been rigorously proven by Gaifman [57], that these grammars, which are being discussed in other lectures given before this Institute, are equivalent to CF grammars in a certain sense, which is somewhat stronger than the one used above, but that this is not necessarily so with regard to what might be called *natural strong equivalence*. More precisely, whereas for every dependency grammar there exists, and can be effectively constructed, a CF grammar naturally and strongly equivalent to it, this is not necessarily the case in the opposite direction, not if the CF grammar is of *infinite degree*. Let me add that the dependency grammars are very closely related to a type of categorial grammars which I discussed in an early publication (Chapter 5) but later on replaced by grammars of a seemingly simpler structure. In the original categorial grammars, I did consider categories of the form $\beta_m \dots \beta_2\beta_1\backslash\alpha/\gamma_1\gamma_2 \dots \gamma_n$, with α, β_i, and γ_j being either fundamental or operator categories themselves, with a corresponding cancellation rule. It should be rather obvious how to transform a dependency grammar into a categorial grammar of this particular type. These grammars are equivalent to grammars in which all categories have the form $\beta\backslash\alpha/\gamma$ where α, β, and γ are fundamental categories and where β and γ may be empty (in which case the corresponding diagonal will be omitted, too, from the symbol). Finally, in view of Gaifman's theorem mentioned above, these grammars in their turn are equivalent to grammars all of whose categories are of the form $\alpha/\beta\gamma$ (or $\gamma\beta\backslash\alpha$), with the same conditions. I think that these remarks (strongly connected with considerations of combinatory logic [46]) should definitely settle the question of the exact formal status of the dependency grammars and their like. One side result is that dependency grammars are weakly reducible to *binary dependency grammars*, i.e., grammars in which each unit governs at most two other units. This result, I presume, is not particularly surprising, especially if we remember that the equivalence proven will in general not be a natural one.

Still another class of grammars, sometimes [39] called *push-down store grammars* and originating, though not in a very precise form, with Yngve [153;154], has recently been shown by Chomsky to be once more equivalent to CF grammars, again to nobody's particular surprise. Since push-down stores are regarded by many workers in the fields of MT and programming languages as particularly useful devices for the mechanical determination of syntactic structure of sentences belonging to natural and programming languages, respectively, this result should be helpful in clarifying the exact scope of those schemes of syntactic analysis which are based on these devices.

Of theoretically greater importance is the fact that push-down store grammars form a proper subset of *linear bounded automata*, one of the many classes of automata lying between Turing machines and finite automata which have recently been investigated by many authors, due to the fact that Turing machines are too idealized to be of much direct applicability, whereas finite automata are too restricted for this purpose.

The investigation of these automata, initiated by Myhill [107], is, however, still in its infancy, similar to that of many other classes of automata reported by McNaughton in his excellent review [97]. Still more in the dark is the linguistic relevance of all these models though, judging from admittedly limited experience, almost every single one of them will sooner or later be shown to have such relevance.

To wind up this discussion, let me only mention that during the last few years various classes of grammars whose potency is intermediate between FS and CF grammars have been investigated. These intermediate grammars will probably turn out to be of greater importance for the study of grammars of programming and other artificial formalized languages than for natural languages. In addition to the sequential grammars mentioned before, let me just mention the *linear* and *metalinear grammars* studied by Chomsky.

It might be useful to present, at this stage, a picture of the various grammars discussed in the present lecture, together with the two important classes of transformational and context-sensitive phrase structure grammars (which I could not discuss, for lack of time) in the form of a directed graph

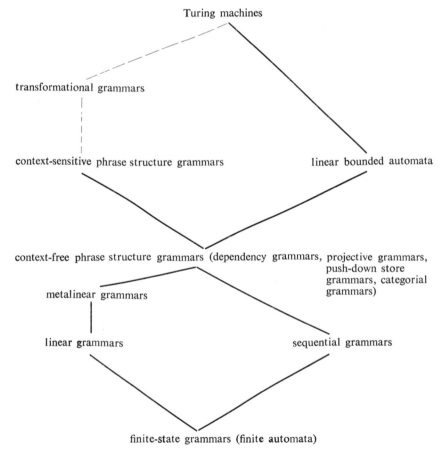

based on the (partial) ordering relation Determine-a-more-extensive-class-of-languages-than (the staggered lines indicating that the exact relationship has not yet been fully determined).

Two further questions I would now like to discuss are the following: (1) In view of the fact that so many models of linguistic structure have turned out to be (weakly) equivalent, how do they compare from the point of view of pedagogy and MT-directed application? (2) What is the degree of adequacy with which natural languages can be described by CF grammars and their equivalents?

As to the first question, I am afraid that not much can be said at this stage. I am not aware of any experiments made as yet to determine the pedagogical status of the various equivalent grammars. Some programmatic statements have been made on occasion, but I would not want to attribute much weight to them. I myself, for instance, have a feeling that the governor-dependent terminology of the dependency and projective grammars has an unfortunate, and intrinsically of course unwarranted, side-effect of strengthening dogmatic approaches to the decision of what governs what. The operator-operand terminology of the categorial grammars seems to be emotionally less loaded, but again, these are surely minor issues. Altogether, I would advocate the performance of pedagogical experiments in which the same miniature language would be taught with the help of various equivalent grammars. I do not foresee any particular complications for such projects.

Turning now to the second question which has been much discussed during the last few years, often with great fervor, the situation should be reasonably clear. FS grammars are definitely inadequate for describing any natural language, unless this last term is mutilated, for what must be regarded as arbitrary and ad hoc reasons. I am sorry that Yngve's otherwise extremely useful recent contributions did becloud this issue. As to CF grammars, the situation is more complex and more interesting. It is almost, but not quite, certain that such grammars, too, are inadequate in principle, for reasons which I shall not repeat here, since they have been stated many times in the recent literature and been authoritatively restated by Chomsky [28]. But of even greater importance, particularly for applications, such as MT, is the fact that such grammars seem definitely to be inadequate in practice, in the sense that the number and complexity of grammatical rules of this type, in order to achieve a tolerable, if not perfect, degree of adequacy, will have to be so immense as to defeat the practical purpose of establishing these rules. Transformational grammars seem to have a much better chance of being both adequate and practical, though this point is still far from being settled. In view of this fact, which does not appear to have been seriously challenged by most workers on MT, it is surprising to see that most, if not all, current programs of automatic syntactic analysis are based on impractical grammars. In some groups, where the impracticability and/or inadequacy has received serious attention, attempts are being made at present to classify the "recalcitrant" phenomena and to find ad hoc remedies for them. You will not be surprised if I say that I take a rather dim view of these attempts. But this already leads to issues which will be to discussed in subsequent lectures.

Second Lecture: SYNTACTIC COMPLEXITY

Extremely little is known about syntactic complexity, though this notion has come up in many discussions of style, readability and, more recently, of mechanization of syntactic analysis. Its explication has been universally regarded as a matter of great difficulty, this probably being the reason why it has also been, to my knowledge, universally shunned. When such authors as Flesch [53] developed their readability measures, they could not help facing the problem but, unable to cope with it, replaced syntactic complexity in their formulas by length, whose measure poses incomparably fewer problems, while still standing in some high statistical correlation with the elusive syntactic complexity.

Very often one hears, or reads, of an author, a professional group, or even a whole linguistic community being accused of expressing themselves with greater syntactic complexity than necessary. Such slogans as "What can be said at all, can be said simply and clearly in any civilized language, or in a suitable system of symbols", formulated by the British philosopher C. D. Broad in elaboration of a well-known dictum by Wittgenstein, were used by philosophers of certain schools to criticize philosophers of other schools, and have gained particular respectability in this context. On a less exalted level, most people interested in information processing and, in particular, in the condensation of information, preferably by machine, seem to be convinced that most, if not all, of what is ordinarily said could be said not only in syntactically *simpler* sentences but in syntactically *simple* sentences, the analysis of which would be a pleasure for a machine. Often, informationlossless transformation into syntactically simple sentences is regarded as a helpful, perhaps even necessary step prior to further processing. In the context of machine translation, Harris, e.g., once expressed the hunch that mechanical translation of kernel sentences, which would presumably rank lowest on any scale of syntactic complexity, should be a simpler affair than translation of any old sentences.

It is my conviction that the topic of syntactic complexity is, beyond certain very narrow limits of a vaguely felt consensus, ridden with bias, prejudice and fallacies to such a degree as to make almost everything that has been said on it completely worthless. In particular, I think that the "Wittgensteinian" slogan mentioned above is misleading in the extreme. I tend to believe that its attractiveness is due to its being understood not as a statement of fact but rather as a kind of general and vague advice to say whatever one wants to say as simply and clearly "as possible," some· thing to which one could hardly object, though, as we shall see, even in this interpretation it is not unequivocally good advice, when simplicity is understood as syntactic simplicity, since the price to be paid for reducing syntactic complexity, even when it is "possible," may well turn out to be too high.

So far, I have been using "syntactic complexity" in its pre-theoretical and unanalyzed vague sense. It is time to become more systematic.

One should not be surprised that the explication of syntactic complexity to which we shall presently turn will reveal that the pre-theoretical term is highly equivocal, though one might well be surprised to learn *how* equivocal it is.

When I said in the opening phrase that "extremely little is known about syntactic complexity," I intended the modifier "extremely little" to be understood literally and not as a polite version of "nothing." Such terms as "nesting," "discontinuous constituents," "self-embedding" and "syntactic depth" are being used in increasing frequency by linguists in general and — perhaps unfortunately so—by applied linguists in particular, especially when programming for machine analysis is discussed. But not until very recently have these notions been provided with a reasonably rigid formal definition which alone makes possible their responsible discussion. The most recent and most elaborate discussion that has come to my attention is that by Miller and Chomsky [101]. They discuss there various explicata for "syntactic complexity," with varying degrees of tentativeness, as befits such a first attempt, and I shall make much use of this treatment in what follows.

Let me first discard one notion which, as already mentioned, has a certain *prima facie* appeal to serve as a possible explicatum for syntactic complexity, namely *length*, measured, say, by the number of words in the sentence (or in whatever other construction is under investigation). Though, as said before, it is obvious that there should exist a fairly high statistical correlation between syntactic complexity and length, it should be equally obvious that length is entirely inadequate to serve as an explicatum for syntactic complexity. Take as many sentences as you wish of the form "... is —" (such as "John is hungry", "Paul is thirsty", etc.) whose intuitive degree of syntactic complexity is close, if not equal, to the lowest one possible, join them by repeated occurrences of "and" (a procedure resulting in something like "John is hungry and Paul is thirsty and Mary is sleepy and..."),

and you will get sentences of any length you wish whose intuitive degree of syntactic complexity should still be close to the minimum. True enough, a sentence of this form, containing 50 clauses of the type mentioned, always with different proper names in the first position and different adjectives in the third position would be difficult to remember exactly. Therefore such a sentence will be "complex," in one of the many senses of this word, but surely not syntactically so. No normal English-speaking person will have the slightest difficulty in telling the exact syntactic form, up to a parameter, of the resulting sentence, and there will be no increase in this difficulty even if the number of clauses will be 100, 1000, or any number you wish. In one very important sense of "understanding," the increased length of sentences of this type will *not* increase the difficulty of understanding them. And the sense in question is, of course, precisely that of grasping the syntactic structure.

The next remark, prior to presenting some of the more interesting explicata, refers to a fact which I want very much to call to your careful attention. I hope it will not be as surprising to you as it was to me, the first time I hit upon it. For a time, I thought that the only relativization needed for explicating syntactic complexity would be the trivial one to a given language. (Logicians, and some linguists, know plenty of examples where the "same" sentence may belong to entirely different languages; in that case, nobody would be surprised to learn that it also has—or rather that they also have—different degrees of syntactic complexity, relative to their respective languages.) What did shock me, however, though only for a moment until I realized that it could not be otherwise, was that degree of complexity must also be explicated as being relative to a grammar, that the same sentence of the same language may have one degree of complexity when analyzed from the point of view of one grammar and a different one when analyzed from the point of view of another grammar, and that, of two different sentences, one may have a higher degree of complexity than the other relative to one grammar, but a lower degree relative to another grammar.

This doubtless being the case, may I be allowed a certain amount of speculation for a minute? It is a simple and well-known fact that the same sentence will sometimes be better understood by person A than by B, though they have about the same IQ, about the same background knowledge, and though they read or hear it with about equal attention, as far as one can make out. Could it be that they are (subconsciously, of course) analyzing this same sentence according to different grammars, relative to which this sentence has different degrees of syntactic complexity? Could it be that part of the improvement in understanding obtained through training and familiarization is due to the trainees' learning to employ another grammar (whose difference from the one he was accustomed to employ before might be only minimal, so that the acquisition of this new grammar might not have been too difficult, perhaps)? Could it be that many, if not all, of us work with more than one grammar simultaneously, switching from the one to the other when the employment of the one runs us into trouble, e.g., when according to one grammar the degree of complexity of a given sentence is greater than one can stand? More about this later. Attractive as these speculations are, let me stress that at this moment I don't know of any way of putting them to a direct empirical test. But I wish someone would think up such a way. Let me also add that he who does not like this picture of different grammars for the same language lying peacefully side by side in our brain, may look upon the situation as *one* system of grammatical rules (the set-theoretical union of the *two* sets discussed so far) being stored in the brain, and allowing the same sentence to be analyzed and understood in two different ways with two different degrees of complexity, with a control element deciding which rules to apply in a given case and allowing the switch to other rules when trouble strikes. That there are syntactically ambiguous sentences has, of course, always been well known, but I am speaking at the moment about a particular kind of syntactic ambiguity, one that has no semantic ambiguities in its wake, but where the difference in the analysis still creates a difference in comprehensibility. At this point it is probably worthwhile to present an extremely simple example. The English sentence, "John loves Mary.", can be analyzed (and has been analyzed) in two different ways, each of which will be expressed here in two different but equivalent notations which have been simplified for our present purposes:

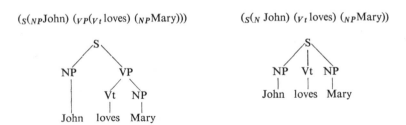

$$(_S(_{NP}\text{John})\ (_{VP}(_{Vt}\text{loves})\ (_{NP}\text{Mary})))$$ $$(_S(_N\text{John})\ (_{Vt}\text{loves})\ (_{NP}\text{Mary}))$$

These analyses correspond to the following two "grammars," G_1 and G_2:

G_1:   S   → NP + VP G_2:   S   → NP + Vt + NP
     VP → Vt + NP   NP → John, Mary
     NP → John, Mary   Vt → loves
     Vt → loves

or, if you prefer, they both correspond to the grammar G_3, which is the set-theoretical union of G_1 and G_2, and consists therefore of just the rules of G_1 plus the first rule of G_2. (Both G_1 and G_2 are of course CF grammars; G_1 is *binary*, but G_2, and therefore also G_3, is not.)

Though the difference in structure assigned to this sentence by the two analyses is palpable, it is less clear whether this difference implies a difference in the intuitive degree of syntactic complexity, and if so, according to which analysis the sentence is more complex. As a matter of fact, good reasons can be given for both views: in the first analysis, more rules are applied but each rule has a particularly simple form; in the second analysis fewer rules are applied, but one of them has a more complicated form. This situation seems to indicate that we have more than one explicandum before us, more than one notion which, in the pre-theoretical stage, is entitled to be called "syntactic complexity."

There are still more aspects to the intuitive uses of "syntactic complexity," but perhaps it is time to turn directly to the explicata which, hopefully, will take care of at least some of these aspects.

To follow Chomsky once again [101] rather closely, we might introduce the terms *"depth of postponed symbols"* and *"node/terminal-node ratio"* to denote the following two relevant measures: the first for Yngve's well-known depth-measure, which, I trust, will again be explained in his lectures at this Institute, the second for a new concept which has not yet been discussed in the literature. Both measures refer to the tree representing the sentence and are therefore applicable only to such grammars which assign tree structure to each sentence generated by them.

If we assign, in the Yngve fashion, numbers to the nodes and branches (with the branches leading to the terminal symbols left out), we see that the greatest number assigned to any of the nodes of the left tree is 1, so that its depth of postponed symbols is also 1, whereas the corresponding number for the second tree is 2. On the other hand, the total number of nodes of the first tree is 5, the number of its terminal nodes is 3, so that its node/terminal-node ratio is 5/3, whereas the corresponding numbers for the second tree are 4, 3, and 4/3, respectively.

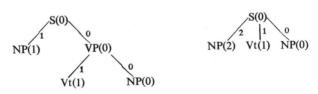

Each node number (in parentheses) is equal to the sum of the number assigned to the branch leading to this node and the number of the node from which the branch comes.

There are at least three more notions that are entitled to be considered as explicata for other aspects of syntactic complexity. The one that has been most studied is the *degree of nesting*. The reasons for the attention given to it are that it has been known for a long time that a highly nested sentence causes difficulties in comprehension and, more recently, that it creates troubles for mechanical syntactic analysis. One rough explication of this notion (there are others) might run as follows, again relative to tree grammars: The degree of nesting of a labeled tree is the largest integer m, such that there exists in this tree a path through $m + 1$ nodes $N_0, N_1, .., N_m$, with the same or different labels, where each N_i ($i \geqq 1$) is an inner node in the subtree rooted in N_{i-1}. The same degree of nesting is also assigned to the terminal expression as analyzed by this tree.

A special case of nesting is *self-embedding*, to whose importance Chomsky has called attention. In order to define the degree of self-embedding of a labeled tree, one has only to change in the above definition of degree of nesting the phrase "with the same or different labels" by the phrase "each with the same label." (Other definitions are again possible.)

To present one more stock example, the following tree has a degree of nesting (equal, in this particular case, to its degree of self-embedding) of 4. (Its depth, incidentally, is 7 and its node/terminal-node ratio is $21/15 = 7/5$.)

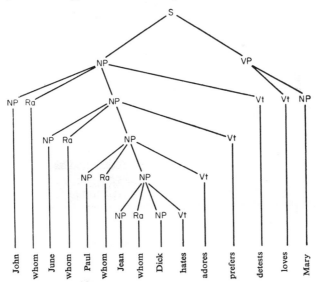

Though this tree could have been derived from a grammar G_4 differing from G_3 only by containing the additional rules

$$NP \rightarrow NP + Ra + NP + Vt$$
$$Ra \rightarrow whom$$

there are very good reasons why sentences of the type

John whom Ann loves hates Mary

and their ramifications should, in the framework of the whole English language, not be regarded as being produced by a CF grammar containing G_4 as a proper part, but rather by a transformational grammar built upon a CF grammar of English containing, in addition, a transformational rule, which I shall not specify here, allowing the derivation of

$$NP_1 + Ra + NP_3 + Vt + Vt + NP_2$$

from

$$NP_1 + Vt + NP_2$$

and

$$NP_3 + Vt + NP_1.$$

(There is no need to stress that all this is only a very rough approximation to the incomparably more refined treatment which a full-fledged transformational grammar of English would require. The transformational rule, for instance, should refer to the trees representing the strings under discussion rather than to the strings themselves.) It is worthwhile noticing that the node/terminal-node ratio (7/5) of the resulting tree is smaller than the ratios (5/3) of the underlying trees.

The fifth aspect of syntactic complexity is, then, *transformational history*. I am, of course, not using the term "measure" now, because it is very doubtful whether measures can be usefully assigned to this concept. So far, no attempt in this direction has been made. I shall, therefore, say no more about this notion here.

It is not particularly difficult to develop these five notions, and many more could be thought of. The decisive questions are twofold: What are the exact formal properties of the various notions and, perhaps even more important, what is their psychological reality, to use a term of Sapir's? In general, one would tend to require that if one sentence is syntactically more complex than another, then, *ceteris paribus*, it should, perhaps only on the average, create more difficulties in its comprehension. What can we say on this point?

Well, very little, and nothing so far under controlled experimental conditions. Highly nested constructions just don't occur at all in normal speech and very rarely in writing, with the notable exception of logical or mathematical formulas. Their syntactic structure can be grasped only by using extraordinary means such as going over them more than once and using special markers for pairing off expressions that belong together but between which other expressions have been nested. A formula such as

$$[[p \supset [q \supset [[r \supset [s \supset t]] \supset u]]] \supset v]$$

is certainly not a very complex one among the formulas of the propositional calculus, as they go, but testing its well-formedness would either require some artificial aids, such as the use of a pencil for marking off paired brackets, or the acquisition of a special algorithm based upon a particular counting procedure, or else just an extraordinary (and unanalyzed) effort and concentration. It is doubtful whether any effort, without external aids, would suffice to determine that the "literal" English rendition of the formula as

If if p then if q then if if r then if s then t then u then v

is well-formed, when one listens to such a sentence without prior warning.

It is interesting that in order to explain our difficulties in either uttering or grasping the structure of such sentences we need assume nothing more than that we are finite automata with a finite number of internal states. For Chomsky [35], in effect, has shown that when the number of these states is some number n, then, relative to a given grammar G, there exists a number m (depending on n) such that this device will not be able to correctly analyze the syntactic structure of all sentences whose degree of nesting is greater than or equal to m. (As a matter of fact, Chomsky showed this for degree of self-embedding rather than for nesting, but the proof can be trivially extended to this case.)

On the incomparably stronger assumptions that natural languages (such as English) can be adequately determined by tree grammars, that human speakers of such a language have at least one such tree grammar stored in their permanent memory, that they utter the sentences of these languages by going through (one of) their tree(s) "from top to bottom and from left to right," that all storage required for this process is done in an immediate memory of the push-down store form containing, say, n cells, we arrive at the conclusion that only sentences whose depth of postponed symbols is no higher than n can be uttered by such speakers.

Now, though Yngve continues to believe that there exists good evidence for the soundness of these assumptions, Chomsky has on various occasions [37;38] expressed his doubts as to this evaluation of the evidence. He believes that most of the positive evidence invoked by Yngve can already be explained on the basis of the weaker assumption mentioned above, whereas he mentions the existence of other evidence which tends to refute Yngve's stronger assumptions though not his own weak one. I have no time to go further into this controversy. Let me only state that Chomsky's arguments seem to me to be the more conclusive ones. This, of course, by no means diminishes the credit due to Yngve for having been the first to have raised certain types of questions that were never asked before, and to have ventured to provide for them interesting answers, though they may well turn out to be the wrong ones.

It is time now to say at least a few words on the "Wittgensteinian Thesis." In one sense, this thesis is of course perfectly true: After all, all of us do manage to say most of what we have to say in sentences of a low degree of nesting and, if really necessary, could rephrase even those things for the expression of which we do use highly nested strings, such as occur in many mathematical formulas, in syntactically less complex ways, which will be presently investigated. But in this sense, the thesis is no more than a rather uninteresting truism. What Wittgenstein, Broad and the innumerably many other people who invoked this slogan doubtless had in mind was that most, if not all, of the things that are expressed (usually, by such and such an author, by such and such a cultural group, etc.) by sentences with high syntactic complexity could have been expressed with sentences of lower syntactic complexity, *without any compensation*. In this interesting interpretation, Wittgenstein's Thesis seems to me wrong, almost demonstrably so. I would, on the contrary, want to express and justify, if not really demonstrate, the following "Anti-Wittgensteinian Thesis": *For most languages, and for all interesting (sufficiently rich) ones, there are things worth saying which cannot be expressed in sentences with a low degree of syntactic complexity, without a loss being incurred in other communicationally important respects.*

Though a fuller justification will have to be postponed for another occasion, let me make here the following remarks. Consider one of the simplest calculi ever invented by logicians, the so-called *implicational propositional calculus* [41: 140]. We are here interested only in its rules of formation but not in its axioms or theorems.

The rules of formation of one of the many formulations of this calculus are as follows: Its primitive symbols are the three improper symbols

$$], \qquad \supset, \qquad [$$

and the infinitely many proper symbols

$$p_1, p_2, p_3, \cdots .$$

Its rules of formation are just the following two:

F1.   Each proper symbol is well-formed (wf).

F2.   Whenever α and β are wf, so is $[\alpha \supset \beta]$

(with the understanding that nothing is wf unless it is so by virtue of F1 and F2). There exists no bound to the degree of nesting of the wf formulas of this calculus, as is obvious from the series of wf formulas

$$p_1, [p_1 \supset p_2], [p_1 \supset [p_2 \supset p_3]], [p_1 \supset [p_2 \supset [p_3 \supset p_4]]], \cdots .$$

It is less obvious, but can at any rate be rigorously proved, that for none of these formulas does there exist in the calculus another formula which is logically equivalent to it but has a lesser degree of nesting. (The term "logically equivalent" needs explanation in our context, but I shall nevertheless not provide it. For logicians the required explanation would be rather obvious, for non-logicians it would take too much time.) Wittgenstein's Thesis does not hold in this calculus.

Consider now the (logically utterly uninteresting) *conjunctional propositional calculus*, whose rules of formation are analogous to those of the implicational calculus, except that '$\supset$' is to be replaced by '$\wedge$' in both the list of improper symbols and F2. Here, too, it can be shown, by a somewhat more complicated argument, that for each n there exist wf formulas whose degree of nesting is higher than n such that they are not logically equivalent to any wf formula with a lesser degree of nesting.

But there exists the following interesting difference between the two calculi. The conjunctional calculus, as presented here, looks unduly complex. Since conjunction is "associative," i.e., since $[p_1 \wedge [p_2 \wedge p_3]]$ and $[[p_1 \wedge p_2] \wedge p_3]$ are equivalent, the brackets fulfill no semantically important function within the calculus and could as well have been omitted from the list of improper symbols, with a corresponding simplification in rule F2. In this version, all wf formulas would have had a degree of nesting 0, as can easily be verified. True enough, all formulas with at least two conjunction signs would have become syntactically ambiguous, but, in this particular calculus, syntactic ambiguity would not have entailed semantic ambiguity. Syntactic simplification could have been achieved, and in the most extreme fashion, without any semantic loss whatsoever!

This is by no means the case for the implicational calculus. Implication is not associative, so that the syntactic ambiguity introduced by omission of brackets would have entailed semantic ambiguity, a price no logician could possibly be ready to pay in this connection, though again all resulting formulas would have a degree of nesting 0.

(As for the conjunctional calculus, as soon as it is combined with some other calculus, say the disjunctional calculus, omission of brackets would again entail semantic ambiguity, since, say, $[p_1 \wedge [p_2 \vee p_3]]$ and $[[p_1 \wedge p_2] \vee p_3]$ are not equivalent.)

For those of you who have heard of the so-called Polish bracket-free notation, let me add the following remark. One might have thought that the nesting (which in this particular case is also self-embedding) is due to the use of brackets for scoping purposes, in accordance with standard mathematical usage, since it seems that the brackets "cause" the branchings to be "inner" ones, and might therefore have cherished the hope that a bracket-free notation would eliminate, or at least reduce, nesting. But this hope is illusory. Inner branching, thrown out through the front door, would re-enter through the back door. With 'C' as the only improper symbol and F2 changed to: Whenever α and β are wf, so is $C\alpha\beta$, expansion of α (though not of β) causes inner branching. Notice further that in Polish notation calculi you cannot introduce syntactic ambiguity, harmless or harmful, even if you want to, by omitting symbols, since there are no special scoping symbols to omit.

As far as natural languages are concerned, the situation is much more confused. In speech, it seems that we can express distinctions of scope up to a degree of nesting of 3, anything beyond that becoming blurred, whereas in writing things are still worse, punctuation marks not being consistently used for scoping purposes and anyhow not being adequate for this task, with the result that syntactic ambiguities abound, which may or may not be reduced through context or background knowledge. Sometimes, when the resulting semantic ambiguity becomes intolerable, extraordinary measures are taken, such as using scoping symbols like parentheses in ways ordinarily reserved for mathematical formulas only, indentation at various depths, ad hoc abbreviations, etc.

Natural languages have many so-to-speak built-in devices for syntactic simplification. These devices, and their effectiveness, are badly in need of further study, after the extremely interesting beginnings by Yngve [153].

Certain "simplifications," beloved by editors who are out to split up involved sentences, may well turn out to be spurious and perhaps even downright harmful, in spite of appearances. An editor who rewrites an author's "Since p and q and r, therefore s." (where you have to imagine the letters p, q, r, and s replaced by sentences which on occasion will themselves have considerable syntactic complexity) by "$p. q. r.$ Therefore s." is probably under the illusion that he has simplified something and therefore improved something. Now, he has doubtless replaced one long sentence with a degree of syntactic complexity of, say, n, by four shorter sentences, each with a degree of syntactic compexity of at most $n-1$, and has even used three words less for this purpose. But there is a price connected with this procedure, even a twofold one. First, the word "therefore" has become semantically much more indefinite. What for? "s, for r.", or "s, for q and r.", or "s, for p and q and r."? (And this might not be all. p will be preceded by other sentences, so that, at least from a purely syntactic point of view, it is totally indefinite how far back one has to go in the list of possible antecedents to s.) Secondly, even if the exact antecedent is settled, in order to understand the full content of the argument and to judge its validity, the reader (or listener) will have to recall, or re-read, the antecedent (which, so let us speculate, might have been removed into some larger, more permanent and less easily accessible storage than the immediate memory it was occupying during the syntactic processing), with the result that the overall economy of the "improvement" is, to say the least, very doubtful. There is at least a good chance that the total effort required of the receiver of the message will be higher in the case of the "split-up" sentence than with regard to the original sentence, though it might well be easier on the sender, had he wanted to express himself originally in this less definite way. (I used to teach geometry in high school and still remember the type of student who, when required to demonstrate a certain theorem, would start rattling off a list of congruences or inequalities, as the case might be, and finish with a triumphant "Therefore (or "From this it follows that)...". And he was not even wrong. Because from his list, and in accordance with certain theorems already proved, his conclusion did indeed follow. Except that he left the task of finding out how, *in detail*, the conclusion followed from the premises, to the listeners, including myself in that case, and provided no indication of the fact that he himself knew the details.)

An investigation, recently begun in Jerusalem, seems to lead to interesting results as to the mutual relationships between (semantic) equivalence among the sentences of a given formal system, the (syntactic) simplicity of these sentences and the existence of a recursive simplification function for this system. The results will be published in forthcoming Technical Reports [12;75]. Let me only mention here one of the more significant results (I hope to nobody's particular surprise). The existence of a syntactic simplification algorithm is rather the exception, and the proof of such existence, if at all, will in general require that the system fulfill fairly tough conditions. The details, unfortunately, require a good knowledge of recursive function theory and shall therefore not be given here.

Third Lecture: LANGUAGE AND SPEECH: THEORY VS. OBSERVATION IN LINGUISTICS

As already mentioned in the opening paragraph of my first lecture, many of us believe that during the last few years we have gained valuable insights into the relationship between theory and observation in science. I myself have already tried on a few occasions to apply these insights to certain controversial issues of modern linguistics [3;7]. I would now like to do the same with regard to the central term of linguistics, namely 'language' itself. As you will soon realize, this methodological point is of vital importance for the so-called "research methodology" in MT, and insufficient understanding of it has already caused superfluous controversies.

The term 'language' has, of course, been "defined" innumerably many times, but the fact that these definitions are usually mutually inconsistent, at least at first sight, has equally often been forgotten and neglected, so that seemingly contradictory statements about 'language' were usually interpreted as inconsistent statements about the same explicatum (in Carnap's terminology) rather than consistent statements about different explicata.

You will, for instance, find in the literature that language has often been treated as a *set of sentences* (or *utterances*, which two terms will not be distinguished for the moment). This, of course, is an abstraction from ordinary usage, and has been recognized as such. Leaving aside for our present purposes the discussion of how good and useful this abstraction is, let me point out that the characterization can be understood (and has been understood) in at least the following five senses:

(1) A given set of utterances, such as recorded on a certain tape by so-and-so on such-and-such an occasion, or of inscriptions, found on such-and-such a tablet. Such sets are, of course, finite and most of them contain relatively few members. They can be, and sometimes are, represented as lists, under certain transcriptions. As a matter of fact, such sets are only exceptionally called 'languages', the more usual term being 'corpus'.

(2) The set of all utterances (spoken and/or written) made until July 1962, say, by the members of such and such a community during their lifetime until then. This set is certainly finite, too, but cannot, in general, be presented in list form and is rather indefinite, due to the indefiniteness of the term "community" and for dozens of other obvious reasons, such as those centering around idiolects, dialects, bilingualness, not to forget the vagueness of 'utterance' itself.

(3) The set of all utterances, past, present, and future, made by members of such a community. This set differs from that treated under (2) only in having a still greater degree of indeterminacy.

(4) The set of all "possible" utterances of a certain kind. The notion "possible" occurring in this characterization is notorious for its complexities and philosophical perplexities, and I trust I shall be forgiven if I don't go any deeper into this hornet's nest here. Under most conceptions, this set will turn out to be infinite.

(5) The set of all "sentences" (well-formed expressions, grammatical expressions, etc.). (For recent discussions of this and related hierarchies see, e.g., Quine [126] and Ziff [155].)

It is true, of course, that (1) is a subset of (2), which again is a subset of (3), but this is not the crucial point. Much more important is that the term 'utterance' occurring in their characterization changes its meaning in the transition from (3) to (4), becomes less observational and more theoretical. At the same time, there is a change from a concrete, physical, three- or four-dimensional entity, a "token", in Peirce's terminology, to an abstract entity, a "type". (When Paul and John say "I am hungry", we have two members of the set (1), since they utter two different "utterance-tokens," but only one member of the set (4), since these tokens are replicas of the same utterance-type.) The elements of set (5), finally, are so overtly theoretical that the term 'utterance' seemed definitely inappropriate for them, and I had to shift to the term 'sentence'. Though these two terms in ordinary usage, as well as in the usage of most linguists, are almost synonymous, I have already proposed once before [7] to distinguish artificially between them *qua* technical terms and use 'utterance' for observational entities and 'sentence' for theoretical ones (with the adjective 'possible' performing as a *category shifting modifier*, an extremely important and not fully analyzed semantical fact). That 'sentence' is ordinarily used in both these senses, as is 'word' and many terms of this area, is, of course, one of the major sources of confusion and futile controversies.

Sets (2) and (3) have little linguistic importance. Because of their indefiniteness it is difficult to make interesting statements about them. Sets (4) and (5) — in all rigor I should have spoken about the *classes* of sets (4) and (5) — are by and large identical, at least under certain plausible interpretations of 'possible', the characterization of (4) being what Carnap [28] called "quasi-psychologistic," while (5) is presumably characterized in an overtly and purely syntactical fashion.

In many linguistic circles, it has been standard procedure to make believe that linguists, in their professional capacity, are dealing with sets of type (1) (or of types (2) or (3)). This fiction gave their endeavor, so they believed, a closeness-to-earth, an operational solidity which they were anxious not to lose. In fact, they all, with hardly an exception, dealt with sets of types (4) or (5). All the talk about "corpora" was only lip-service. Today we know that no science worth its salt could possibly stick to observation exclusively. Whoever is out to describe and nothing else will not describe at all. *Theorizare necesse est.* Though I don't think that it is necessary, or even helpful, to say that *every* description already contains theoretical elements — as some recent methodologists are fond of stressing — it must be said that theorophobia is a disease, fashionable as it might be. All scientific statements must surely be connected with observations, but this connection can, and must, be much more oblique that many methodological simplicists believe.

Returning from these generalities to our present problem of the relation between language and speech — with MT hovering in the back as a kind of proving ground — it should be superfluous to insist that the proper business of the theoretical linguist is to describe not the actual linguistic *performance* of some individual (or of so many individuals) — this "natural history" stage being of limited interest only — but his linguistic *competence* (or that of a certain community of individuals), to use a dichotomy that has recently been much stressed by Miller and Chomsky[101]. Now competence is a disposition, perhaps even a higher-order disposition. To be a competent native speaker of English means not just to have performed in the past in a certain way, not even that he will (in all likelihood) perform in a certain way when presented with certain stimuli, but rather that one *would* perform, or would have performed (in all likelihood), in a certain way, were he to be presented (or had he been presented) with certain stimuli — in addition to many other things. I know perfectly well that no competent English speaker will ever in his life be presented with a certain utterance consisting of a few billion words, say of the form "Kennedy is hungry, and Khrushchev is thirsty, and De Gaulle is tired, ... , and Adenauer is old.", going over the whole present population of the world, but I know, and everybody else knows perfectly well, that were such a speaker, contrary to fact, to be presented with such an utterance, he would understand it as a perfect specimen of an English sentence.

There is no mechanical procedure to move from someone's performance to his competence, just as there is no mechanical procedure to move from any number of physical observations to a physical theory. But just as this fact does not free the physicist from his professional obligation to develop theories, so there is nothing to absolve the linguists from presenting theories of linguistic competence. Testing the validity of these theories will, again as in the other theoretical sciences, in general proceed not in any straightforward way but by standard indirect methods. That John is competent to understand a certain ten-billion-word sentence will not be tested by presenting John with a token of this sentence, but, as we all know, by entirely different, oblique methods. For the above sentence, for instance, it would suffice to find out that John understands such sentences as "Paul is hungry." and "David is thirsty." as well as that he has mastered the rule that whenever α and β are sentences, α followed by 'and' followed by β is a sentence. This latter finding might not be a very simple one or a very secure one, but we do often claim to have found out just such things.

One often hears, in certain philosophical circles as well as among people interested in applied linguistics, statements to the effect that natural languages have no grammar. These people are aware of the paradoxical character of such statements, but nevertheless insist that they are true, and even trivially so. Every grammar, so they say, determines a certain fixed, "static," set of sentences. But a natural language is a living affair, "dynamic," constantly in change, and it is utterly impossible that the set of sentences should coincide with the set of utterances, as it should for an adequate grammar. It should now be obvious where the fallacy lies in this argument: in the unthinking identification of sentences and utterances, and in the complete misunderstanding of the relation between theory and observation. It is as if one wanted to argue that natural gases obey no physical laws, since these laws apply only to the fictitious "ideal gases." (Incidentally, such statements have indeed been made by obscurantists at all times.) To understand the exact relationship between the laws of gases of theoretical physics and the behavior of real gases requires a lot of methodological sophistication, and no less should be expected for the understanding of the exact relationship between the grammatical rules of an artificial language and the utterances made by the members of the community speaking this language. Any naive identification will quickly result in paradox, futile discussions, and irrational distrust of theory.

That the question of the adequacy of a given grammar is much more complex than ordinarily assumed does not mean that this question is a pointless one. On the contrary, since there exists no simple criterion for deciding which of two proposed grammars is "better," more adequate than the other, the problem of finding *any* criterion, however partial and indirect, becomes of overwhelming importance. The fact is, of course, that extremely little is known here beyond programmatic declarations. We know that "grammatical" should not be identified with "comprehensible," nor is one of these concepts subsumed under the other, but neither are these two concepts incommensurable. In that connection we have the large complex of questions arising around degrees of grammaticalness, deviancy, oddness, and anomaly; all of vital importance to linguists and philosophers alike. Some of you know the valiant beginnings made toward an investigation of this problem by Chomsky, Ziff [155] and others, but it will, I hope, not deter you from following in their footsteps, if I state, rather dogmatically, that these attempts are woefully inadequate, while admitting that I have nothing better to offer, for the moment.

As soon as it is understood that competence and performance are to be kept clearly apart, one will no longer be tempted to feel oneself obliged to impose upon, say, the English language a grammar which will not allow the generation of sentences of a higher degree of syntactic complexity than some small number, say 4, acccrding to one or the other measures discussed in the previous lecture. True enough, "corresponding" utterances are not normally found in speech or writing, and if artificially produced will not be grasped unless certain artificial auxiliary means are invoked. These limitations of human performance are doubtless of vital importance; have to be clearly stated and investigated; and should, sooner or later, be backed up by some neurophysiological theory. They are of equal importance for the programming of machines which are charged with determining the syntactic structure of all sentences of any given text of a given language. That sentences of a high degree of complexity can be disregarded for this purpose, because of their extreme rarity or just plain non-occurrence, may allow an organization of the computer's working space that could make all the difference between the economically feasible and the economically utopian. But in order to do all this, it is by no means necessary to impose these restrictions on the grammar of English as such. Nothing is gained, and much is lost. Not only will certain arbitrary-looking restrictions on the recursive generation rules have to be imposed, thereby increasing the complexity of the grammar to a degree that can hardly be estimated at present, but this procedure is self-defeating. It is done in the name of "sticking to the brute facts," but doing so in such a crude way will force the adherents of this approach to disregard other brute facts, such as that with the aid of certain auxiliary means, the syntactic structure of English word sequences of a degree of syntactic complexity of 5, or of 100 for that matter, will be perfectly grasped. Since these word sequences are not English sentences, according to the grammarians of performance, how come they are understood and what is the language they belong to?

This does not mean, of course, that restrictions of performance will not reflect themselves in the grammar. I am convinced, e.g., that Professor Yngve has made a remark full of insight when he noticed and stressed the fact that by changing its mood from the active to the passive, the syntactic complexity of a given sentence can be reduced. And I have no objection to formulating this insight in the form that there exists a passive in English (and the same or other devices in other languages) *in order* to allow, among other things, the formulation of certain thoughts in sentences of a lower degree of complexity than would otherwise have been possible. But trying to obliterate the distinction between competence and performance, to say it for the last time, is only a sign of confusion and will breed further confusion. The sooner we get rid of these last traces of extreme operationalism, the better for all of us, including MT research workers.

In order to describe and explain the facts of speech exhaustively and revealingly, a full-fledged, formal theory of language is needed, among many other things. Philosophical prejudice aside, there is no particular merit in keeping this theory "close to the facts," in assuming that the rules of correspondence which connect the theory (in the narrower sense of the word) with observation will have a particularly simple form. Experience from other sciences should have taught us that such an assumption is baseless. Physics, e.g., has reached its present heights only because the free flight of fancy, "the free play of ideas," has not been fettered by a narrow conception of scientific methodology. True enough, the particular logical status of these rules of correspondence has still not been investigated deeply enough, and I fully understand the attitude of those who, for this reason, regard this whole business with suspicion, and are afraid that the free flight of fancy will reintroduce uncontrollable metaphysics into science in general and linguistics in particular. But I hope that the necessary controls will be developed and better understood in the future and that in the meantime one will manage somehow. Occasional metaphysical aberrations are probably less damaging in the long run than the curtailment of creative scientific imagination.

Let me stress, in this connection, that the extensive use of symbolism in the formulation of generative grammars has induced many linguists to accuse the authors of these formulations of having lost all connection with empirical science and indulged instead in some mathematical surrogate. I hope that it is now perfectly clear that this accusation is baseless. A formal grammar of English is an *empirical* theory of the English language, and its symbolic formulation, while it increases its precision and therefore its testability, by no means turns it into a mathematical theory. When according to a certain grammar "Sincerity admires John." turns out not to be a (formal) sentence whereas this very sequence is considered by someone to be an (intuitive) sentence, then this grammar is to that degree inadequate to his intuitions. It should only be kept in mind that the determination of the intuitive sentence-hood of "Sincerity admires John." is by no means such a straightforward affair of observation, experimentation and statistics as some people believe. The notion of "intuitive sentence" is highly theoretical itself (though with-out the benefit of a complete theory being formulated back it up, which fact is, of course, the whole crux of this peculiar modifier 'intuitive'), and observations of utterances of people or their reaction to utterances alone will never settle in any clearcut way the question of the sentencehood of a particular word sequence. This is as it should be, and only wishful thinking and naive methodology make people believe otherwise. Confirmation and refutation of linguistic theories, as of theories in any other science, is not such a simple operation as one is taught to believe in high school. But the complexity of refutation does not make a linguistic theory empirically irrefutable and therefore does not turn it into a mathematical theory.

Fourth Lecture: WHY MACHINES WON'T LEARN TO TRANSLATE WELL

My arguments against the feasibility of high-quality fully-automatic translation can be assumed to be well known in this audience. I have gone through them often enough in lectures and publications. I also have the impression that, after occasionally rather strong initial negative reactions, a good number of people who have been active in the field of MT for some years tend more and more to agree with these arguments, though they might prefer a more restrained formulation. On the other hand, the number of research groups which have taken up MT as their major field of activity is still on the increase, and by now there is hardly a country left in Europe and North America which does not feature at least one such group, with Japan, China, India and a couple of South American countries joining them for good measure. Though a certain amount of involvement in MT, and in particular in its theoretical aspects, is certainly helpful and apt to yield fresh insights into the working language, most of the work that is at present going on under the auspices of MT seems to me to be a wanton expenditure of research money that could be put to better use in other fields and, still worse, a deplorable waste of research potential.

The combined interest in MT is sometimes defended on the grounds that though it is indeed extremely unlikely that computers working according to rigid algorithms will ever produce high-quality translations, there still exists a possibility that computers with considerable learning ("self-organizing") abilities will be able through training and experience to improve their initial algorithms and thereby constantly improve their output until adequate quality is achieved. I myself mentioned the possiblity in some prior publications but refrained from evaluating it, at that time regarding such an evaluation as premature ([10] and Chapter 13).

During the last two years, however, while going through the pertinent literature once more and pondering over the whole issue of artificial intelligence, I came to more radical conclusions which I would like to expose and defend here. Today, I am convinced that even machines with learning abilities, as we know them today or foresee them according to known principles, will not be able to improve by much the quality of the translation output.

For this purpose, let us notice once more the obvious prerequisites for high-quality human translation. There are at least the following five of them, though deeper analysis would doubtless reveal more:

(1) competent mastery of the source language,
(2) competent mastery of the target language,
(3) good general background knowledge,
(4) expertness in the field,
(5) intelligence (know-how).

(I admit of course, that the last of these prerequisites, intelligence, is not too well defined or understood, and shall therefore have to use it with a good amount of caution.)

All this was surely common knowledge at all times, and certainly known to all of us "machine translation pioneers" a dozen years ago. I knew then that nothing corresponding to items (3) and (4) could be expected of electronic computers, but thought that (1) and (2) should be within their reach, and entertained some hopes that by exploiting the redundance of natural language texts better than human readers usually do, we should perhaps be in a position to enable the computers to overcome, at least partly, their lack of knowledge and understanding. True enough, scientists (and almost everyone else) write their articles with a reader in mind who, in addition to having a good command of the language, has a general background knowledge of, say, college level, has so many years of study behind him in the respective field and is intelligent enough to know how to apply these three factors when called upon to do so. But it could have been, couldn't it, that, perhaps inadvertently, they do introduce sufficient formal clues in their publications to enable a very ingenious team of linguists and programmers to write a translation program whose output, though produced by the machine without understanding, would be indistinguishable from a translation done out of understanding? After all, cases are known of human translations that were done under similar conditions and were not always recognized as such.

Well, it could have been so, but it just didn't turn out this way. For any given source language, there are countless sentences to which a competent human translator will provide in a given target language many, sometimes very many, distinct renderings which will sometimes differ from each other only by minor idiosyncrasies, but will at other times be *toto coelo* different. The original sentence will very often be, as the standard expression goes, multiply ambiguous by itself, morphologically, syntactically, and semantically, but the competent human translator will render it, in its particular context, uniquely to the general satisfaction of the human reader. The translator will resolve these ambiguities out of the last three factors mentioned. Though it is undoubtedly the case that some reduction of ambiguity can be obtained through better attention to certain formal clues, and though it has turned out many times that what superficial thinking regarded as definitely requiring understanding could be handled through certain refinements of purely formal methods, it should by now be perfectly clear that there are limits to what these refinements can achieve, limits that definitely block the way to autonomous, high-quality, machine translation.

Could not perhaps computers with learning capacity do the job? Let me say rather dogmatically that a close study of one of the most publicized schemes for the mechanization of problem solving and a somewhat less detailed study of the whole field of Artificial Intelligence, has shown an amount of careless and irresponsible talk which is nothing short of appalling and sometimes close to lunatic. There is absolutely nothing in all this talk which shows any promise to be of real help in mechanizing translation. There is nothing to indicate how computers could acquire what the famous Swiss linguist de Saussure called, at the beginning of this century, the *faculté de langage*, an ability which is today innate in every human being, but which took evolution hundreds of millions of years to develop. Let nobody be deceived by the term "machine language" which may be suggestive for other purposes but which has turned out to be detrimental in the present context. Surely computers can manipulate symbols if given the proper instructions and they do it splendidly, many times quicker and safer than humans, but the distance from symbol manipulation to linguistic understanding is enormous, and loose talk will not diminish it.

Though certain electronic devices (such as perceptrons) have been built which can be "trained" to perform certain tasks (such as pattern recognition) and indeed perform better after training than before, and though computers have been programmed to do certain things (such as playing checkers) and do these things better after a period of learning than before, it would be disastrous to extrapolate from these primitive exhibitions of artificial intelligence to something like translation. There just is no serious basis for such extrapolation. As to checkers, the definition of "legal move" is extremely simple and is, of course, given the computer in full. After a few years of work the inventor of the checkers playing program [134] succeeded in formalizing a good set of strategies so that the training had nothing more to achieve than to introduce certain changes in the rank-ordering of these strategies. There never was any question of training the computer to discover the rules of checkers, or to expand an incomplete set of rules into a complete one, or to add new strategies to those given it beforehand. But some people do talk about letting computers discover rules of grammar or expand an incomplete set of such rules fed into it, by going over large texts and using "induction." But let me repeat, this talk is quite irresponsible and "induction" is nothing but a magic word in this connection. All attempts at formalizing what they believe to be inductive inference have completely failed, and inductive inference machines are pipe dreams even more than autonomous translation machines.

Now children do learn, as we all know, their native language up to an almost complete mastery of its grammar by the time they are four or five years old. But by the time they reach this age, they have heard (and spoken) surely no more than a few hundred thousand utterances in their native language (only a part of which are good textbook specimens of grammatical sentences). If they succeed in mastering the grammar, apparently "by induction" from these utterances, why shouldn't a computer be able to do so? Even if we add the fact that these children were also told that so many word sequences were not grammatical sentences—whatever the form was by which they were given these pieces of instruction—, could not the same procedure be mirrored for computers? Well, the answer to these two questions can be nothing but an uncompromising No. The children are able to perform as splendidly as they do because, in addition to the training and learning, their brain is not a *tabula rasa* general purpose computer but a computer which, after all those hundreds of millions of years of evolution mentioned before, is also special purpose structured in such a way that it possesses the unique *faculté de langage* which makes it so different from the brain of mice, monkeys, and machines. The fact that we know close to nothing about this structure does not turn the previous statement into a scholastic truism.

Years of most patient and skillful attempts at teaching monkeys to use language intelligently succeeded in nothing better than making them use four single words with understanding, and monkeys' brains are in many respects vastly superior to those of computers. True enough, computers can do many things better than monkeys or humans, computing for instance, but then we know the corresponding algorithms, and know how to feed them into the computer. In some cases we know algorithms which, when fed into the computer, will enable it to construct for itself computing algorithms out of other data and instructions that can be fed into it. But nothing of the kind is known with respect to linguistic abilities. So long as we are unable to wire or program computers so that their initial state will be similar to that of a newborn human infant, physically or at least functionally, let's forget about teaching computers to construct grammars.

Let me now turn to the first two items. What is the outlook for computers to master a natural language to approximately the same degree as does a native speaker of such a language? And by "mastering a language" I now mean, of course, only a mastery of its grammar, i.e. vocabulary, morphology, and syntax, to the exclusion of its semantics and pragmatics. Until recently, I think that most of us who dealt with MT at one time or another believed that not only was this aim attainable, but that it would not be so very difficult to attain it, for the practical purpose at hand. One realized that the mechanization of syntactic analysis, based on this mastery, would lead on occasion to multiple analyses whose final reduction to a unique analysis would then be relegated to the limbo of semantics, but did not tend to take this drawback very seriously. It seems that here, too, a more sober appraisal of the situation is indicated and already is gaining ground, if I am not mistaken. More and more people have become convinced that the inadequacies of present methods of mechanical determination of syntactic structure, in comparison with what competent and linguistically trained native speakers are able to do, are not only due to the fact that we don't know as yet enough about the semantics of our language—though this is surely true enough—but also to the perhaps not too surprising fact that the grammars which were in the back of the minds of almost all MT people were of too simple a type, namely of the so-called immediate constituent type, though it is quite amazing to see how many variants of this type came up in this connection.

Leaving aside the question of the theoretical inadequacy of immediate constituent grammars for natural languages, the following fact has come to the fore during the last few years: If one wants to increase the degree of approximate practical adequacy of such grammars, one has to pay an enormous price for this, namely a proliferation of rules (partly, but not wholly, caused by a proliferation of syntactic categories) of truly astronomic nature. The dialectics of the situation is distressing: the better the understanding of linguistic structure, and the greater our mastery of the language —the larger the set of grammatical rules we need to describe the language, the heavier the preparatory work of writing the grammar, and the costlier the machine operations of storing and working with such a grammar.

It is very often said that our present computers are already good enough for the task of MT and will be more than sufficient in their next generation, but that the bottleneck lies mostly in our insufficient understanding of the workings of language. As soon as we know all of it, the problem will be licked. I shall not discuss here the extremely dubious character of this "knowing all of it," but only point out that the more we shall know about linguistic structure, the more complex the description of this structure will become, so long as we stick to immediate constituent grammars. It is known that in some cases transformational grammars are able to reduce the complexity of the description by orders of magnitude. Whether this holds in general remains to be seen, but the time has come for those interested in the mechanical determination of syntactic structure, whether for its own sake, for MT or for other applications, to get out of the self-imposed straitjacket of immediate constituent grammars and start working with more powerful models, such as transformation grammars.

Let me illustrate by just one example: one of the best programs in existence, on one of the best computers in existence, recently needed 12 minutes (and something like $100 on a commercial basis) to provide an exhaustive syntactic analysis of a 35-word sentence [81]. I understand that the program has been improved in the meantime and that the time required for such an analysis is now closer to one minute. However, the output of this analysis is multiple, leaving the selection of the single analysis, which is correct in accordance with context and background, to other parts of the program or to the human posteditor. But there are other troubles with using immediate constituent grammars only for MT purposes. In his lecture to this Institute, Mr. Maurice Gross gave an example of a French sentence in the passive mood which could be translated into English only by ad hoc procedures so long as its syntactic analysis is made on an immediate constituent basis only. The translation into English is straightforward as soon as the French sentence is first detransformed into the active mood. A grammar which is unable to provide this conversion, besides being scientifically unsatisfactory, will increase the difficulties of MT.

In the time left to me I would like to return to what is perhaps the most widespread fallacy connected with MT, the fallacy I call, in variation of a well known term of Whitehead, The Fallacy of Misplaced Economy. I refer to the idea that indirect machine translation through an *intermediate language* will result in considerable to vast economies over direct translation from source to target language, on the obvious condition that should MT turn out to be feasible at all, in some sense or other, many opportunities for simultaneous translation from one source language into many target languages (and vice versa) will arise. I already once before discussed both the attractiveness of this idea and the fallaciousness of the reasoning behind it [10]. Let me therefore discuss here at some length only what I regard to be the kernel of the fallacy.

The following argument has great *prima facie* appeal: Assume that we deal with 10 languages, and that we are interested in translating from each language into every other, i.e., altogether 90 translation pairs. Assume, for simplicity's sake, that each translation algorithm—never mind the quality of the output—requires 100 man-years. Then the preparation of all the algorithms will require 9000 man-years. If one now designates one of these languages as the pivot-language, then only 18 translation pairs will be needed, requiring 1800 man-years of preparation, an enormous saving. True enough, translation time for any of the remaining 72 language pairs will be approximately doubled, and the quality of the output will be some-what reduced, but this would be a price worth paying. (In general, the argument is presented with some artificial language serving as the pivot. Though this move changes the appeal of the argument for the better—since this artificial pivot language is supposed to be equipped with certain magical qualities—as well as for the worse—since the number of translation algorithms now increases to 20—I don't think that thereby the substance of the following counterargument is weakened.) However, in order to counteract even this deterioration, let us double our effort and spend, say, 200 man-years on the preparation of the algorithms for translating to and from the pivot language. We would still wind up with no more than 3600 man-years of work, vs. the 9000 originally needed. Well?

The fallacy, so it seems to me, lies in the following: the argument would hold if the preparation of the 90 algorithms were to be done independently and simultaneously by different people, with nobody learning from the experience of his co-workers. This is surely a highly unrealistic assumption. If preparing the Russian-to-English and German-to-English algorithms were to take 100 man years each, when done this way, there can be no doubt that preparing the German-to-English algorithm after completion (or even partial completion) of a successful Russian-to-English algorithm will take much less time, perhaps half as much. The next pair, say Japanese-to-English, will take still less time, etc. All these figures being utterly arbitrary, I don't think we should go on bothering about the convergence of this series. Though we might still wind up with a larger time needed for the preparation of the 90 than of the 18 "double precision" algorithms, it is doubtful, to say the least, whether the overall quality/preparation-time/ translation-time balance would be in favor of the pivot language approach.

Add to this the fact that 100 man-years would be enough, by assumption, to start a working MT outfit along the direct approach, whereas 400 man-years will be needed even to start translating the first pair along the indirect approach, and the initial appeal of the intermediate language idea should completely vanish, when judged from a practical point of view. As to its speculative impact, enough has been said on other occasions.

I think it is my duty to state at the end of this lecture series where all this leaves us. Autonomous, high-quality machine translation between natural languages according to rigid algorithms may safely be considered as dead. Such translation on the basis of learning ability is still-born. Though machines could doubtless provide a great variety of aids to human translation, so far in no case has economic feasibility of any such aid been proven, though the outlook for the future is not all dark. So much for the debit side. On the credit side of the past MT efforts stands the enormous increase of interest which has already begun to pay off not only in an increased understanding of language as such, but also in such applications as the mechanical translation between programming languages. But this could already be a topic for another Institute.

PART IV

Semantic Information

An Outline of a Theory of Semantic Information* | 15

1. THE PROBLEM

[The concepts of information and amount of information are distinguished. The explication of these concepts is attempted only insofar as they apply to (declarative) sentences or, alternatively, to propositions. Prevailing theory of communication (or transmission of information) deliberately neglects the semantic aspects of communication, i.e., the meaning of the messages. This theoretical restraint is, however, not always adhered to in practice, and this results in many misapplications. The theory outlined here is fully and openly of a semantic character and is therefore deemed to be a better approximation to a future theory of pragmatic information. For didactic purposes, the present theory of semantic information may be identified with a theory of pragmatic information for an "ideal" receiver.]

It seems desirable that one should be able to say not only what information a message or an experiment has supplied but also how much. Hence we are going to distinguish between information (or content) and amount of information.

We shall deal with these concepts only insofar as they apply to either sentences or propositions, where 'sentences' is short for 'declarative sentences' or 'statements', and propositions are the nonlinguistic entities expressed by sentences. The theory we are going to develop will presuppose a certain language system and the basic concepts of this theory will be applied to the sentences of that system. These concepts, then, will be semantic concepts, closely connected with certain concepts of inductive logic, as we shall show below. Since inductive logic has been treated at length in [28; 29], we shall make extensive use of the results achieved there. Relevant definitions and theorems will, however, be repeated to such an extent as to make the present treatment stand almost completely on its own.

---

* First appeared as **Technical Report No. 247** of the Research Laboratory of Electronics, Massachusetts Institute of Technology, 1952.

The restriction of the range of application of the concepts to be explicated to sentences (or propositions) is probably not serious, since other applications seem to be reducible to this one. Instead of dealing with the information carried by letters, sound waves, and the like, we may talk about the information carried by the sentence, 'The sequence of letters (or sound waves, etc.)...has been transmitted'. The situation is similar to that prevailing with regard to the concept of truth, which is used presystematically as applying not only to sentences or propositions but also to many other entities such as concepts and ideas. There, too, these latter usages seem to be reducible to the former ones.

In recent authoritative presentations of the so-called Mathematical Theory of Communication, or Theory of (Transmission of) Information, great care has been taken to point out that this theory is not interested in the semantic aspects of communication.

The following two quotations may be regarded as representative. Claude E. Shannon states [136:3]: "These semantic aspects of communication are irrelevant to the engineering problem." E. Colin Cherry [31:383] says: "It is important to emphasize, at the start, that we are not concerned with the meaning or the truth of messages; semantics lies outside the scope of mathematical information theory."

It has, however, often been noticed that this asceticism is not always adhered to in practice and that sometimes semantically important conclusions are drawn from officially semantics-free assumptions. In addition, it seems that at least some of the proponents of communication theory have tried to establish (or to reestablish) the semantic connections which have been deliberately dissevered by others.

In 1948, Donald MacKay conceived a theory of information that should be broad enough to cover both theory of communication and theory of scientific information, the latter dealing with the formation of representations or their arrangement in the representational space of the observer, the former dealing with the replication of representations in the mind of the receiver, which were already present in the mind of the sender of a message (Cf. [92; 93]).

Jean Ville [147] also treats information as a basically semantic concept and develops functions and theorems which stand in close correspondence to some of the functions and theorems with which we deal in this report. A more thorough evaluation of these and other contributions to the foundations of information theory, as well as a comparison between the theory presented here and the theory of communication, is given in Chapter 16.

Our theory lies explicitly and wholly within semantics.

It does not deal, however, with what has been termed by Weaver in his contribution to the afore-mentioned book " the semantic problem of communication", which, as defined by him, is "concerned with the identity, or satisfactorily close approximation, in the interpretation of meaning by the receiver, as compared with the intended meaning of the sender." We would rather prefer to consider an investigation in which sender and receiver are explicitly involved as belonging to pragmatics.

We shall talk about the information carried by a sentence, both by itself and relative to some other sentence or set of sentences, but not about the information which the sender intended to convey by transmitting a certain message nor about the information a receiver obtained from this message. An explanation of these usages is of paramount importance, but it is our conviction that the best approach to this explication is through an analysis of the concept of semantic information which, in addition to its being an approximation by abstraction to the full-blooded concept of pragmatic information, may well have its own independent values.

Anticipating later results, it will turn out, under all explications envisaged by us, that the amount of information carried by the sentence '$17 \times 19 = 323$' is zero and that the amount of information of 'The three medians of the sides of a plane triangle intersect in one point', relative to some set of sentences serving as a complete set of axioms for Euclidean geometry, is likewise zero. This, however, is by no means to be understood as implying that there is no good sense of 'amount of information', in which the amount of information of these sentences will not be zero at all, and for some people, might even be rather high. To avoid ambiguities, we shall use the adjective 'semantic' to differentiate both the presystematic senses of 'information' in which we are interested at the moment and their systematic explicata from other senses (such as "amount of psychological information for the person P") and their explicata. This adjective will, however, be dropped in those cases where ambiguities are unlikely to arise.

The following comparison might be of value for pointing out one of the services which a clarification of the semantic concept of information should render for a future theory of pragmatic information. The theory of so-called ideal gases is of great importance in physics despite the fact that no actual gas is ideal and that many gases are very far from being ideal. The semantic information carried by a sentence with respect to a certain class of sentences may well be regarded as the "ideal" pragmatic information which the sentence would carry for an "ideal" receiver whose only empirical knowledge is formulated in exactly this class of sentences. By an "ideal" receiver we understand, for the purposes of this illustration, a receiver with a perfect memory who "knows" all of logic and mathematics, and together with any class of empirical sentences, all of their logical consequences. The interpretation of semantic information with the help of such a superhuman fictitious intellect should be taken only as an informal indication. We shall not refer to this fiction in the technical part of this paper.

Our task can now be stated much more specifically. We intend to explicate the presystematic concept of information, insofar as it is applied to sentences or propositions and inasmuch as it is abstracted from the pragmatic conditions of its use. We shall then define, on the basis of this systematic concept of semantic information, various explicata for the presystematic concept (or concepts) of amount of semantic information and shall investigate their adequacy and applicability.

2. GENERAL EXPLANATIONS

[The language-systems relative to which the present theory of information is developed are described as containing a finite number of individual constants and primitive one-place predicates. The following fundamental syntactic and semantic concepts are explained: atomic sentence, molecular sentence, basic sentence, molecular predicate, L-true, L-false, factual, L-implies, L-equivalent, L-disjunct, L-exclusive, Q-predicator, Q-property, Q-sentence, state-description, and range. Some terms and symbols of class-theory (set-theory) are introduced, mainly complement, sum, and product.]

The language-systems relative to which our theory of information will be developed are very simple ones, so simple indeed that the results to be obtained will be of only restricted value with regard to language-systems complex enough to serve as possible languages of science. The restriction, however, was partly imposed by the fact that inductive logic — on which we shall have to rely heavily — has so far been developed to a sufficiently elaborate degree only for languages that are not much richer than those treated here [28: §§15, 16], and partly for the sake of simplicity of presentation. It is hoped that in spite of this the results will be immediately applicable to certain simple situations and will be suggestive with respect to more complex ones.

Our language-systems $\mathscr{L}_n^\pi$ contain n different individual constants which stand for n different individuals (things, events, or positions) and π primitive one-place predicates which designate primitive properties of the individuals. (n and π are finite numbers; under certain assumptions, however, it is easy to extend the results obtained here to systems with a denumerably infinite number of individual constants.) In an atomic sentence, for example, '*Pa*' ('the individual *a* has the property *P*'), a primitive property is asserted to hold for an individual. Other molecular sentences are formed out of atomic sentences with the help of the following five customary connectives:

~	not	negation
$\lor$	or	disjunction
·	and	conjunction
$\supset$	if...then	(material) implication
$\equiv$	if and only if (written iff)	(material) equivalence

All atomic sentences and their negations are called basic sentences. Analogously, other molecular predicates or predicators are formed out of primitive predicates with the help of the (typographically) same connectives (for example, '*M*. ~ *P*' standing for '*M* and not *P*'). A sentence consisting of a predicator and an individual constant is called a full sentence of this predicator. Though our systems do not contain individual variables, quantifiers, or an identity sign, their expressive power is thereby not essentially affected. Sentences like 'There are exactly three individuals having the property *P*' can still be rendered in these systems, though only in the form of a rather clumsy disjunction of conjunctions of basic sentences. Hence absolute frequencies (cardinal numbers of classes or properties) and relative frequencies can be expressed in these systems (but not measurable quantities like length and mass).

Any sentence is either *L*-true, logically true, analytic, e.g., '*Pa* $\lor$ ~ *Pa*', or *L*-false (logically false, self-contradictory, e.g., '*Pa*. ~ *Pa*') or factual (logically indeterminate, synthetic, e.g., '*Pa* $\lor$ [*M*. ~ *N*]*b*'). Logical relations between sentences *i* and *j* can be defined:

$$
\begin{aligned}
&i \text{ } L\text{-implies } j & &=_{Df} i \supset j \text{ is } L\text{-true} \\
&i \text{ is } L\text{-equivalent to } j & &=_{Df} i \equiv j \text{ is } L\text{-true} \\
&i \text{ is } L\text{-disjunct with } j & &=_{Df} i \lor j \text{ is } L\text{-true} \\
&i \text{ is } L\text{-exclusive of } j & &=_{Df} i.j \text{ is } L\text{-false}
\end{aligned}
$$

We shall use '*t*' as the name of a particular *L*-true sentence, a "tautology", say, of '*Pa* $\lor$ ~ *Pa*'.

A *Q*-predicator is a conjunction (of predicates) in which every primitive predicate occurs either unnegated or negated (but not both) and no other predicate occurs at all. The property designated by a *Q*-predicator is called a Q-property. A full sentence of a Q-predicator is a Q-sentence. A state-description is a conjunction of n Q-sentences, one for each individual. Thus a state-description completely describes a possible state of the universe of discourse in question[1]. For any sentence j of the system, the class of those state-descriptions in which j holds, that is, each of which L-implies j, is called the range of j. The range of j is null if, and only if, j is L-false; in any other case, j is L-equivalent to the disjunction of the state-descriptions in its range.

The following theorems will be of use later:

T 2–1.

a. The number of atomic sentences is $\beta = \pi n$.

b. The number of Q-predicators is $\kappa = 2^\pi$.

c. The number of state-descriptions is $z = 2^\beta = 2^{\pi n} = (2^\pi)^n = \kappa^n$.

In our metalanguage, that is, the language in which we talk about our language-systems $\mathscr{L}_n^\pi$ (in our case a certain unspecified sublanguage of ordinary English enriched by a few additional symbols), we shall use some customary terms and symbols of the theory of classes (or sets). The class of all those entities (of a certain type) which do not belong to a certain class K will be called the complement (-class) of K and denoted by '$-K$'. The class of those entities which belong either to a class K or to a class L (or to both) will be called the (class-theoretical) sum of these classes and will be denoted by '$K \cup L$'. The class of those entities which belong to each of the classes K and L will be called the (class-theoretical) product of these classes and denoted by '$K \cap L$'.

Those readers who might not be familiar with abstract logical concepts and terms will profit from the following illustration, which will be carried through this whole chapter. Let a census be taken in a small community of only three inhabitants, and let the census be interested only in whether the inhabitants counted are male or non-male (female) and young or non-young (old), respectively. Let the three individuals be designated by 'a', 'b', 'c', and the properties by 'M', '$\sim M$' (or 'F'), 'Y', and '$\sim Y$' (or 'O'), respectively. The language-system in which the outcome of the census can be exhaustively described is therefore a $\mathscr{L}_3^2$-system, in our notation. 'Ma' is an atomic sentence, '$Ma . Fb . (Mc \supset Oc)$' another molecular sentence, '$F . \sim Y$' a Q-predicator, '$[F . \sim Y]b$' a Q-sentence, '$[M . Y]a . [\sim M . Y]b . [\sim M . \sim Y]c$' a state-description. For later references, the list of all 64 state-descriptions is given in Table I, in abbreviated form.

---

[1] This holds, strictly speaking, only if the primitive properties are logically independent. For a discussion of the problems involved here, see [30] and the literature mentioned there.

Line 10 of this table, for example, is to be interpreted as short for the state-description '$[M.Y]b.[M \cdot Y]c.[F.Y]a$'. Later (§4), however, a different interpretation of the same table will be given.

TABLE I

	M. Y	M. O	F. Y	F. O		M. Y	M. O	F. Y	F. O
1.	a, b, c	–	–	–	33.	b	–	–	a, c
2.	–	a, b, c	–	–	34.	a	–	–	b, c
3.	–	–	a, b, c	–	35.	–	c	–	a, b
4.	–	–	–	a, b, c	36.	–	b	–	a, c
5.	a, b	c	–	–	37.	–	a	–	b, c
6.	a, c	b	–	–	38.	–	–	c	a, b
7.	b, c	a	–	–	39.	–	–	b	a, c
8.	a, b	–	c	–	40.	–	–	a	b, c
9.	a, c	–	b	–	41.	a	b	c	–
10.	b, c	–	a	–	42.	a	c	b	–
11.	a, b	–	–	c	43.	b	a	c	–
12.	a, c	–	–	b	44.	b	c	a	–
13.	b, c	–	–	a	45.	c	a	b	–
14.	c	a, b	–	–	46.	c	b	a	–
15.	b	a, c	–	–	47.	a	b	–	c
16.	a	b, c	–	–	48.	a	c	–	b
17.	–	a, b	c	–	49.	b	a	–	c
18.	–	a, c	b	–	50.	b	c	–	a
19.	–	b, c	a	–	51.	c	a	–	b
20.	–	a, b	–	c	52.	c	b	–	a
21.	–	a, c	–	b	53.	a	–	b	c
22.	–	b, c	–	a	54.	a	–	c	b
23.	c	–	a, b	–	55.	b	–	a	c
24.	b	–	a, c	–	56.	b	–	c	a
25.	a	–	b, c	–	57.	c	–	a	b
26.	–	c	a, b	–	58.	c	–	b	a
27.	–	b	a, c	–	59.	–	a	b	c
28.	–	a	b, c	–	60.	–	a	c	b
29.	–	–	a, b	c	61.	–	b	a	c
30.	–	–	a, c	b	62.	–	b	c	a
31.	–	–	b, c	a	63.	–	c	a	b
32.	c	–	–	a, b	64.	–	c	b	a

The reader will easily verify that the range of the sentence '$Ma.Ya.Fb.Yb$', which might profitably be rewritten in the form '$[M.Y]a.[F.Y]b$', contains exactly 4 state-descriptions, namely, 9, 25, 42, and 53. The range of 'Fa' contains 32 state-descriptions. The range of '$Ma \lor Ya \lor Fb \lor Yb \lor Fc \lor Oc$' contains 63 state-descriptions, that is, all state-descriptions except 52. A reader with some training in propositional logic will see immediately that this last sentence is L-equivalent to '$\sim (Fa.Oa.Mb.Ob.Mc.Yc)$', hence to the negation of state-description 52.

3. THE PRESYSTEMATIC CONCEPT OF SEMANTIC INFORMATION

[A requirement of adequacy for any proposed explication of semantic information—In—is stated: In(i) includes In(j) if and only if i L-implies j.

From this requirement various theorems are derived. In addition to the absolute information carried by a sentence, the information carried by a sentence j in excess to that carried by some other sentence i is often of importance. This concept of relative information is defined by: $\text{In}(j/i) = \text{In}(i.j) - \text{In}(i)$. One of the theorems is: if t is any L-true sentence $\text{In}(j/t) = \text{In}(j)$. Two concepts that fulfill the requirement but differ in some aspect are investigated but neither of them is accepted as an explicatum for In.]

To disperse, at least partially, the haziness which envelops the inevitably vague discussions of the adequacy of the explication to be offered later for the concept of semantic information, let us state a requirement which will serve as a necessary condition for this adequacy.

Whenever i L-implies j, i asserts all that is asserted by j, and possibly more. In other words, the information carried by i includes the information carried by j as a (perhaps improper part) part. Using 'In($\cdots$)' as an abbreviation for the presystematic concept 'the information carried by...', we can now state the requirement in the following way:

R3-1.   In(i) includes In(j) iff i L-implies j.

By this requirement we have committed ourselves to treat information as a set or class of something. This stands in good agreement with common ways of expression, as for example, "The information supplied by this statement is more inclusive than (or is identical with, or overlaps) that supplied by the other statement."

We shall now state some theorems which hold for 'In' and, therefore, also for that concept which we shall offer, in the following section, as the explicatum for 'In.' These theorems follow from R1[2] and well-known theorems of the theory of classes.

T3-1.   In(i) =In(j) iff i is L-equivalent to j.

If a class K of classes contains a class which is included in every member of K, this class will be called "the minimum class (of K)". If K contains a class which includes every member of K, this class will be called "the maximum class (of K)". The minimum class and the maximum class may coincide with the null-class and the universal-class (of the corresponding type), respectively, but need not do so.

Since an L-true sentence is L-implied by every sentence, and an L-false sentence L-implies every sentence, we have:

---

[2] For the sake of brevity, theorems, definitions, or requirements, when found in the same section in which they are first stated, will be referred to only by the corresponding letter 'T', 'D', or 'R' and by their second numbers. Here, for instance, we have 'R1' instead of the longer 'R3-1'.

T3–2. In(i) = the minimum class of K (where K is now the class of the In-classes of sentences) iff i is L-true.

T3–3. In(i) = the maximum class of K iff i is L-false.

It might perhaps, at first, seem strange that a self-contradictory sentence, hence one which no ideal receiver would accept, is regarded as carrying with it the most inclusive information. It should, however, be emphasized that semantic information is here not meant as implying truth. A false sentence which happens to say much is thereby highly informative in our sense. Whether the information it carries is true or false, scientifically valuable or not, and so forth, does not concern us. A self-contradictory sentence asserts too much; it is too informative to be true.

T3–4. In(i) properly includes In(j) iff i L-implies j but j does not L-imply i.

T3–5. In(i) properly includes the minimum class and is properly included in the maximum class iff i is factual.

T3–6. In(i) includes In($i \lor j$) and is included in In($i.j$).

When we use the term 'information' in ordinary language, we often refer to the information carried by a sentence absolutely, so to speak. At least as often, however, we intend to refer to the information carried by a sentence in excess of that carried by some other sentence (or class of sentences). If not otherwise stated or implicitly understood through the context, this other sentence will often be that in which the total knowledge available to the receiver of the information, before he receives the new information, is stated. In contradistinction to the concept of absolute information treated so far, we shall now define, still on the presystematic level, the concept of relative (or additional or excess) information of j with respect to i as the class-theoretical difference of In($i.j$) and In(i), that is, the class-theoretical product of In($i.j$) with the complement of In(i); in symbols:

D3–1. $\text{In}(j/i) =_{Df} \text{In}(i.j) - \text{In}(i) (= \text{In}(i.j) \cap - \text{In}(i))$.

In(j/i) is again a class. Its members belong to the same type as the members of In(i). The following theorems follow immediately from **D1, R1,** and the previous theorems.

Complete formal proofs will be given only when an indication of the theorems, definitions, and requirements from which a theorem follows will not enable most readers to grasp the proof by inspection. In very simple cases (as in the first 8 theorems), these hints will be omitted.

T3–7. In(j/i) includes the null class and is included in the maximum class.

T 3–8.   If i is L-equivalent to j, then $\text{In}(k/i) = \text{In}(k/j)$ and $\text{In}(i/l) = \text{In}(j/l)$.

T 3–9.   If i L-implies j, then $\text{In}(j/i) =$ the null class.

Proof: In this case, $i.j$ is L-equivalent to i. The theorem follows from T1 and D1.

T3–10.   If j is L-true, then $\text{In}(j/i) =$ the null class.

T3–11. $\text{In}(j/i)$ properly includes the null class iff i does not L-imply j.

Proof: In this case, $\text{In}(i.j)$ properly includes $\text{In}(i)$.

So far, we have committed ourselves to treat the information carried by a sentence as a class of something and have stated one requirement which every adequate explicatum will have to meet. This, of course, leaves many possibilities open. With respect to the information carried by an L-true sentence, we were able to state only that it is a minimum and is contained in the information carried by any sentence. It might perhaps seem plausible to require, in addition, that the information carried by an L-true sentence should be empty; hence, the null-class of the appropriate type. But this feeling is due to the fact that we do not always distinguish carefully between information and amount of information. What we really have in mind is rather that the amount of semantic information carried by an L-true sentence should be zero. But this can be achieved by a suitable explicatum even if the information carried by such a sentence is not the null-class.

On the other hand, there also exists no good reason so far why the information of an L-true sentence should not be the null-class. The best procedure is, therefore, to leave this decision open.

There are indeed two plausible explicata for $\text{In}(i)$, which differ in exactly this point: according to the one, the information carried by an L-true sentence will be the null-class; according to the other, it will not. Let us denote the first concept by 'Inf_1' and the second by 'Inf_2'. Their definitions are as follows:

D3–2. $\text{Inf}_1(i) =_{Df}$ the class of all sentences (in $\mathscr{L}$) which are L-implied by i and not L-true.

D3–3. $\text{Inf}_2(i) =_{Df}$ the class of all sentences (in $\mathscr{L}$) which are L-implied by i.

We shall not dwell here on an elaborate comparison of the relative merits and faults of these two definitions; first, because such a comparison has already been carried out in a closely related context [26: §23; 28: 406]; second, because we shall adopt neither of these definitions for future work but a third one to be explained in the following section.

4. CONTENT-ELEMENTS AND CONTENT

[A content-element is defined as the negation of a state-description, and the content of i —Cont(i)—as the class of the content-elements L-implied by i. Cont is taken as the explicatum for In. Cont(j/i) is defined and various theorems derived.]

In §2, we defined the range of a sentence i, $R(i)$, as the class of all state-descriptions Z in which i holds or which, in other words, L-imply i. The sentence i says that the state of the universe (treated in $\mathscr{L}$) is one of the possible states which are described by the Z in $R(i)$. Alternatively formulated, i says that the universe is not in one of those states which are described by the Z in $V_Z - R(i)$, where V_Z is the class of all Z. Just as i is L-implied by every Z in $R(i)$, so it L-implies the negation of every Z in $V_Z - R(i)$. We call these negations the content-elements E of i and their class the content of i, in symbols Cont(i). In general, we call the negations of the Z in a given system $\mathscr{L}$ the E of this system [28: §73].

In our $\mathscr{L}_3^2$, there are, of course, 64 content-elements, namely, the negations of its 64 state-descriptions. These content-elements appear in Table I, when interpreted in a different way from that given before. We can now read line 10, for example, as '$[M \vee Y]b \vee [M \vee Y]c \vee [F \vee Y]a$', a content-element which is L-equivalent to the negation of state-description 37, as the reader will verify for himself.

The content of the sentence '$Ma.Ya.Fb.Yb$' contains 60 content-elements, namely, the negations of all state-descriptions except 9, 25, 42, and 53.

The following theorem, T4-1, can be deduced from the theorems concerning state-descriptions and L-concepts in [28: §§18A, 18D, 19, 20, 21B].

T4-1. For every E_i the following holds:

a. E_i is factual [28: T20–5b, T20–6].

b. If E_j is distinct from E_i, then E_i and E_j are L-disjunct.

Proof: $\sim E_i . \sim E_j$ is L-false [28: T21–8a]. Therefore the negation of this conjunction is L-true. But this negation is L-equivalent to $E_i \vee E_j$.

c. The conjunction of all E_i is L-false.

Proof: Let d be the disjunction of the negations of the E_i, hence L-equivalent to the disjunction of all Z. Therefore d is L-true [28: T21–8b]; hence $\sim d$ is L-false. But $\sim d$ is L-equivalent to the conjunction of all E_i.

d. If E_i L-implies j, then j is either L-true or L-equivalent to E_i; in other words, E_i is a weakest factual sentence.

Just as a state-description says the most that can be said in the given universe of discourse, short of self-contradiction, so a content-element says the least, beyond a tautology. 'a is male and young, b is female and young, and c is female and old' is a strongest factual sentence in the census; its negation 'a is female or old (or both), or b is male or old, or c is male or young' (where 'or' is always to be understood in its nonexclusive sense) a weakest one.

T4–2.
a. $\mathrm{Cont}(i) =$ the null-class of E, Λ_E, iff i is L-true.
b. $\mathrm{Cont}(i) =$ the class of all E, V_E, iff i is L-false.
c. $\mathrm{Cont}(i) =$ neither Λ_E nor V_E iff i is factual.
d. $\mathrm{Cont}(i)$ includes $\mathrm{Cont}(j)$ iff i L-implies j.
e. $\mathrm{Cont}(i) = \mathrm{Cont}(j)$ iff i is L-equivalent to j.
f. $\mathrm{Cont}(i)$ and $\mathrm{Cont}(j)$ are exclusive (i.e., have no members in common) iff i and j are L-disjunct [28: D20–1e].

The contents of 'Ma' and of '$Fa \vee Mb$' are exclusive since '$Ma \vee Fa \vee Mb$' is L-true. The reader can verify from Table I, in its second interpretation, that these contents have indeed no members in common.

T4–3.
a. $\mathrm{Cont}(\sim i) = -\mathrm{Cont}(i)$ (short for '$V_E - \mathrm{Cont}(i)$' [28: T18–1e]).
b. $\mathrm{Cont}(i \vee j) = \mathrm{Cont}(i) \cap \mathrm{Cont}(j)$.

Proof: Let $\bar{R}(\ldots)$ be the class of the negations of the members of $R(\ldots)$. Then
$\mathrm{Cont}(i \vee j) = \bar{R}(\sim(i \vee j)) = \bar{R}(\sim i . \sim j) = \bar{R}(\sim i) \cap \bar{R}(\sim j) = \mathrm{Cont}(i) \cap \mathrm{Cont}(j)$.
c. $\mathrm{Cont}(i . j) = \mathrm{Cont}(i) \cup \mathrm{Cont}(j)$.

Proof: $\mathrm{Cont}(i . j) = -\mathrm{Cont}(\sim(i . j)) = -\mathrm{Cont}(\sim i \vee j) = -(\mathrm{Cont}(\sim i) \cap \mathrm{Cont}(\sim j)) = -(-\mathrm{Cont}(i) \cap -\mathrm{Cont}(j)) = \mathrm{Cont}(i) \cup \mathrm{Cont}(j)$.
To verify T3b,c take, for instance, i as '$Ma \vee Fb \vee [M \vee Y]c$' and j as '$Fa \vee Mb$'.

T2d shows that Cont fulfills requirement R3–1. We decide to take Cont as our explicatum for In. The explication of the information carried by a sentence j as the class of the negations of all those Z which are excluded by j, is intuitively plausible and in accordance with the old philosophical principle, "*omnis determinatio est negatio.*" Our main reason, however, for giving it preference over the two explicata mentioned in the previous section, Inf_1 and Inf_2, lies in the fact that an explanation of amount of information will turn out to be rather simple if based on Cont, in accordance with the fourth requirement for a good explication stated in [28: 7].

Let us notice that according to T2a, Cont shares with Inf_1 the **property** that their value for an L-true sentence as argument is the null-class.

We now have to define the relative content of j with respect to i. What has to be done is, of course, simply to replace 'In' in D3–1 by 'Cont'.

D4–1. $\text{Cont}(j/i) =_{Df} \text{Cont}(i.j) - \text{Cont}(i)$.

Let us state only one theorem on the relative content:

T4–4.

a. If i is an L-true sentence, $\text{Cont}(j/i) = \text{Cont}(j)$.

Proof: In this case, $i.j$ is L-equivalent to j. The theorem follows from D1 and T2a.

b. Cont $(j/t) = $ Cont (j).

Thus the relative content of j with respect to t equals the absolute content of j. Therefore it would be possible to begin with the relative content as primitive and define the absolute content as the value of the relative content with respect to t. However, it seems more convenient to begin with the simple concept of absolute content, because it has only one argument and the relative content can be defined on the basis of it. This is the procedure we have chosen here.

5.   THE PRESYSTEMATIC CONCEPT OF AMOUNT OF INFORMATION

[Requirements of adequacy for the explication of amount of semantic information—*in*—are stated, and theorems for in derived. No formal requirement of additivity is accepted, since the conditions under which additivity is to hold cannot be given unambiguously, so far. in(j/i), the amount of information of j relative to i, is defined and theorems derived.] Our next task is to find an explicatum, or perhaps various explicata, for the presystematic concept of amount of information. This will again be preceded by the statement of some requirements, the fulfillment of which will be a necessary condition for the adequacy of the explicata to be proposed.

We shall use 'in' as the symbol for the presystematic concept of amount of information and distinguish between the absolute amount of information of a sentence i, in(i), and the relative amount of information of the sentence j with respect to i, in(j/i). The relative amount is clearly definable on the basis of the absolute amount:

D5–1. $\text{in}(j/i) =_{Df} \text{in}(i.j) - \text{in}(i)$

(where the ' $-$ '-sign is this time the symbol for numerical difference and not, as in D3–1 or D4–1, for class-difference). Therefore it is sufficient to state only the requirements with respect to the absolute amount. It seems plausible to require that the amount of information of i should be not less than the amount of information of j, if the content of i includes the content of j; that the amount of information of an L-true sentence should be zero; and, for finite systems, that the amount of information of a factual sentence should be greater than zero. (The qualification 'for finite systems' might perhaps look superfluous. It can, however, be shown that with regard to the explicata envisaged by us, this requirement would not be fulfilled in an infinite system.) More formally:

R5–1. $\text{in}(i) \geq in(j)$ if (but not only if) Cont(i) includes Cont(j).

R5–2. $\text{in}(j) = 0$ if Cont(j) = Λ_E.

R5–3. $\text{in}(j) > 0$ if Cont(j) properly includes Λ_E.

Instead of R3 we might also have required the following somewhat stronger condition from which R3 follows immediately:

R5–4. $\text{in}(i) > \text{in}(j)$ if Cont(i) properly includes Cont(j).

We could also have stated these requirements directly in terms of 'L-implies' and 'L-true', without recourse to Cont. For the benefit of those who, for some reason, are not satisfied with our explication of 'information' and who therefore might try to explicate 'amount of information' on the basis of some other explicatum for 'information' or perhaps even without reference to any such explicatum (a perfectly reasonable and achievable goal), the following version is given:

R5–1*. $\text{in}(i) \geq \text{in}(j)$ if (but not only if) i L-implies j.

R5–2*. $\text{in}(j) = 0$ if j is L-true.

R5–3*. $\text{in}(j) > 0$ if j is not L-true.

The following theorems follow from R1 through R3 and the previously stated properties of Cont.

T5–1.   If Cont(i) = Cont(j), then $\text{in}(i) = \text{in}(j)$.

T5–2.   If i is L-false, then $\text{in}(i)$ has the maximum in-value.

Proof: An L-false sentence L-implies every sentence.

T5–3. $0 < \text{in}(i) <$ the maximum in-value iff i is factual.

T5–4. $\text{in}(i \vee j) \leq \text{in}(i) \leq \text{in}(i . j)$.

The requirements R1 through R3 are clearly rather weak, and one might look for further requirements. One that recommends itself immediately would be that of additivity, that is, to have $\text{in}(i . j) = \text{in}(i) + \text{in}(j)$ if i and j are independent of each other in a certain sense. However, we shall not make this one of our formal requirements because the sense of the independence involved is not clear at this moment. We shall find later that each of our explicata is indeed additive but not all of them in the same sense, because the conditions of independence are not the same in the various cases.

The additivity holds, of course, only under certain conditions, whatever those conditions may be in exact terms. It is clear that, in general,

$in(i.j) \neq in(i) + in(j)$. It is further clear that there will be cases where $in(i.j) < in(i) + in(j)$. This will be the case, for example, whenever i L-implies j and j is not L-true, because under these circumstances i is L-equivalent to $i.j$, so that $in(i.j) = in(i)$, whereas $in(j) > 0$, and hence $in(i) < in(i) + in(j)$. So far, we can state only a lower limit for $in(i.j)$, viz:

T5–5. $in(i.j) \geqq \max[in(i), in(j)]$.

Does there exist a general upper limit for $in(i.j)$ that is not trivial? No theorem to this effect can be deduced from the requirements of this section. They do not exclude, for instance, the possibility that sometimes $in(i.j) > in(i) + in(j)$. This possibility might perhaps look so implausible that one would like to exclude it by the explicit additional requirement $in(i.j) \leqq in(i) + in(j)$. However, it seems better not to require this. We shall see later that the second of our explicata (inf) violates this condition, and we shall then make this violation plausible. If someone insists that the requirement just stated has to be fulfilled, then he can accept only the first of our explicata (cont). For this concept the requirement is indeed fulfilled (T6–4m).

The following theorems correspond to T3–7 through T3–11 and T4–4a.

T5–7.   The maximum in-value $\geqq in(j/i) \geqq 0$.

T5–8.   If i is L-equivalent to j, then $in(k/i) = in(k/j)$ and $in(i/l) = in(j/l)$.

T5–9.   If i L-implies j, then $in(j/i) = 0$.

T5–10.   If j is L-true, then $in(j/i) = 0$.

T5–11. $in(j/i) > 0$ iff i does not L-imply j.

T5–12.

a.   If i is an L-true sentence, $in(j/i) = in(j)$ (T4–4a, T1).

b. $in(j/t) = in(j)$.

6. THE FIRST EXPLICATUM: CONTENT-MEASURE (CONT)

[One way of fulfilling the requirements stated in the previous section is outlined. It consists, essentially, in defining a measure-function over the content-elements, fulfilling certain conditions, and then taking as the measure of the content of a sentence the sum of the measures ascribed to the elements of its content. Since measure-functions over state-descriptions—m-functions—have been treated at length before [28], a shorter way of introducing content-measures—cont—is chosen, simply by equating cont(i) with $m_P(\sim i)$, where 'm_P' stands for proper m-function, i.e., m-function fulfilling certain conditions. Many theorems for cont(i) are derived, among them theorems for the content-measures of basic sentences, for disjunctions and conjunctions of such, for Q-sentences, and for sentences in disjunctive and conjunctive normal form. Cont(j/i) is defined, and among others, the important theorem cont(j/i) = cont($i \supset j$) is derived.]

We could have defined an adequate explicatum for the amount of information carried by a sentence with the help of measure-functions ranging over the contents of the sentences of $\mathscr{L}$ and fulfilling the conditions laid down in the previous section. Since there exist, however, close relations between contents and ranges (§4), we shall make use of the fact that the definitions of various measure-functions over ranges have already been treated at length in [28] and define the functions in which we are now interested simply on the basis of those measure-functions.

It seems profitable to start with a kind of measure-function ranging over state-descriptions and other sentences which has not been discussed explicitly in [28] or [29], namely, with proper m-functions, to be denoted by 'm_P'.

We define:

D6–1. m is a proper m-function (in $\mathscr{L}$) $=_{Df}$ m fulfills the following nine conditions:

a.   For every Z_i, $m(Z_i) > 0$.

b.   The sum of the m-values of all $Z = 1$.

c.   For any L-false sentence j, $m(j) = 0$.

d.   For any non-L-false sentence j, $m(j) =$ the sum of the m-values for the Z in $R(j)$.

e.   If Z_j is formed from Z_i by replacing the individual constants of Z_i by those correlated to them by any permutation of the individual constants, then $m(Z_k) = m(Z_i)$. (Less strictly but more suggestively: all individuals are treated on a par.)

f.   If Z_j is formed from Z_i by replacing the primitive predicates of Z_i by those correlated to them by any permutation of the primitive predicates, then $m(Z_j) = m(Z_i)$ (i.e., all primitive properties are treated on a par).

g.   If Z_j is formed from Z_i by replacing any of the primitive predicates of Z_i by their negations (omitting double negation signs), then $m(Z_j) = m(Z_i)$ (i.e., each primitive property is treated on a par with its complement).

The last three conditions could have been stated in a somewhat weaker form, but no attempt was made to reduce redundancy by sacrificing psychological clarity.

h.   If i and j have no primitive predicates in common, then $m(i.j) = m(i) \times m(j)$.

i. $m(i)$ is not influenced by the number of individuals of $\mathscr{L}$ not mentioned in i. (This condition will be used only in the derivation of formula (6) in §10.)

An m-function fulfilling   conditions (a) through (d) is called regular [28: 295]. If it fulfills, in addition, condition (e), it is called symmetrical [28:

485]. All theorems that hold for regular m-functions hold a fortiori for any proper m-function.

m_P is believed to be an adequate explicatum for one of the senses in which 'probability' is used, namely that which might be termed 'absolute logical probability', that is, logical probability on no evidence (or tautological evidence or irrelevant evidence).

Similarly, c_P, to be defined in D7–3, is believed to be an adequate explicatum of relative logical probability.

Any two sentences (not only state-descriptions) that stand in the relation stated in D1e are called isomorphic.

The following theorem holds for all regular m-functions [28: §§55A, 57A], hence also for all proper m-functions:

T6–1.
a. $0 \leqq m(i) \leqq 1$.
b. $m(i) = 1$ iff i is L-true.
c. $m(i) = 0$ iff i is L-false.
d. $0 < m(i) < 1$ iff i is factual.
e. If i L-implies j, then $m(i) \leqq m(j)$.
f. If i is L-equivalent to j, then $m(i) = m(j)$.
g. $m(i.j) \leqq m(i) \leqq m(i \vee j)$.
h. $m(i \vee j) = m(i) + m(j) - m(i.j)$.
i. $m(i \vee j) = m(i) + m(j)$ iff $i.j$ is L-false (i.e., iff i and j are L-exclusive).
j. $m(i.j) = m(i) + m(j) - m(i \vee j)$.
k. $m(i.j) = m(i) + m(j) - 1$ iff $i \vee j$ is L-true (i.e., iff i and j are L-disjunct).
l. $m(\sim i) = 1 - m(i)$.
m. $m(i.j) \leqq m(i) + m(j)$.

The measure-function in which we are interested and which we shall call from now on *content-measure* and denote by 'cont' is defined by

D6–2. $\text{cont}(i) =_{Df} m_P(\sim i)$.

From this definition it immediately follows that the cont-value of any E equals the m_P-value of the corresponding Z.

T6–2. For every Z_i, if E_i is $\sim Z_i$, $\text{cont}(E_i) = m_P(Z_i)$.

D2 and D11 entail
T6–3.
a. $\text{cont}(i) = 1 - m_P(i)$.
b. $m_P(i) = 1 - \text{cont}(i)$.
c. $\text{cont}(\sim i) = m_P(i)$.

The following theorem follows from T1 and T3b:

T6–4.

a. $1 \geqq \text{cont}(i) \geqq 0$.

b. $\text{cont}(i) = 0$ iff i is L-true.

c. $\text{cont}(i) = 1$ iff i is L-false.

d. $1 > \text{cont}(i) > 0$ iff i is factual.

e. If i L-implies j, then $\text{cont}(i) \geqq \text{cont}(j)$.

f. If i is L-equivalent to j, then $\text{cont}(i) = \text{cont}(j)$.

g. $\text{cont}(i.j) \geqq \text{cont}(i) \geqq \text{cont}(i \vee j)$.

h. $\text{cont}(i \vee j) = \text{cont}(i) + \text{cont}(j) - \text{cont}(i.j)$.

i. $\text{cont}(i \vee j) = \text{cont}(i) + \text{cont}(j) - 1$ iff i and j are L-exclusive.

j. $\text{cont}(i.j) = \text{cont}(i) + \text{cont}(j) - \text{cont}(i \vee j)$.

k. $\text{cont}(i.j) = \text{cont}(i) + \text{cont}(j)$ iff i and j are L-disjunct.

l. $\text{cont}(\sim i) = 1 - \text{cont}(i)$.

m. $\text{cont}(i.j) \leqq \text{cont}(i) + \text{cont}(j)$.

T4e, b and c–d show that cont fulfills the requirements of adequacy R5–1*, R5–2*, and R5–3*, respectively.

The condition under which additivity is stated in T4k to hold for cont appears quite plausible at first glance. If i and j are L-disjunct, then the contents of i and j are exclusive (T4–2f). Nothing in that which is asserted by i is simultaneously asserted by j; in other words, there is no factual sentence which is L-implied both by i and by j. However, we shall later (§7) present certain considerations which will raise some doubts with respect to this special condition of additivity.

The relative content-measure of j with respect to i is meant as the increase of the value of cont by adding j to i. Hence, in conformance with D5–1:

D6–3. $\text{cont}(j/i) =_{Df} \text{cont}(i.j) - \text{cont}(i)$.

T6–5.

a. $\text{cont}(j/i) = \text{cont}(j) - \text{cont}(i \vee j)$ (D3, T4j)

b. $= \text{cont}(j)$ iff i and j are L-disjunct ((a), T4b).

T6–6. $\text{cont}(j/i) = \text{cont}(i \supset j)$.

Proof: j is L-equivalent to $(i \vee j).(\sim i \vee j)$. The components of this conjunction are L-disjunct. Therefore $\text{cont}(j) = \text{cont}(i \vee j) + \text{cont}(\sim i \vee j)$ (T4k). Hence, with T5a, $\text{cont}(j/i) = \text{cont}(\sim i \vee j)$. But $\sim i \vee j$ is L-equivalent to $i \supset j$.

The last theorem is especially interesting. It shows that the relative content-measure of j with respect to i is the same as the absolute content-measure of the (material) implication $i \supset j$. If an "ideal" receiver possesses the knowledge i and then acquires the knowledge j, his possession of information is only increased in the same amount as if $i \supset j$ were added instead of j. This is, indeed, highly plausible since j is a logical consequence of the sentences i and $i \supset j$, and an "ideal" receiver, by definition, is able to draw such consequences instantaneously.

From T6 we also see that if i L-implies j, $\text{cont}(j/i) = 0$. We know this already since it holds for all our explicata for the relative amount of information in virtue of T5–9.

The following inequality, an immediate consequence of T5a, is of interest:

T6–7. $\text{cont}(j/i) \leqq \text{cont}(j)$.

We can express $\text{cont}(j/i)$ directly in terms of m_P in various ways:

T6–8.

a. $\text{cont}(j/i) = m_P(i) - m_P(i.j)$ (D3, T3a)

b. $\qquad\qquad = m_P(i. \sim j)$ (T6, $i \supset j$ is L-equivalent to $\sim (i. \sim j)$, T3a)

c. $\qquad\qquad = m_P(i \lor j) - m_P(j)$ (D3, T5a).

Two sentences, i and j, that fulfill the condition, $m_P(i.j) = m_P(i) \times m_P(j)$, are called inductively independent (or initially irrelevant, in the terminology of [28: 356]) with respect to that m_P. We get

T6–9.   If i and j have no primitive predicate in common, then

$$m_P(i \lor j) = m_P(i) + m_P(j) - m_P(i) \times m_P(j) \text{ (T1h, D1h)}.$$

T6–10.

a. For any basic sentence B, $m_P(B) = 1/2$.

Proof: $B \lor \sim B$ is L-true. Therefore, by T1b, $m_P(B \lor \sim B) = 1$. Hence the assertion with D1g and T1–i.

b. For any conjunction, C_n, of n basic sentences with n distinct primitive predicates, $m_P(C_n) = (1/2)^n$ (D1h,(a)).

c. If i and i' are isomorphic, then $m_P(i) = m_P(i')$ (D1e).

We now get

T6–11.   If i and j have no primitive predicate in common, then

a. $\text{cont}(\sim(i.j)) = \text{cont}(\sim i) \times \text{cont}(\sim j)$ (D1h, T3c).

b. $\text{cont}(i \lor j) = \text{cont}(i) \times \text{cont}(j)$.

Proof: $i \lor j$ is L-equivalent to $\sim (\sim i. \sim j)$. $\sim i$ and $\sim j$ have no primitive predicate in common since i and j do not. Hence the assertion from (a).

c. $\text{cont}(i.j) = \text{cont}(i) + \text{cont}(j) - \text{cont}(i) \times \text{cont}(j)$ (T4j, (b)).

In our $\mathscr{L}_3^2$, $\text{cont}('Ma \lor Yb') = \text{cont}('Ma \lor Ya') = 1/4$ and $\text{cont}('Ma. \sim Yb') = 3/4$.

T6–12.   Let D_n be a disjunction of n ($\geqq 2$) sentences with no primitive predicate occurring in more than one of these sentences. Then $\text{cont}(D_n) =$ the product of the cont-values of the n components (T11b).

T6–13.

a. For any basic sentence B, $\text{cont}(B) = 1/2$ (T3a, T10a).

b. For any disjunction, D_n, of n basic sentences with n distinct primitive predicates, $\text{cont}(D_n) = (1/2)^n$ (T3a, T12, (a)).

c. For any conjunction, C_n, of n basic sentences with n distinct primitive predicates, $\text{cont}(C_n) = 1 - (1/2)^n$ (T3a, T10b, (a)).

d. For any Q-sentence i, $\text{cont}(i) = 1 - (1/2)^\pi((c)) = 1 - 1/\kappa$ (T2–1b) $= (\kappa - 1)/\kappa$.

$$\text{cont}('[M. \sim Y]a') = 3/4 \text{ (since } \pi = 2, \ \kappa = 4 \text{ (T2 − 1b))}.$$

e. Let i have the form $C_1 \vee C_2 \vee \cdots \vee C_m$, where each C is a conjunction of n basic sentences with n distinct primitive predicates, the same n atomic sentences occurring in all conjunctions. (Under these circumstances, i has disjunctive normal form. See [28: 94] or any textbook on Symbolic Logic.) Then

$$\text{cont}(i) = 1 - \frac{m}{2^n}.$$

Proof: Any two distinct conjunctions are L-exclusive. Therefore, from T4i, $\text{cont}(i) = \text{cont}(C_1) + \text{cont}(C_2) + \cdots + \text{cont}(C_m) - (m-1)$. Hence the conclusion with (c).

$$\text{cont}('(Ma.Yb) \vee (\sim Ma.Yb) \vee (Ma. \sim Yb)') = 1 - \frac{3}{2^2} = \frac{1}{4}.$$

Notice that this disjunction is L-equivalent to '$Ma \vee Yb$', that is, a disjunction fulfilling (b).

f. Let i have the form $D_1.D_2.\cdots.D_m$, where each D is a disjunction of n basic sentences with n distinct primitive predicates, the same n atomic sentences occurring in all disjunctions. (Under these circumstances, i has conjunctive normal form. See [28: 95].) Then

$$\text{cont}(i) = \frac{m}{2^n}.$$

Proof: Any two distinct disjunctions are L-disjunct. Therefore, from T4k, $\text{cont}(i) = \text{cont}(D_1) + \text{cont}(D_2) + \cdots + \text{cont}(D_m)$. Hence the assertion with (b).

$$\text{cont }('(Ma \vee Yb).(\sim Ma \vee Yb).(Ma \vee \sim Yb)') = \frac{3}{2^2} = \frac{3}{4}.$$

Notice that this conjunction is L-equivalent to '$Ma \cdot Yb$', that is, a conjunction fulfilling (c).

T6–14. If i and i' are isomorphic and j and j' are isomorphic on the basis of the same permutation of the individual constants, then $\text{cont}(j'/i') = \text{cont}(j/i)$ (T8b, T10c).

T6–15.

a. For any two basic sentences, B_i and B_j, with different primitive predicates, $\text{cont}(B_j/B_i) = 1/4$ (T13c, T10a) $= 1/2 \ \text{cont}(B_i)$ (T13a).

$$\text{cont}(\text{'}Ya\text{'}/\text{'}Ma\text{'}) = \frac{1}{4}.$$

b. Let $B_1, B_2, \cdots, B_n$ be basic sentences with n distinct primitive predicates. Let C_m be the conjunction of the first m of them, Then, for every m $(m = 2, \cdots, n-1)$,

$$\text{cont}(B_{m+1}/C_m) = \frac{1}{2^{m+1}}.$$

Proof: $C_m \cdot B_{m+1} = C_{m+1}$. Hence

$$\text{cont}(B_{m+1}/C_m) = \text{cont}(C_{m+1}) - \text{cont}(C_m)$$

$$= 1 - \frac{1}{2^{m+1}} - \left(1 - \frac{1}{2^m}\right) \text{(T13c)} = \frac{1}{2^{m+1}}.$$

T6–16. Let i and j be molecular sentences with no primitive predicate in common. Then $\text{cont}(j/i) = \text{cont}(j) - \text{cont}(i) \times \text{cont}(j)$ (T11c) $= \text{cont}(j) \times (1 - \text{cont}(i)) = \text{cont}(j) \times \text{cont}(\sim i)$ (T4l) $= \text{cont}(j) \times m_P(i)$ (T3c).

7. THE SECOND EXPLICATUM: MEASURE OF INFORMATION (INF)

[One of the theorems derived in the previous section states that if i and j are basic sentences with different primitive predicates, then $\text{cont}(j/i) = \frac{1}{2} \text{cont}(i)$. Since basic sentences with different primitive predicates are inductively independent, this result makes cont look inadequate as an explicatum for in. It turns out that no explicatum fulfilling all our intuitive requirements for an amount-of-information function is possible, indicating a certain inconsistency between these requirements. cont fulfills a partial set of these requirements, and a different, though overlapping, partial set is fulfilled by another function, called measure of information, denoted by 'inf', and defined as

$$\text{inf}(i) = \text{Log} \frac{1}{1 - \text{cont}(i)}.$$

It is shown that

$$\inf(h, e) = \text{Log} \frac{1}{c_P(h, e)}$$

where $c_P(h, e)$ is the degree of confirmation of the hypothesis h on the evidence e, defined as

$$\left. \frac{m_P(e \cdot h)}{m_P(e)} \cdot \right]$$

The last-but-one theorem of the preceding section (T6–15) may not appear entirely plausible. According to this theorem, if an "ideal" receiver with no previous knowledge receives a sequence of n basic sentences with n different primitive predicates, the amount of information he gets from the first sentence is 1/2, from the second only 1/4, from the third 1/8, from each only half as much as from the preceding one. And this will be the case despite the fact that these basic sentences are independent from each other not only deductively but also inductively. One has the feeling that under such conditions the amount of information carried by each sentence should not depend upon its being preceded by another of its kind.

An inconsistency in our intuitions, at which we already hinted above (§6), becomes now even more prominent. The feeling to which we referred in the preceding paragraph may be expressed also as a requirement that additivity should hold for the amount of information carried by the conjunction of two sentences if these sentences are inductively independent. We saw, however, that additivity holds for cont only if these sentences are L-disjunct and have no content in common. Now, it is clear that two basic sentences, B_1 and B_2, with different primitive predicates, have content in common: the factual sentence $B_1 \lor B_2$, for instance, is L-implied by each. Nevertheless, this condition of additivity looked plausible in its context.

It seems best to resolve this conflict of intuitions by assuming that there is not one explicandum "amount of semantic information" but at least two, for one of which cont is indeed a suitable explicatum whereas the explicatum for the other still has to be found.

Let us now state the additional requirement in a formal way:

R7–1.   If i and j are inductively independent, then $\text{in}(i . j) = \text{in}(i) + \text{in}(j)$.

From R1 and D5–1 follows immediately:

T7–1.   If B_i and B_j are two basic sentences with distinct primitive predicates, then $\text{in}(B_j/B_i) = \text{in}(B_j)$.

Let us also decide, for the sake of normalization, to assign to each basic sentence an in-value of 1.

R7–2. For any basic sentence B, $\text{in}(B) = 1$.

We have now

T7–2. For a conjunction of n basic sentences, C_n, with n distinct primitive predicates, $\text{in}(C_n) = n$ (R1, R2).

T6–13c stated that $\text{cont}(C_n) = 1 - (1/2)^n$, hence

$$2^n = \frac{1}{1 - \text{cont}(C_n)}$$

hence

$$n = \text{Log} \frac{1}{1 - \text{cont}(C_n)}$$

(where 'Log' is short for 'logarithm to the base 2'). This, combined with T2, yields

T7–3. For a conjunction of n basic sentences, C_n, with n distinct primitive predicates,

$$\text{in}(C_n) = \text{Log} \frac{1}{1 - \text{cont}(C_n)}.$$

T3 gives us the lead for defining the second explicatum for "amount of information". This new function will be called measure of information and denoted by 'inf'. Extending the relationship stated in T3 to hold for all sentences, we define

D7–1. For any sentence i,

$$\text{inf}(i) = \text{Log} \frac{1}{1 - \text{cont}(i)}.$$

D1 may be usefully transformed into

T7–4.

a. $\text{inf}(i) = - \text{Log}(1 - \text{cont}(i)) = - \text{Log}\,\text{cont}(\sim 1) = \text{Log} \dfrac{1}{\text{cont}(\sim i)}.$

b. $\text{inf}(\sim i) = - \text{Log}\,\text{cont}(i).$

c. $\text{cont}(\sim i) = 2^{-\text{inf}(i)}.$

d. $\text{cont}(i) = 1 - 2^{-\text{inf}(i)}.$

T7–5.

a. $\qquad\qquad \text{inf}(i) = \text{Log} \dfrac{1}{m_P(i)}$ (D1, T6–3)

b. $\qquad\qquad\quad = - \text{Log}\,m_P(i).$

The form of T5a is analogous to the customary definition of amount of information in communication theory. In the place of the ocncept of probability in the statistical sense (relative frequency) used in that definition, we have here the logical (inductive) probability m_P. For a detailed discussion of the relation between these two concepts, see [28: §§3,10].

T7-6. $m_P(i) = 2^{-inf(i)}$.

A host of other theorems for inf can easily be derived. We shall mention only a few of them.

T7-7. $\inf(\sim i) = \text{Log}\dfrac{1}{1 - m_P(i)} = -\text{Log}(1 - m_P(i))$.

T7-8.

a. $0 \leqq \inf(i) \leqq \infty$ (T6–4a).
b. $\inf(i) = 0$ iff i is L-true (T6–4b).
c. $\inf(i) = \infty$ iff i is L-false (T6–4c).
d. $\inf(i)$ is positive finite iff i is factual (T6–4d).
e. If i L-implies j, then $\inf(i) \geqq \inf(j)$ (T6–4e).
f. If i is L-equivalent to j, then $\inf(i) = \inf(j)$ (T6–4f).
g. $\inf(i.j) \geqq \inf(i) \geqq \inf(i \vee j)$ (T6–4g).
h. $\inf(i.j) = -\text{Log}\,\text{cont}(\sim i \vee \sim j)$ (T4a)
    $= -\text{Log}(\text{cont}(\sim i) + \text{cont}(\sim j) - \text{cont}(\sim i. \sim j))$ (T6–4h)
    $= -\text{Log}(2^{-inf(i)} + 2^{-inf(j)} - 2^{-inf(i \vee j)})$ (T4c).
i. If i and j are L-disjunct, then $\inf(i.j) = -\text{Log}(2^{-inf(i)} + 2^{-inf(j)} - 1)$
    ((h),(b)).
j. $\inf(i \vee j) = -\text{Log}\,\text{cont}(\sim i. \sim j)$ (T4a) $= -\text{Log}(1 - 2^{-inf(\sim i. \sim j)})$.
k. If i and j are L-exclusive (hence $\sim i$ and $\sim j$ L-disjunct), then
    $\inf(i \vee j) = -\text{Log}(\text{cont}(\sim i) + \text{cont}(\sim j))$ ((j), T4k)
    $= -\text{Log}(2^{-inf(i)} + 2^{-inf(j)})$ (T4c).
l. $\inf(\sim i) = \inf(i) - \text{Log}(2^{inf(i)} - 1)$ (T4b,d).

Whereas the correspondence between T8a through 9 and T6–4a through g is straightforward, T8h through l are much more complicated and much less convenient for computation than their corresponding theorems T6–4h through l.

As against the complicated formula T8i, we have, however,

T7-9.   (Additivity) $\inf(i.j) = \inf(i) + \inf(j)$ iff i and j are inductively independent.

Proof: $\inf(i.j) = -\text{Log}\,m_P(i.j)$ (T5b);
   $\inf(i) + \inf(j) = \text{Log}\,2^{inf(i)} + \text{Log}\,2^{inf(j)} = -\text{Log}(2^{-inf(i)} \times 2^{-inf(j)})$
   $= -\text{Log}(m_P(i) \times m_P(j))$ (T6);

$m_P(i \cdot j) = m_P(i) \times m_P(j)$ iff i and j are inductively independent (by definition).

To T6–13 corresponds

T7–10.

a. For any basic sentence B, $\inf(B) = 1$.

b. For any disjunction, D_n, of n basic sentences with n distinct primitive predicates,

$$\inf(D_n) = \mathrm{Log}\frac{1}{1-(1/2)^n} = \mathrm{Log}\,\frac{2^n}{2^n-1} = n - \mathrm{Log}(2^n - 1).$$

c. For any conjunction, C_n, of n basic sentences with n distinct primitive predicates, $\inf(C_n) = n$.

d. For any Q-sentence i, $\inf(i) = \pi$.

e. Let i have disjunctive normal form: $C_1 \vee C_2 \vee \cdots \vee C_m$. Let every C be a conjunction of n basis sentences with n distinct primitive predicates, the same n atomic sentences occurring in all conjunctions. Then

$$\inf(i) = n - \mathrm{Log}\,m.$$

$\inf('(Ma \cdot Yb) \vee (\sim Ma \cdot Yb) \vee (Ma \cdot \sim Yb)') = 2 - \mathrm{Log}\,3 (= 0.412)$.

f. Let i have conjunctive normal form: $D_1 \cdot D_2 \cdot \cdots \cdot D_m$. Let every D be a disjunction of n basic sentences with n distinct primitive predicates, the same n atomic sentences occurring in all disjunctions. Then

$$\inf(i) = n - \mathrm{Log}(2^n - m).$$

$\inf('(Ma \vee Yb) \cdot (\sim Ma \vee Yb) \cdot (Ma \vee \sim Yb)') = 2 - \mathrm{Log}(2^2 - 3) = 2$.

T8e, b and d show that inf fulfills R5–1* through R5–3*. T9 corresponds to R1, and T10a to R2. Thereby it is shown that inf fulfills all our requirements for the second explicatum for amount of information.

The following table gives approximate inf-values for D_2 (T10b) through D_{10}:

TABLE II

n	$\inf(D_n)$
2	0.412
3	0.192
4	0.093
5	0.046
6	0.023
7	0.0113
8	0.0056
9	0.0028
10	0.0014

We define now the relative measure of information in the already familiar way:

D7–2. $\inf(j/i) =_{Df} \inf(i \cdot j) - \inf(i)$.

T7–11.

a. For any two basic sentences, B_i and B_j, with distinct primitive predicates, $\inf(B_j/B_i) = 1$ (D2, T10c, a) $= \inf(B_i)$ (T10a).

$$\inf(\text{‘}Ma\text{’} / \text{‘}Yb\text{’}) = \inf(\text{‘}Ma\text{’} / \text{‘}Ya\text{’}) = 1.$$

b. Let $B_1, B_2, \cdots, B_n$ be basic sentences with n distinct primitive predicates. Let C_m be the conjunction of the first m of them. Then, for every m $(m = 2, \cdots, n - 1)$,

$$\inf(B_{m+1}/C_m) = 1 \, (\text{D2}, \text{T10c}, (\text{a})).$$

T7–12.

a. $\inf(j/i) = \inf(j)$ iff i and j are inductively independent (D2, T9).

b. If i and j have no primitive predicates in common, $\inf(j/i) = \inf(j)$ (T6–9a, (a)).

In [28: §55] the concept of degree of confirmation of an hypothesis h on the evidence e, on the basis of a given range measure m, is defined as follows:

$$c(h, e) \ = \ \frac{m(e \cdot h)}{m(e)}.$$

e L-implies h if, and only if, the range of e is wholly contained in the range of h. If, however, only a part of $R(e)$ is contained in $R(h)$, then none of the customary relations of deductive logic hold between e and h. If, say, that part of $R(e)$ which is contained in $R(h)$ is three fourths of $R(e)$, as measured by m, if, in other words,

$$\frac{m(e \cdot h)}{m(e)} = \frac{3}{4},$$

then we shall say that the hypothesis h is confirmed by the evidence e to the degree 3/4 and write this relation, which is fundamental for inductive logic, as '$c(h, e) = 3/4$'. c is meant as an explicatum for (relative) inductive probability.

Figure 1 might be of some help for a visualization of the difference between L-implication and degree of confirmation as dependent upon the relations between the ranges of the hypothesis and the evidence.

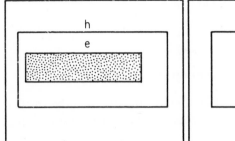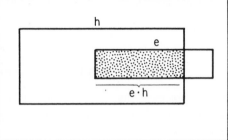

Figure 1

Deductive Logic
'e L-implies h' means that the range
of e is entirely contained in that of h.

Inductive Logic
'c(h,e) = 3/4' means that three-fourths of the
range of e is contained in that of h.

For an m_P-function, we have more specifically

D7–3. $c_P(h,e) =_{Df} \dfrac{m_P(e\,.\,h)}{m_P(e)}$.

T7–13.   If inf and c_P are based on the same m_P, then

$$\inf(h/e) = \text{Log } \frac{1}{c_P(h,e)} = -\text{Log}\,c_P(h,e).$$

Proof: $\inf(h/e) = \inf(e\,.\,h) - \inf(e) = \text{Log}\,m_P(e) - \text{Log}\,m_P(e\,.\,h)$

$$= \text{Log}\frac{m_P(e)}{m_P(e\,.\,h)} = \text{Log}\frac{1}{c_P(h,e)}.$$

This theorem shows the strong connection that exists between the relative measure of information of a new message h with respect to the knowledge e and the degree of confirmation of an hypothesis h on the evidence e, in other words, the relative inductive probability of an hypothesis h on the evidence e. The characterization of h as message and e as knowledge, on the one hand, or as hypothesis and evidence, on the other, has didactive value only; h and e are, strictly speaking, simply any sentences of the given system. T13 shows that $\inf(h/e)$ is the greater the more improbable h is on the evidence e. That the relative amount of information carried by a sentence should increase with its degree of improbability seems plausible. This holds also for cont, if e remains fixed, as shown by the following theorem.

T7–14.   If cont and c_P are based on the same m_P, then

$$\text{cont}(h/e) = m_P(e) \times (1 - c_P(h,e)) = m_P(e) \times c_P(\sim h,e).$$

Proof: $\text{cont}(h/e) = m_P(e) - m_P(e \cdot h)$ (T6–8a)

$$= m_P(e) \times \frac{m_P(e) - m_P(e \cdot h)}{m_P(e)}$$

$$= m_P(e) \times (1 - c_P(h,e)) \text{(D3)}.$$

Notice, however, that for variable e it need not be the case that the smaller $c_P(h,e)$ is, the larger $\text{cont}(h/e)$ will be, because of the factor $m_P(e)$. (See end of §10, below.)

8.   COMPARISON BETWEEN CONT AND INF

[The cont and inf measures are compared in greater detail. Both exhibit properties which look intuitively plausible and others which look intuitively implausible. The formally most striking comparison is given by the following pair of theorems:

$$\text{cont}(h/e) = m_P(e) - m_P(e \cdot h),$$
$$\text{inf}(h/e) = \text{Log}\, m_P(e) - \text{Log}\, m_P(e \cdot h).]$$

We are now ready for a comparison between the two explicata for amount of information. Let us begin with stating some corresponding theorems one beside the other for better confrontation.

T6–4k. $\text{cont}(i.j) = \text{cont}(i) + \text{cont}(j)$ iff i and j are L-disjunct.
T6–4m. $\text{cont}(i.j) \leqq \text{cont}(i) + \text{cont}(j)$.
T6–13a. For any basic sentence B, $\text{cont}(B) = 1/2$.

T6–13c. For any conjunction, C_n, of n basic sentences with n distinct primitive predicates, $\text{cont}(C_n) = 1 - (1/2)^n$.

T6–15a. For any two basic sentences, B_i and B_j, with distinct primitive predicates, $\text{cont}(B_j/B_i) = 1/4 = 1/2\,\text{cont}(B_i)$.

T6–15b. Let $B_1, B_2, ..., B_n$ be basic sentences with n distinct primitive predicates. Let C_m be the conjunction of the first m of them. Then, for every m $(m = 2, ..., n-1)$,

$$\text{cont}(B_{m+1}/C_m) = (1/2)^{m+1}.$$

T6–5b. $\text{cont}(j/i) = \text{cont}(j)$ iff i and j are L-disjunct.

T6–7. $\text{cont}(j/i) \leqq \text{cont}(j)$.

T6–4l. $\text{cont}(\sim i) = 1 - \text{cont}(i)$.

T7–9. $\text{inf}(i.j) = \text{inf}(i) + \text{inf}(j)$ iff i and j are inductively independent.
T7–10a. For any basic sentence B, $\text{inf}(B) = 1$.

T7–10c. For any conjunction, C_n, of n basic sentences with n distinct predicates, $\text{inf}(C_n) = n$.

T7–11a. For any two basic sentences, B_i and B_j, with distinct primitive predicates, $\text{inf}(B_j/B_i) = 1 = \text{inf}(B_i)$.

T7–11b. Let $B_1, B_2, ..., B_n$ be basic sentences with n distinct primitive predicates. Let C_m be the conjunction of the first m of them. Then, for every m $(m = 2, ..., n-1)$,

$$\text{inf}(B_{m+1}/C_m) = 1.$$

T7–12a. $\text{inf}(j/i) = \text{inf}(j)$ iff i and j are inductively independent.

T7–8l. $\text{inf}(\sim i) = \text{inf}(i) - \text{Log}(2^{\text{inf}(i)} - 1)$.

We see that the conditions of additivity for cont and inf are entirely different. This divergence is not surprising at all. On the contrary, dissatisfaction with the condition of additivity stated for cont in T6–4k was one of the reasons for our search for another explicatum of amount of information. It is of some psychological interest to notice that common sense would probably prefer T7–9 to T6–4k, whereas inf has no property comparable to that exhibited by cont in T6–4m, a theorem that looks highly intuitive.

The counter-intuitiveness of the lack of a counterpart to T6–4m might be reduced by the following example. Consider a system with 6 primitive predicates, P_1 to P_6, hence with $2^6 = 64$ Q-properties. All proper m-functions have equal values for the 64 Q-sentences with the same individual constant, hence the value $1/64$ for each. Let i be '$P_1 a$'. P_1 is the disjunction of the first 32 Q's. Hence $m_P(i) = 1/2$. Therefore $\inf(i) = - \mathrm{Log}(1/2) = 1$. Let M be a disjunction of 32 Q's, that is, of Q_1 and the last 31 Q's. Let j be 'Ma'. Then $m(j) = 1/2$ and $\inf(j) = 1$. $i.j$ is L-equivalent to '$Q_1 a$'; hence, it is a very strong sentence. $m(i.j) = 1/64$. $\inf(i.j) = - \mathrm{Log}(1/64) = 6$. This is three times as much as the sum of the inf-values of the two components. This result becomes plausible if we realize that i says merely that a has one of certain 32 Q's, but that by the addition of j, which by itself also says no more than that a has one of 32 Q's, our information about the situation is at once made completely specific; that is, it is specified as saying that a has one particular Q.

Continuing the comparison, we may dismiss the difference between T6–13a and T7–10a as inessential, the number 1 in T7–10a being only a matter of normalization. However, the differences between T6–13c and T7–10c, T6–15a and T7–11a, and T6–15b and T7–11b are decisive. Whereas the cont-value of a basic sentence relative to a conjunction of basic sentences with primitive predicates is always less than its absolute cont-value and decreases, moreover, with the number of components in the conjunction, the inf-value of a basic sentence relative to such a conjunction is equal to its absolute inf-value and is therefore also independent of the number of components in this conjunction.

The relation between cont and inf is exhibited in the perhaps simplest and most striking fashion by the following pair of formulas which appear in the proofs of T7–13 and T7–14:

$$\inf(h/e) \;=\; \mathrm{Log}\, m_P(e) - \mathrm{Log}\, m_P(e.h), \tag{1}$$

$$\mathrm{cont}(h/e) \;=\; m_P(e) - m_P(e.h). \tag{2}$$

For the tautological evidence t, we get

$$\inf(h/t) \;=\; \inf(h) \;=\; - \mathrm{Log}\, m_P(h) \tag{3}$$

and

$$\operatorname{cont}(h/t) = \operatorname{cont}(h) = \quad 1- \quad m_P(h), \qquad (4)$$

formulas that are nothing else than variants of T7–5b and T6–3a but look now much more akin, especially if we write (3) as

$$\operatorname{inf}(h/t) \quad = \operatorname{inf}(h) \quad = \operatorname{Log} 1 - \operatorname{Log} m_P(h). \qquad (3')$$

Let us illustrate the relation between cont and inf also in the following numerical example.

Let $B_1, B_2, \cdots$ be basic sentences with distinct primitive predicates. Let C_1 be B_1, C_2 be $B_1 . B_2, \cdots, C_n$ be $B_1 . B_2 . \cdots . B_n, \cdots$. Then cont and inf have the following values for these C, according to T6–13c and T7–10c:

TABLE III

C_i	$\operatorname{cont}(C_i)$	$\operatorname{inf}(C_i)$
C_1	1/2	1
C_2	3/4	2
C_3	7/8	3
C_4	15/16	4
.	.	.
.	.	.
.	.	.
C_n	$1 - (1/2^n)$	n
.	.	.
.	.	.
.	.	.

9.   D-FUNCTIONS AND I-FUNCTIONS

[Not all m_P-functions can be regarded as equally adequate explicata of initial inductive probability. It seems that only those which fulfill the additional requirement of instantial relevance—m_I-functions—are adequate for ordinary scientific purposes, whereas that m_P-function which exhibits instantial irrelevance—m_D—has properties which make it suitable for situations where inductive reasoning is of minor importance. Computations with m_D and the in-functions based upon it, are relatively easy due to the fact that m_D assigns equal values to all state-descriptions. One consequence is, for instance, that a sufficient conditions for $m_D(i.j) = m_D(i) \times m_D(j)$ is already that i and j should have no atomic sentences in common, whereas only the much stronger condition that i and j should have no primitive predicates in common is sufficient for the corresponding theorem concerning m_I.]

Not every m_P can serve as a basis for an inductive method that is in agreement with customary scientific procedures [29: §2]. There is at least one additional requirement for the adequacy of an m-function to serve as an explicatum for (absolute, initial) inductive probability. This is

R9–1. (Requirement of instantial relevance) Let 'M' be a factual, molecular predicate. Let e be any non-L-false molecular sentence. Let i and h be full sentences of 'M' with two distinct individual constants which do not occur in e. Then

$$\frac{m(e.\,i.\,h)}{m(e.\,i)} > \frac{m(e.\,h)}{m(e)}.$$

(This can be formulated more simply in terms of 'c' as

$$c(h, e.\,i) > c(h, e).)$$

The requirement says, in effect, that one instance of a property is positively relevant to (the prediction of) another instance of the same property. This seems a basic feature of all inductive reasoning concerning the prediction of a future event.

We therefore define inductive m-function (in the narrower sense), to be denoted by 'm_I', as

D9–1. m is an inductive m-function $=_{Df} m$ is an m_P and fulfills R1.

Among the proper m-functions which do not fulfill R1, there is one which fulfills, so to speak, a requirement of instantial irrelevance. For this m-function, to be denoted by 'm_D' ('D' for 'deductive' since this function plays a special role in deductive logic), observed instances of a molecular property have no influence on the prediction of future instances of this property. Experience cannot teach us anything about the future if this function is applied. It has, nevertheless, great importance: its definition is of extreme simplicity, calculations on its basis are relatively easy, and results obtained by its use may have at least approximative value in cases where experience is estimated to be of little or no influence.

The definition of m_D incorporates a principle which looks very plausible to untrained common sense, viz. the principle of assigning equal m-values to all state-descriptions. It is of some psychological interest that this rather obvious procedure should lead to an inductive method that is unacceptable as a final method. (The function designated here by 'm_D' has been denoted by '$m\dagger$' in [28: §110A] and by 'm_∞' in [29: §13].)

We define

D9–2.

a. For every Z_i, $m_D(Z_i) =_{Df} 1/z$.

b. For every L-false sentence j, $m_D(j) =_{Df} 0$.

c. For every non-L-false sentence j, $m_D(j) =_{Df}$ the sum of the m_D-values for the Z in $R(j)$; this is $r(j)/z$, where $r(j)$ is the number of the state-descriptions in $R(j)$.

It can easily be verified that m_D fulfills conditions D6–1a through D6–1g and D6–1i. That m_D also fulfills D6–1h and is therefore an m_P-function, follows from the much stronger theorem

T9–1.   If i and j have no atomic sentences in common, then

$$m_D(i.j) = m_D(i) \times m_D(j).$$

Proof: Let K_1 be the class of those atomic sentences which occur in i, K_2 the class of those atomic sentences which occur in j, K_3 the class of all other atomic sentences. Let C_1 be the class of those conjunctions which contain, for each atomic sentence in K_1, either it or its negation, but not both nor any other component. Let C_2 and C_3 be determined analogously with respect to K_2 and K_3. Let c_1 be the number of the conjunctions in C_1. Let c_2 and c_3 be determined analogously with respect to C_2 and C_3. (However, if C_3 is empty, let $c_3 = 1$.) Each Z is a conjunction of three conjunctions (disregarding the order) belonging respectively to C_1, C_2, and C_3. Therefore

$$z = c_1 \times c_2 \times c_3 \text{ (T2–1c).} \tag{1}$$

Let $c_1(i)$ be the number of those conjunctions in C_1 which L-imply i, and let $c_2(j)$ be the number of those conjunctions in C_2 which L-imply j. (Notice that i cannot be L-implied by any conjunction of C_2 or C_3, nor can j be be L-implied by any conjunction of C_1 or C_3.) Therefore

$$r(i) = c_1(i) \times c_2 \times c_3 \tag{2}$$

and

$$r(j) = c_2(j) \times c_1 \times c_3. \tag{3}$$

But for the same reason we have also

$$r(i.j) = c_1(i) \times c_2(j) \times c_3. \tag{4}$$

From (2) and (3) we get

$$\begin{aligned} r(i) \times r(j) &= c_1(i) \times c_2 \times c_3 \times c_2(j) \times c_1 \times c_3 \\ &= r(i.j) \times c_1 \times c_2 \times c_3 \text{ (from (4))} \\ &= r(i.j) \times z \text{ (from (1)).} \end{aligned} \tag{5}$$

Dividing by z^2 we get finally

$$\frac{r(i)}{z} \times \frac{r(j)}{z} = \frac{r(i.j)}{z} \tag{6}$$

from which the assertion follows, by D2c.

Since m_D is an m_P-function, all theorems stated in §6 for m_P hold also for m_D. But some of them, having conditional form, can be strengthened by weakening the antecedent. We get, for instance, in analogy to T6–9,

T9–2. If i and j have no atomic sentence in common, then

$$m_D(i \lor j) = m_D(i) + m_D(j) - m_D(i) \times m_D(j),$$

and in analogy to T6–10b,

T9–3. For any conjunction, C_n, of n basic sentences with n distinct atomic sentences, $m_D(C_n) = (1/2)^n$.

For that cont-function which is based on m_D according to D6–2, cont_D, we have

T9–4.
a. For every E_i, $\text{cont}_D(E_i) = 1/z$.
b. For every sentence j, $\text{cont}_D(j) = n/z$, where n is the number of E which belong to $\text{Cont}(j)$.

cont_D has advantages and disadvantages similar to those of m_D. T4b points to the extreme simplicity, at least in principle, of its computation. All theorems on cont stated in §6 also hold, of course, for cont_D and all cont_I, the cont-functions defined on the basis of the m_I, analogously to D3. With respect to cont_I, no additional theorems in the form of equalities can be derived from R1. We shall not care to derive some inequalities from R1 and the previous theorems, especially since we shall treat later (§10) at some length a numerical example based on a specific cont_I-function.

With respect to cont_D, however, various theorems holding for cont_P can be strengthened by weakening the condition in the antecedent, in complete analogy to the relation between m_D and m_P. T6–11, T6–12, T6–13b, c, e, f, T6–15, and T6–16 hold for cont_D, even if the expression 'primitive predicate(s)' in their antecedents is replaced by 'atomic sentence(s)'. That this should be so is plausible in view of T1. But it is also easy to check the truth of our general assertion by inspecting the proofs of these theorems.

Let us state, however, also one theorem which is not a counterpart of a previous theorem:

T9–5.
a. For every conjunction, C_n, of n distinct E, $\text{cont}_D(C_n) = n/z$ (T4b).
b. For every conjunction, C_n, of n distinct E, different from E_i,

$$\text{cont}_D(E_i/C_n) = 1/z \,(\text{D6-2},(a)).$$

The relation between $\inf_D$, defined on the basis of cont_D following D7-1 and inf is the same as that between cont_D and cont. We shall therefore state only those theorems which are based on T4 and T5.

T9-6.

a. For every E, $\inf_D(E) = \beta - \text{Log}(z - 1)$.

Proof: $\inf_D E = \text{Log}[1/(1 - 1/z)]\,(\text{T4a}) = \text{Log}(z/(z-1)) = \beta - \text{Log}(z-1)$ (T2-1c).

b. For every conjunction, C_n, of n distinct E, $\inf_D(C_n) = \beta - \text{Log}(z - n)$.

Proof: $\inf_D(C_n) = \text{Log}[1/(1 - n/z)]\,(\text{T5a}) = \text{Log}(z/(z-n)) = \beta - \text{Log}(z-n)$ (T2-1c).

c. For every conjunction, C_n, of n distinct E, different from E_i,

$$\inf_D(E_i/C_n) = \text{Log}(z - n) - \text{Log}(z-n-1)\,(\text{D7-2}, \text{ (b)}).$$

According to the correlate of T7-10e, $\inf_D(i) = n - \text{Log}\,m$, where i has disjunctive normal form: $C_1 \lor C_2 \lor \cdots \lor C_m$, each C being a conjunction of basic sentences with n distinct atomic sentences, the same n atomic sentences occurring in all conjunctions. According to a well-known theorem in the sentential calculus, there exists for every molecular sentence a sentence in disjunctive normal form L-equivalent to it (see, for instance [28: D21-2]). It follows that for every molecular sentence i, $\inf_D(i)$ has the form $n - \text{Log}\,m$, where both n and m are integers. Hence it is easy to calculate the $\inf_D$-value of any molecular sentence. Such a sentence has to be transformed into

TABLE IV

m	Log m	m	Log m	m	Log m
1	0.0000	39	5.2853	57	5.8328
2	1.0000	40	5.3219	58	5.8579
3	1.5849	41	5.3575	59	5.8826
4	2.0000	42	5.3923	60	5.9068
5	2.3219	43	5.4262	61	5.9307
6	2.5849	44	5.4594	62	5.9541
7	2.8073	45	5.4918	63	5.9772
8	3.0000	46	5.5235	64	6.0000
9	3.1699	47	5.5545	100	6.6438
10	3.3219	48	5.5849	128	7.0000
16	4.0000	49	5.6147	250	7.9657
32	5.0000	50	5.6438	251	7.9715
33	5.0443	51	5.6724	252	7.9772
34	5.0874	52	5.7004	253	7.9829
35	5.1292	53	5.7279	254	7.9886
36	5.1699	54	5.7548	255	7.9943
37	5.2094	55	5.7813	256	8.0000
38	5.2479	56	5.8073	1000	9.9657

one of its disjunctive normal forms, according to some standard procedure available for this purpose. Then the number of its components has to be counted as well as the number of atomic sentences in one of these components. Finally, a table for $\text{Log}\, m$, for integer m, will have to be consulted and a simple subtraction performed. For purposes of reference, such a table (Table IV) is given above for some selected integral values of m.

Let the E in our $\mathscr{L}_3^2$ be $E_1, E_2, \cdots, E_{64}$. Let C_m be the conjunction of the first m E. Then $\text{cont}_D(C_m) = m/64$ (T5a) and $\inf_D(C_m) = 6 - \text{Log}(64 - m)$ (T6b). Table V gives the values of the absolute and relative cont_D for the first six values of m and for the last six values of m.

TABLE V

m	$\text{cont}_D(C_m)$	$\text{cont}_D(E_m/C_{m-1})$	$\inf_D(C_m)$	$\inf_D(E_m/C_{m-1})$
1	1/64	1/64	0.0228	0.0228
2	2/64	1/64	0.0459	0.0231
3	3/64	1/64	0.0693	0.0234
4	4/64	1/64	0.0931	0.0238
5	5/64	1/64	0.1174	0.0242
6	6/64	1/64	0.1421	0.0247
.	.	.	.	.
.	.	.	.	.
.	.	.	.	.
59	59/64	1/64	3.6781	0.2630
60	60/64	1/64	4.0000	0.3219
61	61/64	1/64	4.4151	0.4151
62	62/64	1/64	5.0000	0.5849
63	63/64	1/64	6.0000	1.0000
64	1	1/64	∞	∞

We see from this that if a series of messages is received, each being an E, then cont_D grows by every one of these messages by the same amount, namely, by 1/64, from 0 to 1. $\inf_D$, however, behaves in a different way. It grows from 0 to ∞ by unequal amounts. The first message contributes only a small fraction. Every further message contributes a little more than the preceding one. The last-but-three message contributes less than 1/2. The last-but-two contributes more than 1/2. The last-but-one contributes 1. And the last message contributes ∞. This behavior of $\inf_D$ becomes plausible when we realize that the different messages, although each of them is an E, nevertheless play different roles in the series of messages. When we have received sixty messages (in other words, when we have the knowledge C_{60}), then we know that sixty of the sixty-four possible states of the universe are excluded. There still remain four possible states; that is, our knowledge C_{60} means that the universe is in one of the four remaining states The sixty-first message excludes among these four possible states a further one; hence, the range of those that are still open decreases from four to three. By the sixty-second message the range is further decreased from three to two, and this may well be regarded as a stronger addition to our knowledge than the decrease from four to three. At this moment, only two possibilities are left open. The sixty-third message gives us information concerning which of these two remaining sentences is the actual one and hence completes our knowledge of the universe. Thus, this step has a great weight, more than any of those prior to it. After this step, nothing can be added to our knowledge in a consistent way. The sixty-fourth message is incompatible with the conjunction of the sixty-three preceding ones. If this message is nevertheless added, then this is a still more weighty step which leads to contradiction. The strongest factual message, which is a state-description, a conjunction of 6 basic sentences, carries 6 units of information as measured by $\inf_D$. The only messages that carry more units of information, and then by necessity infinitely many such units, are the messages that contradict either themselves or prior messages.

10.   CONT* AND INF*

[Two special cont_I and $\inf_I$ functions, cont* and inf*, are defined and theorems regarding them developed. These functions are based upon that m_I—m^*—which assigns equal values to all structure-descriptions, i.e., disjunctions of isomorphic state-descriptions. Since m^* seems to have a special status among the various m_I-functions, cont* and inf* are deemed to be of special importance. Various computations and tables regarding these functions are presented.]

We shall now define and investigate two special I-functions that might turn out to be of special importance. They are based on the function m^* defined in [28: §110] essentially as a proper m-function which has the same values for all structure-descriptions, that is, disjunctions of isomorphic state-descriptions.

Recalling the definition of 'isomorphic sentences' given in §6, the reader will easily see that our $\mathscr{L}_3^2$ has exactly 20 structure-descriptions. Let the Z of $\mathscr{L}_3^2$, as presented in Table I, be $Z_1, Z_2, \cdots, Z_{64}$. Then the structure-descriptions 'T_1', 'T_2', $\cdots$, 'T_{20}', are:

T_1: Z_1

T_2: Z_2

T_3: Z_3

T_4: Z_4

T_5: $Z_5 \vee Z_6 \vee Z_7$

T_6: $Z_8 \vee Z_9 \vee Z_{10}$

T_7: $Z_{11} \vee Z_{12} \vee Z_{13}$

T_8: $Z_{14} \vee Z_{15} \vee Z_{16}$

T_9: $Z_{17} \lor Z_{18} \lor Z_{19}$
T_{10}: $Z_{20} \lor Z_{21} \lor Z_{22}$
T_{11}: $Z_{23} \lor Z_{24} \lor Z_{25}$
T_{12}: $Z_{26} \lor Z_{27} \lor Z_{28}$
T_{13}: $Z_{29} \lor Z_{30} \lor Z_{31}$
T_{14}: $Z_{32} \lor Z_{33} \lor Z_{34}$
T_{15}: $Z_{35} \lor Z_{36} \lor Z_{37}$
T_{16}: $Z_{38} \lor Z_{39} \lor Z_{40}$
T_{17}: $Z_{41} \lor Z_{42} \lor Z_{43} \lor Z_{44} \lor Z_{45} \lor Z_{46}$
T_{18}: $Z_{47} \lor Z_{48} \lor Z_{49} \lor Z_{50} \lor Z_{51} \lor Z_{52}$
T_{19}: $Z_{53} \lor Z_{54} \lor Z_{55} \lor Z_{56} \lor Z_{57} \lor Z_{58}$
T_{20}: $Z_{59} \lor Z_{60} \lor Z_{61} \lor Z_{62} \lor Z_{63} \lor Z_{64}$

For all i, $m^*(T_i) = 1/20$, hence $m^*(Z_1) = m^*(Z_2) = m^*(Z_3) = m^*(Z_4) = 1/20$, $m^*(Z_5) = \cdots = m^*(Z_{40}) = 1/60$, $m^*(Z_{41}) = \cdots = m^*(Z_{64}) = 1/120$.

In [29: §18], an argument is presented which shows that the function c^* based on m^* is in a certain sense simpler than other c_P-functions. Explicata for amount of information based on m^* would share this special status.

$c^*(h, e)$, cont$^*(e)$, cont$^*(h/e)$, inf$^*(e)$, and inf$^*(h/e)$ can all be expressed as simple functions of $m^*(e)$ and $m^*(e.h)$:

$$c^*(h,e) = \frac{m^*(e.h)}{m^*(e)} \text{ (D7–3).} \tag{1}$$

$$\text{cont}^*(e) = 1 - m^*(e) \text{ (T6–3a).} \tag{2}$$

$$\text{cont}^*(h/e) = m^*(e) - m^*(e.h) \text{ (T6–8a).} \tag{3}$$

$$\text{inf}^*(e) = - \log m^*(e) \text{ (T7–5b).} \tag{4}$$

$$\text{inf}^*(h/e) = \log m^*(e) - \log m^*(e.h) \text{ (formula (1) in §8).} \tag{5}$$

Let e be '$Ma.Mb$' and h be 'Mc'. Then, by inspection of Table I, we see that

$$m^*(\text{'}Ma.Mb\text{'}) = 2 \times \frac{1}{20} + 10 \times \frac{1}{60} + 4 \times \frac{1}{120} = 0.3.$$

Notice that $m_D(e) = 0.25$. The larger value of m^* is due to instantial relevance. We also have

$$m^*(\text{'}Ma.Mb.Mc\text{'}) = 2 \times \frac{1}{20} + 6 \times \frac{1}{60} = 0.2.$$

Hence

$$c^*(\text{'}Mc\text{'}, \text{'}Ma.Mb\text{'}) = \frac{0.2}{0.3} = \frac{2}{3}.$$

$$\text{cont*}(\text{'}Ma.Mb\text{'}) = 0.7.$$

$$\text{cont*}(\text{'}Mc\text{'}/\text{'}Ma.Mb\text{'}) = 0.3 - 0.2 = 0.1.$$

On the other hand,

$$\text{cont}_D(\text{'}Mc\text{'}/\text{'}Ma.Mb\text{'}) = 0.125.$$

$$\text{inf*}(\text{'}Ma.Mb\text{'}) = -\,\text{Log}\,0.3 = \text{Log}\,10 - \text{Log}\,3 = 1.7370,$$

as against an inf_D-value of 2. Finally,

$$\text{inf*}(\text{'}Mc\text{'}/\text{'}Ma.Mb\text{'}) = \text{Log}\,\frac{0.3}{0.2} = \text{Log}\,3 - \text{Log}\,2 = 0.5849,$$

whereas the corresponding relative inf_D-value is 1.

It might perhaps be worthwhile to investigate now another sample language, this time with only one primitive predicate and n distinct individual constants. In this case, c^* yields the same values as Laplace's rule of succession [28: §110C]. Let e be a conjunction of $s < n$ basic sentences with s distinct individual constants, among them s_1 atomic sentences with 'P' and $s - s_1$ negations of such. Let h be 'Pb', where 'b' is an individual constant not occurring in e. Then the following holds (according to [28:566, formula (4)], cf. remark to D6–1i).

$$m^*(e) = \frac{s_1!(s-s_1)!}{(s+1)!} = \frac{1}{(s+1)\binom{s}{s_1}}. \tag{6}$$

$$m^*(e.h) = \frac{(s_1+1)!(s-s_1)!}{(s+2)!} = m^*(e) \times \frac{s_1+1}{s+2}. \tag{7}$$

$$c^*(h,e) = \frac{s_1+1}{s+2}\ ((1),(6),(7)). \tag{8}$$

$$\text{cont*}(h/e) = m^*(e) \times \left(1 - \frac{s_1+1}{s+2}\right)((3),(6),(7)) = m^*(e) \times \frac{s-s_1+1}{s+2}. \tag{9}$$

To have a numerical example, assume $s = 10$. We get

$$m^*(e) = \frac{1}{11\binom{10}{s_1}}. \tag{10}$$

$$m^*(e.h) = m^*(e) \times \frac{s_1+1}{12}. \tag{11}$$

$$c^*(h,e) = \frac{s_1 + 1}{12}. \tag{12}$$

$$\text{cont}^*(h/e) = m^*(e) \times \frac{11 - s_1}{12}. \tag{13}$$

$$\text{inf}^*(e) = \text{Log} \; \frac{1}{m^*(e)}. \tag{14}$$

$$\text{inf}^*(h/e) = \text{Log} \; \frac{12}{s_1 + 1} \tag{15}$$

The values given in Table VI are calculated according to these formulas.

TABLE VI

s_1	$m^*(e)$	$m^*(e.h)$	$c^*(h,e)$	$\text{cont}^*(e)$	$\text{cont}^*(h/e)$	$\text{inf}^*(e)$	$\text{inf}^*(h/e)$
0	0.09091	0.0076	0.0833	0.90909	0.08333	3.459	3.585
1	0.00909	0.0015	0.1667	0.99091	0.00758	6.781	2.585
2	0.00202	0.0005	0.2500	0.99798	0.00152	8.751	2.000
3	0.00076	0.0003	0.3333	0.99924	0.00051	10.366	1.585
4	0.00043	0.0002	0.4167	0.99957	0.00025	11.174	1.263
5	0.00036	0.0002	0.5000	0.99964	0.00018	11.437	1.000
6	0.00043	0.0003	0.5833	0.99957	0.00018	11.174	0.778
7	0.00076	0.0005	0.6666	0.99924	0.00025	10.366	0.585
8	0.00202	0.0015	0.7500	0.99798	0.00051	8.751	0.514
9	0.00909	0.0076	0.8333	0.99091	0.00152	6.781	0.263
10	0.09091	0.0833	0.9167	0.90909	0.00758	3.459	0.126

In addition to these formulas, we have, of course, also

$$m^*(h) = \tfrac{1}{2}. \tag{16}$$

$$\text{cont}^*(h) = \tfrac{1}{2}. \tag{17}$$

$$\text{inf}^*(h) = 1. \tag{18}$$

A few comments on Table VI might be indicated. The columns for $m^*(e)$ and $m^*(e.h)$ show that this m_I-function, as is to be expected from any adequate m_I-function, puts a premium on homogeneity; that is, those states for which the absolute difference between the individuals having P and those not having P is higher, are treated as initially more probable. When the evidence states that 5 individuals have P and 5 others do not have P, the last column shows that the inf*-value of our hypothesis, which states that an eleventh individual has P, is just 1. Hence it is the same as the absolute inf*-value of this hypothesis. The greater the number of individuals having P, according to the evidence, the larger $c^*(h,e)$ and the smaller $\text{inf}^*(h/e)$. $\text{cont}^*(h/e)$, however, behaves differently. It reaches its minimum for intermediate values of s_1 but increases both when s_1 increases from 6 to 10 and when it decreases from 5 to 0.

11. ESTIMATES OF AMOUNT OF INFORMATION

[A scientist is often interested in the expectation-value of the amount of information conveyed by the outcome of an experiment to be made. If the various possible outcomes can be expressed by $h_1, h_2, \cdots, h_n$, such that these sentences are pairwise exclusive and their disjunction L-true on the given evidence e, in short, when $H = \{h_1, h_2, \cdots, h_n\}$ is an exhaustive system on e, the estimate of the amount of information carried by H with respect to e is given by the formula

$$\text{est(in}, H, e) = \sum_{p=1}^{n} c(h_p, e) \times \text{in}(h_p/e).$$

Various formulas for $\text{est(cont}, H, e)$, $\text{est(inf}, H, e)$, and other functions based upon them are derived. The concepts of posterior estimate of amount of information, amount of specification, estimate of the posterior estimate, and estimate of the amount of specification are defined, and various theorems concerning them proved. A simple illustrative application is given.]

If an experiment is performed, the possible results of which are expressed in n sentences $h_1, \cdots, h_n$ (or in n sentences L-equivalent to them), we can compute the amounts of information which each possible outcome would convey, assuming that an m-function has been defined for all the sentences of the language in which the h's are formulated. So long as the actual outcome is not known, the amount of information it carries is also unknown. But, for certain purposes, it is important to have a good estimate of this amount. The situation is analogous to that existing very often in scientific investigations, where a certain magnitude is unknown and one has to work instead with an estimate of this magnitude.

To give a crude but sufficiently illustrative example: Imagine a thermometer which is divided rather unconventionally into three regions so that in region 1 the pointer indicates Warm, in region 2 Temperate, and in region 3 Cold. Let the thermometer be read in a place where, according to available evidence, most past readings indicated Cold, some Temperate, and only very few Warm. Since the same distribution (approximately) is expected for future readings, an adequate measure of information will assign to the sentence 'Cold(t_1)' (where t_1 is a time-point in the future, that is, one not mentioned in the evidence) a lower value, relative to the evidence, than to 'Temperate(t_1)' which again will have a lower value than 'Warm(t_1)'. Let these sentences be h_1, h_2, and h_3, respectively. What would be a reasonable estimate of the amount of information a future observation is expected to carry? One might at first think of taking the arithmetic mean of the three amounts of information, that is,

$$\frac{\text{in}(h_1/e) + \text{in}(h_2/e) + \text{in}(h_3/e)}{3},$$

but a little reflection will show that this would be utterly inadequate. The amounts have to be weighted differently. It seems rather natural to take as appropriate weights here, as well as in general, the degrees of confirmation which the sentences h_1, h_2, and h_3 have on the available evidence. (For a more thorough discussion of this procedure, see [28: Chap. IX].) We arrive, therefore, at the value

$$c(h_1, e) \times \text{in}(h_1/e) + c(h_2, e) \times \text{in}(h_2/e) + c(h_3, e) \times \text{in}(h_3/e),$$

or, in the convenient customary shorthand,

$$\sum_{p=1}^{3} c(h_p, e) \times \text{in}(h_p/e).$$

Expressions of this type are well known in the theory of probability and statistics (with the degree-of-confirmation subformula usually replaced by a corresponding relative-frequency-formula) under the name 'the mathematical expectation (or hope) of ...', in our case, '...of the amount of information carried by the observation to be made at t_1'.

In general, whenever we have a class of sentences $H = \{h_1, \cdots, h_n\}$ such that the available evidence e L-implies $h_1 \vee h_2 \vee \cdots \vee h_n$ as well as $\sim (h_i . h_j)$, for all $i \neq j$, we shall say that H is an exhaustive system relative to e, and the expression

$$\sum_{p=1}^{n} c(h_p, e) \times \text{in}(h_p/e)$$

will be called 'the (c-mean) estimate of the amount of information carried by (the members of) H with respect to e', symbolized by 'est(in, H, e)'.

So far, our discussion has been proceeding on a partly presystematic, partly systematic level. To switch to a completely systematic treatment, we obviously have only to replace the explicandum 'in' by one or the other of its explicata. We define:

D11–1.   Let H, h_p, e be as above. Then

$$\text{est}(\text{cont}, H, e) =_{Df} \sum_{p} c(h_p, e) \times \text{cont}(h_p/e).$$

D11–2.   Let H, h_p, e be as above. Then

$$\text{est}(\inf, H, e) =_{Df} \sum_p c(h_p, e) \times \inf(h_p/e).$$

E (Example) 11–1. Let, for example, with respect to our $\mathscr{L}_3^2$, $h_1 = $ 'Mc', $h_2 = $ 'Fc', $H = \{h_1, h_2\}$, $e = $ '$Ma \cdot Mb$'. On the basis of Table I, some formulas in the preceding section, and the two following formulas which the reader will easily be able to derive for himself, namely,

$$\text{cont*}(\text{'}Mc\text{'}/\text{'}Ma \cdot Mb\text{'}) = 0.1$$

and

$$\text{cont*}(\text{'}Fc\text{'}/\text{'}Ma \cdot Mb\text{'}) = 0.2,$$

we obtain now

$$\text{est}(\text{cont*}, H, e) = \frac{2}{3} \times 0.1 + \frac{1}{3} \times 0.2 = 0.133$$

and

$$\text{est}(\inf*, H, e) = - \left(\frac{2}{3} \times \text{Log} \, \frac{2}{3} + \frac{1}{3} \times \text{Log} \, \frac{1}{3} \right) = 0.918.$$

$\text{est}(\inf_D, H, e)$, on the other hand, equals 1, of course.

E11–2.   Let h_1, h_2, and H be as before, but let now

$$e = \text{'}Ma \cdot Mb \cdot Ya \cdot Yb \cdot Yc\text{'}.$$

Then

$$m*(e) = \frac{1}{20} + \frac{1}{60} = \frac{1}{15},$$

$$m*(e \cdot h_1) = \frac{1}{20},$$

$$m*(e \cdot h_2) = \frac{1}{60}.$$

Hence

$$\text{cont*}(h_1/e) = \frac{1}{60},$$

$$\text{cont*}(h_2/e) = \frac{1}{20},$$

$$\inf*(h_1/e) = 0.4151,$$

$$\inf*(h_2/e) = 2,$$

$$*(h_1, e) = \frac{3}{4},$$

and

$$c*(h_2, e) = \frac{1}{4}.$$

Hence

$$\text{est}(\text{cont}*, H, e) = \frac{3}{4} \times \frac{1}{60} + \frac{1}{4} \times \frac{1}{20} = \frac{1}{40},$$

and

$$\text{est}(\text{inf}*, H, e) = \frac{3}{4} \times 0.4151 + \frac{1}{4} \times 2 = 0.811$$

(whereas $\text{est}(\text{inf}_D, H, e)$ equals 1).

For the following theorems it is always assumed that H, h_p, and e fulfill the above-mentioned conditions.

T11–1.
$$\text{est}(\text{cont}, H, e) = \sum_p \frac{m(h_p . e)}{m(e)} \times m(e) \times (1 - c(h_p, e)) \quad \text{(T7–14)}$$

$$= \sum m(h_p . e) \times (1 - c(h_p, e))$$

$$= \sum m(h_p . e) \times c(\sim h_p, e)$$

$$= \frac{1}{m(e)} \sum m(h_p . e) \times m(\sim h_p . e)$$

$$= \sum c(h_p, e) \times m(\sim h_p . e)$$

$$= c(e, t) \sum c(h_p, e) \times c(\sim h_p, e).$$

Let $K = \{k_1, \cdots, k_n\}$ be an exhaustive system with respect to e. Then from well-known theorems in the theory of inequalities, the following theorem can be derived:

T11–2. Let $c(k_i, e) = c(k_j, e)$ for all i and j (hence $= 1/n$), and let there be at least one pair i and j such that $c(h_j, e) \neq c(h_j, e)$. Then

$$\text{est}(\text{cont}, K, e) > \text{est}(\text{cont}, H, e).$$

T11–3. For fixed n, $\text{est}(\text{cont}, H_i, e)$ is a maximum for those H_i all of whose members have the same c-values on e. Hence

$$\max_i[\text{est}(\text{cont}, H_i, e)] = m(e) \times \frac{n - 1}{n}.$$

(This is, of course, also the cont-value of each h_p^i belonging to these H_i.)

T11-4.   For fixed n, est(cont, H_i, e) is a minimum for those H_i one member of which has the c-value 1 on e (and hence all the other members the c-value 0 on e); hence

$$\min_i[\text{est}(\text{cont}, H_i, e)] = 0.$$

Theorems similar to T2, T3, and T4 can be obtained for the second explicatum inf. Let us first state a transformation of D2, according to T7-13:

T11-5.

$$\text{est}(\text{inf}, H, e) = \Sigma\, c(h_p, e) \times \text{Log}\, \frac{1}{c(h_p, e)}$$
$$= -\Sigma\, c(h_p, e) \times \text{Log}\, c(h_p, e).$$

We now get

T11-6.   Let $c(k_i, e) = c(k_j, e)$ for all i and j (hence $= 1/n$), and let there be at least one pair i and j such that $c(h_i, e) \neq c(h_j, e)$. Then

$$\text{est}(\text{inf}, K, e) > \text{est}(\text{inf}, H, e).$$

T11-7.   For fixed n, est(inf, H_i, e) is a maximum for those H_i all of whose members have the same c-values on e; hence

$$\max_i[\text{est}(\text{inf}, H_i, e)] = \text{Log}\, n.$$

(This is, of course, also the inf-value of each h_p^i belonging to these H_i.)

T11-8.   For fixed n, est(inf, H_i, e) is a minimum for those H_i one member of which has the c-value 1 on e (and hence all the other members have the c-value 0 on e). Hence

$$\min_i[\text{est}(\text{inf}, H_i, e)] = 0.$$

An expression analogous to

$$`-\Sigma\, c(h_p, e) \times \text{Log}\, c(h_p, e)'$$

but with degree of confirmation replaced by (statistical) probability, plays a central role in communication theory, as well as in certain formulations of statistical mechanics, where the probability concerned is that of a system being in cell p of its phase space. In statistical mechanics, in the formulation given it by Boltzmann, this expression is said to measure the entropy of the system. In analogy to this, some communication-theoreticians call the corresponding expression, which arises when the probabilities concerned are those of the (expected) relative frequencies of the occurrence of certain messages, the entropy of this system of messages. Other terms, used synonymously, though unfortunately without any real effort for terminological clarification, were uncertainty, choice, and even simply as well as confusingly, information.

Let H and K be exhaustive systems with respect to e, let H contain n members, and K contain m members, Let '$H.K$' be short for

$$\text{'}\{h_1.k_1,\ h_1.k_2, \cdots, h_1.k_m,\ h_2.k_1, \cdots, h_n.k_m\}\text{'}.$$

Then we define

D11-3.

$$\text{est(in,} H.K, e) =_{Df} \sum_{q=1}^{m} \sum_{p=1}^{n} c(h_p.k_q, e) \times \text{in}(h_p.k_q/e).$$

With respect to the explicatum inf, the following theorem can be proved:

T11-9. $\text{est(inf,} H.K, e) \leqq \text{est(inf,} H, e) + \text{est(inf,} K, e)$, where equality holds only if, for all p and q, $c(h_p.k_q, e) = c(h_p, e) \times c(k_q, e)$, in other words, when the h's and the k's are inductively independent on e (with respect to that m-function on which c is based).

E11-3. Let $e =$ '$Ma.Mb.Ya.Yb$', $h_1 =$ 'Mc', $h_2 =$ 'Fc', $k_1 =$ 'Yc', $k_2 =$ 'Oc', $H = \{h_1, h_2\}$, and $K = \{k_1, k_2\}$. Then,

$$H.K = \{h_1.k_1,\ h_1.k_2,\ h_2.k_1,\ h_2.k_2\}.$$

We have

$$m^*(e) = \frac{1}{10},$$

$$m^*(h_1.k_1.e) = \frac{1}{20},$$

$$m^*(h_1.k_2.e) = m^*(h_2.k_1.e) = m^*(h_2.k_2.e) = \frac{1}{60},$$

$$c^*(h_1.k_1, e) = \frac{1}{2},$$

$$c^*(h_2.k_2, e) = c^*(h_2.k_1, e) = c^*(h_2.k_2, e) = \frac{1}{6},$$

$$\text{cont}^*(h_1.k_1/e) = \frac{1}{20},$$

$$\text{cont}^*(h_1.k_2/e) = \cdots = \frac{1}{12},$$

$$\text{inf}^*(h_1.k_1/e) = 1,$$

$$\inf^*(h_1 . k_2/e) = \cdots = 2.585.$$

Hence

$$\text{est(cont}^*, H . K, e) = \frac{1}{15}$$

and

$$\text{est(inf}^*, H . K, e) = 1.792.$$

$$\text{est(inf}^*, H, e) = \text{est(inf}^*, K, e) = 0.918.$$

We verify that

$$\text{est(inf}^*, H . K, e) < \text{est(inf}^*, H, e) + \text{est(inf}^*, K, e),$$

the h's and the k's not being inductively independent on this e with respect to m^*. They are, however, independent with respect to m_D, and indeed

$$\text{est(inf}_D, H . K, e) = 2 = \text{est(inf}_D, H, e) + \text{est(inf}_D, K, e).$$

In general, $\text{est(in}, H, e)$ will be different from $\text{est(in}, H, e . k)$, where k is a sentence that has been added to the prior evidence e. Since '$\text{est(in}, H, e . k)$' and similar expressions are of great importance, it is worthwhile to give it a special name. We shall call it the posterior estimate (of the amount of information carried by H on the evidence comprised of e and k). The expression '$\text{est(in}, H, e)$' will then be called, for greater clarity, the prior estimate (of...). It is often important to investigate how such a prior estimate has been changed through some additional evidence. We shall therefore give also to the difference between the prior and the posterior estimate a special name, the amount of specification of H through k on e, and denote this function by a special symbol '$\text{sp(in}, H, k, e)$':

D11–4. $\text{sp(in}, H, k, e) =_{Df} \text{est(in}, H, e) - \text{est(in}, H, e . k)$.

E11–4.   Let e, H and k_1 be as in E3. Then $e . k_1$ is the e of E2. Therefore $\text{est(inf}^*, H, e . k_1) = 0.811$. Since $\text{est(inf}^*, H, e) = 0.918$ (from E3), we have $\text{sp(inf}^*, H, k_1, e) = 0.918 - 0.811 = 0.107$.

It can be easily seen that $\text{sp(in}, H, k, e) = 0$ if (but not only if) k is inductively independent of the h's on e. Otherwise sp can be either positive or negative. Its maximum value is obviously equal to $\text{est(in}, H, e)$ itself. This value will be obtained when $e . k$ L-implies one of the h's. In this case H is maximally specified through k on e.

Situations often arise in which the event stated in k has not yet occurred or, at least, in which we do not know whether or not it has occurred but know only that either it or some other event belonging to an exhaustive system of events will occur or has occurred. In such circumstances, it makes sense to ask for the expectation value of the posterior estimate of the amount of information carried by H on e and (some member of the exhaustive system) K. We are led to the (c-mean) estimate of this posterior estimate which we shall denote by 'est(in, $H/K,e$)' and define as

D11–5.

$$\text{est(in, } H/K,e) =_{Df} \sum_{q=1}^{m} c(k_q,e) \times \text{est(in, } H,e.k_q).$$

E11–5. Let e, H, and K be as in E3. Then

$$\text{est(inf*, } H/K,e) = \frac{2}{3} \times 0.811 + \frac{1}{3} \times 1 = 0.847.$$

The stroke-notation has been chosen instead of a more neutral comma-notation because the following theorem, which stands in a certain analogy to the definitions of relative amounts of information, holds.

T11–10. est(in, $H/K,e$) = est(in, $H.K,e$) − est(in, K,e).

Proof:

$$\begin{aligned}
\text{est(in, } H/K,e) &= \sum_q c(k_q,e) \sum_p c(h_p,e.k_q) \times \text{in}(h_p/e.k_q) \\
&= \sum_q \sum_p c(k_q,e) \times c(h_p,e.k_q) \times \text{in}(h_p/e.k_q) \\
&= \sum_c \sum_p c(h_p.k_q,e) \times \text{in}(h_p/e.k_q) \\
&= \sum_q \sum_p c(h_p.k_q,e) \times [\text{in}(h_p.k_q/e) - \text{in}(k_q/e)] \\
&= \text{est(in, } H.K,e) - \sum_q c(k_q,e) \times \text{in}(k_q/e) \\
&= \text{est(in, } H.K,e) - \text{est(in, } K,e).
\end{aligned}$$

Indeed, est(inf*, $H.K,e$) − est(inf*, K,e) = 1.792 (from E3) − 0.918 (from E3) = 0.874 (as in E5).

One will often be interested in an estimate of the amount of specification of H on e through K. This function will be symbolized by 'sp(in, H,K,e)'. Its definition is

D11–6.

$$\text{sp(in, } H,K,e) =_{Dj} \sum_q c(k_q,e) \times \text{sp(in, } H,k_q,e).$$

E11–6. Let e, H, and K be as in E3. Then

$sp(inf^*, H, K, e) = 2/3 \times 0.107$ (from E4) $+ 1/3 \times (-0.082)$ (computed in the same way) $= 0.044$.

We see immediately that the following theorem holds:

T11–11. $sp(in, H, K, e) = est(in, H, e) - est(in, H/K, e)$.

Indeed, $est(inf^*, H, e) - est(inf^*, H/K, e) = 0.918$ (E3) $- 0.874$ (E5) $= 0.044$ (as in E6).

Though it may happen that, for some q, $sp(in, H, k_q, e)$ is negative, it can be proved that $sp(in, H, K, e)$ is never negative, in other words, that the estimate of the posterior estimate is at most equal to the prior estimate.

T11–12. $sp(in, H, K, e) \geqq 0$, with equality holding iff the h's and the k's are inductively independent.

Combining T10 and T11, we get

T11–13. $sp(in, H, K, e) = est(in, H, e) + est(in, K, e) - est(in, H, K, e)$.

From T13 follows immediately the following theorem of the symmetricity or mutuality of specification:

T11–14. $sp(in, H, K, e) = sp(in, K, H, e)$.

To illustrate the importance and use of the functions defined in this section, let us work out a different numerical example, albeit an artificially simplified one, for ease of computation. Let h_1 be 'Jones is bright', h_2 be 'Jones is average (in intelligence)', and h_3 be 'Jones is dull'. Somebody who is interested in Jones' intelligence makes him undergo a certain test. Let now k_1 be 'Jones achieves more than 80 percent (in his test)', k_2 be 'Jones achieves between 60 percent and 80 percent', and k_3 be 'Jones achieves less than 60 percent'. Let the following degrees of confirmation hold on the available evidence, according to some m-function:

$$c(h_1, e) = c(h_3, e) = \frac{1}{4}$$

$$c(h_2, e) = \frac{1}{2}$$

$$c(k_1, e . h_1) = c(k_2, e . h_1) = c(k_2, e . h_2) = c(k_2, e . h_3) = (k_3, e . h_3) = \frac{1}{2}$$

$$c(k_1, e . h_2) = c(k_3, e . h_2) = \frac{1}{4}.$$

(All other $c(k_q, e . h_p) = 0$.) Figure 2 might help to visualize the situation.

For the following computations, the explicatum inf will be used. First we compute with the help of T5 the value of $est(inf, H, e)$ in our example.

$$est(inf, H, e) = \frac{1}{4} Log 4 + \frac{1}{2} Log 2 + \frac{1}{4} Log 4 = 1.5.$$

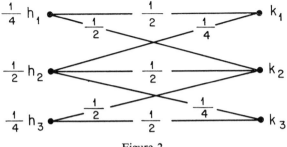

Figure 2.

To evaluate est(inf, K, e) we have first to find the various $c(k_q, e)$. These can be easily read off the diagram.

$$c(k_1, e) = c(k_3, e) = \frac{1}{4},$$
$$c(k_2, e) = \frac{1}{2}.$$

Since $c(k_i, e) = c(h_i, e)$ for all i (this is pure coincidence), we have

$$\text{est(inf}, K, e) = 1.5.$$

For est(inf, $H . K, e$) we get, again by simple inspection of the diagram,

$$\text{est(inf}, H . K, e) = 6 \times \frac{1}{8} \text{Log} 8 + 1 \times \frac{1}{4} \text{Log} 4 = 2.75.$$

This verifies T9. It is obvious that not all h's and k's are inductively independent.

To find the various est(inf, $H, e . k_q$), we compute first all $c(h_p, e . k_q)$. We get

$$c(h_1 . e . k_1) = c(h_2, e . k_1) = c(h_2, e . k_2) = c(h_2, e . k_3) = c(h_3, e . k_3) = \frac{1}{2},$$

$$c(h_1, e . k_2) = c(h_3, e . k_2) = \frac{1}{4}.$$

(All other $c(h_p, e . k_q) = 0$.) Hence we have

$$\text{est(inf}, H, e . k_1) = \text{est(inf}, H, e . k_3) = 1,$$
$$\text{est(inf}, H . e . k_2) = 1.5.$$

Hence we get, according to D4,

$$\text{sp(inf}, H . k_1, e) = \text{sp(inf}, H, k_3, e) = \frac{1}{2},$$
$$\text{sp(inf}, H . k_2, e) = 0.$$

The last result is of special importance. And indeed, if Jones achieves between 60 percent and 80 percent in his test, we are *"so klug als wie zuvor,"* we know exactly as much as we knew before. The addition of k_2 to our evidence left the c-values of the h's unchanged, k_2 is inductively irrelevant to the h's and our knowledge has not become more specific through this addition. The situation is different with respect to the two other outcomes of the test. In both other cases, our knowledge has become more specific. This appears even on the qualitative level: Before the test, Jones could have been bright, average, or dull. After the test, we know that he is not dull if the outcome is k_1, and that he is not bright, if the outcome is k_3. But one has to be careful with this argument. A reduction of the number of possibilities does not always entail an increase of specifity of the situation. If the probability distribution of the remaining possibilities is much more evenly spread than that of the initial possibilities, the situation may become, in a certain important sense, less specific. Examples could be easily constructed. In our case, however, there is a real increase in specificity, though not a large one.

It seems reasonable to measure one aspect of the effectiveness of this intelligence test by the estimate of the amount of specification. One might compare the effectiveness of various proposed tests in this way. In our case, according to D6,

$$\text{sp}(\text{inf}, H, K, e) = \frac{1}{4} \times \frac{1}{2} + \frac{1}{2} \times 0 + \frac{1}{4} \times \frac{1}{2} = \frac{1}{4},$$

a result that could, of course, also have been obtained from T13. Incidentally, it follows that the test was a pretty poor one. Whereas a direct measurement of Jones' intelligence, were it only possible, could be expected to yield 1.5 units of information, the mentioned test can be expected to give us only 0.25 of a unit of information on Jones' intelligence. The difference between 1.5 and 0.25, i.e., 1.25, is the value of est(inf, $H/K, e$), according to T11. The same value would be obtained by using either D5 or T10. We may say that by applying the test instead of measuring the intelligence directly we must content ourselves with expecting a "loss" of 1.25 units of information. The correlate of this function within communication theory has been called by Shannon [136: 36] the equivocation. With fixed H, that test is more efficient whose K (the class of possible outcomes) yields the higher value for the estimate of the amount of specification of H on e through K, or the lower value for the estimate of the posterior estimate of the amount of information carried by H on e and K.

12. SEMANTIC NOISE, EFFICIENCY OF A CONCEPTUAL FRAMEWORK

[Two usages of 'semantic noise' are distinguished and a more general concept of distortion through noise defined. Efficiency of the conceptual framework of a language is introduced, both with respect to some given evidence and absolutely. The symmetrical treatment of a predicate and its negation maximizes initial efficiency. With increasing evidence, the efficiency of a language generally decreases.]

Whenever a receiver of a message is unable to reconstruct immediately the message as originally sent, the communication engineer describes the situation by saying that the message has been distorted by noise. To combat noise is one of his principal tasks.

Sometimes the receiver of a message, in spite of a reception which is physically free of distortion, reacts to it in a way which is different from that expected by the sender. Attempts have been made to formulate this situation in terms of semantic noise. Indeed, the same sentence (more exactly, two tokens of the same sentence-type) may convey different informations (with different or equal amounts of information) to two people (e.g. the sender and the receiver of a message) and this in at least two different ways: first, the two tokens, which are physically alike, are interpreted as belonging to different languages [69], and second, probably more common and interesting, the information carried by them is evaluated with respect to different evidences. Misunderstandings may be due either to physical mishearing or to semantic misevaluation (or to both).

In addition to the two metaphorical usages of 'noise' mentioned above, which seem pretty straightforward and should cause no confusion if properly distinguished among themselves and from the engineer's noise, it seems natural to use this term also in the following general situations. Whenever one is interested in knowing whether a certain event out of an exhaustive system of events, H, has happened (or is going to happen) but is unable, for some reason, to observe directly the occurrence of these events and has to content oneself with the observation of some event out of another exhaustive system, K, where not all of the k_q are irrelevant to the h_p on e [28: §65], one can regard K as a distortion or a transformation through noise of H.

Following this usage, we may not only say that the system of sounds coming out of a telephone receiver is a distortion through noise of the system of sounds coming out of the mouth of the speaker and that the system of symbol printings at the output of a teleprinter is a distortion of the system of symbol printings at the input, but also that the system of positions of a thermometer at a certain time is a distortion of the system of the temperature situations at those times (for somebody who is interested in the temperatures), that the system of weather predictions of a certain weather bureau is a distortion of the system of weather situations at the times for which the predictions are made (for somebody who is interested in the weather), and that the system of IQ-tests results is a distortion of the system of intelligence characteristics (for somebody interested in these characteristics).

Whether it is worthwhile, in the three last examples and in similar cases, to talk about nature communicating with us and about our receiving nature's messages in a noise-distorted fashion in order to drive home a useful analogy, is questionable. Some heuristic value to such a form of speech can hardly be denied, but the strain such usage would put upon terms like 'communication' or 'message' might well be too high.

The twin concepts of code-efficiency and code-redundancy play an important role in communication theory. We shall not discuss here the definitions given these concepts nor dwell on their various applications (and misapplications) but give instead definitions for certain semantic correlates which seem to have some importance.

By the efficiency of (the conceptual framework of) the language L_1, with respect to (the amount-of-information function) in and (the evidence) e, in symbols: ef(L_1, in, e), we understand the ratio of est(in, H_1, e) where H_1 is the class of the full sentences of all Q-predicators (§2) with an argument not mentioned in e, to $\max_i[\text{est(in}, H_i, e)]$, where the H_i are the corresponding classes in other languages L_i covering, intuitively speaking, the same ground. (This loose statement is in need of much elaboration. This is expected to be achieved at a later stage. We have in mind that the languages L_i refer to the same physical magnitudes without, however, there existing a sentence-by-sentence translatability between them.) It seems to us that the choice of the class of the Q-sentences as the class relative to which the efficiency of a language is defined is a natural one, though it certainly is not the only plausible one. The efficiency of a language, as defined here, changes, as a function of e, with a change of the evidence taken into account. A language may become, in a sense, more or less efficient with a change in experience.

For an inhabitant of New York, a language with the predicates 'W', 'T', and 'C', designating Warm (above 75°F.), Temperate (between 40° and 75°), and Cold (below 40°), respectively, would be quite efficient. Should he move to San Francisco, however, its efficiency would be highly reduced because 'T' occurs here much more frequently than the other two.

We would, therefore, like to have also a concept of efficiency that is independent of experience. Such a concept is, of course, readily available. We have only to consider the efficiency relative to the tautological evidence, i.e., $\text{ef}(L_1, \text{in}, t)$. Let us call this concept the initial efficiency and denote it also by '$\text{ef}_t(L_1, \text{in})$'. A language will accordingly have maximal initial efficiency if and only if each of the mentioned Q-sentences will be initially equiprobable, that is, if and only if the m-function upon which it is based ascribes equal values to all Q-sentences with the same argument, which will be the case when (but not only when) this m-function treats each primitive predicate and its negation on a par, as do, for instance, m_D and all m_I.

The symmetrical treatment of a predicate and its negation loses somewhat the arbitrariness with which it has often been charged; it turns out that this treatment, based psychologically upon some principle of indifference and methodologically upon considerations of simplicity, maximizes the initial efficiency of the language.

With an increase in experience and the establishment of empirical laws, which in their simplest form are equivalent to the statement that certain Q-properties are empty [28: §38], the efficiency of the respective language generally decreases. The greater the number of laws which are established, and the stronger they are, the less efficient the languages become. It is plausible that with a continuing decrease of the efficiency of a language, a stage may be reached where this language will be altogether abandoned and replaced by another which, on the same evidence, shows a higher efficiency, mainly through the fact that the (or at least some) empirical laws of the first language have led to a modification of the conceptual framework of the second.

The New Yorker, in our previous illustration, would do well, after having stayed for some time in San Francisco, to adopt a new language in which 'W''' would stand for More-Than-60°, 'T''' for Between-50°-And-60°, and 'C''' for Less-Than-50°, for instance, to save him from making the inefficient and uninteresting statements about the weather in San Francisco, which had before in almost all cases the form '$T(x)$', i.e., 'It is temperate at time x'.

It might be sometimes useful to talk about the inefficiency of a language. The definition is obvious:

$$\text{inef}(L_1, \text{in}, e) =_{Df} 1 - \text{ef}(L_1, \text{in}, e).$$

It is advisable to avoid the term 'redundancy'—the term used for the correlate of our 'inefficiency' in communication theory—since the expression 'redundancy of a conceptual framework' is usually understood in a different sense.

13. CONCLUSIONS

[The concepts of information and information measures explicated here should be of value in various theories, as in the Theory of Design of Experiments and the Theory of Testing. Various extensions are outlined. One of these would take into account the linear arrangements of the individuals.]

The Theory of Semantic Information outlined here is nothing more than a certain ramification of the Theory of Inductive Probability presented in [28]. The explication of the presystematic concept of the information carried by a sentence, which has been attempted here, should be of value for a clarification of the foundations of all those theories which make use of this concept and the measures connected with it. The impact of the concepts presented here for the Theory of Design of Experiments or for the Theory of Testing should be obvious.

The present theory requires extension into various directions. One extension has already been mentioned: no great difficulties are involved in treating language systems with denumerably many individuals. Nor would introduction of individual variables and quantification over them present problems of which we do not know the solution. Language systems of these types have already been treated in [28]. Other extensions, however, will have to be postponed until the corresponding theories of inductive probability are developed.

An Examination of Information Theory*

One of the tasks with which communication engineers are presented is that of devising a mechanism by which a significant sequence of words, a *message*, produced by somebody, the *sender* of the message, is reproduced at some other place, with the shortest practical time lag. The reproduction must be such that the *receiver* of the message will be able to understand what the sender meant by his message, at least, if he knows the sender's language (or, perhaps, his specific use of the language). The following illustration is typical: A writes on a sheet of paper "I love you" and wishes that B, 3000 miles away, should become aware of the full content of this message, with little delay and at a low cost. There will be institutions, in a capitalistic society, which will compete with each other in providing A, for a price, with the required service. Those companies which perform these services most satisfactorily, i.e., with an overall better combination of faithfulness, time lag, and cost, will get the job. The executives of these companies will hire engineers and put them to work on improving this overall combination.

Let us scrutinize the situation somewhat more. A will be dissatisfied if he learns either that his message has been scrambled up, whether into something incomprehensible like "K bogl pou" or into something comprehensible like "A long bow" but with an entirely different meaning, or that an undistorted replica has been delivered a day late (and, of course, even more so if a distorted message is delivered too late). This dissatisfaction may lead to a loss of business for the company. In addition, A would appreciate a reduction in the cost of transmitting future messages. So would the company, at least in enlightened capitalism, if it were able to save on the cost of transmission. Cheaper transmission would mean increased business.

How will the company transmit the message? Assume that a telegraph line stands at the disposal of the company. Assume, further, that at one side of the line a mechanism is available which is able to create electrical pulses in the line for any length of time, and that at the other side a mechanism is

---

* First appeared in **Philosophy of Science,** vol. 22 (1955), pp. 86–105.

available which is able to detect the existence of a pulse in the line as well as measure its exact duration. Under these conditions, one could imagine that the following instructions would be given to the sending operator: "To transmit the letter "a", press the key for 1 second, to transmit "b", press for 2 seconds, ..., to transmit "z", press for 26 seconds. Wait 1 second between letters, 2 seconds between words, 3 seconds between sentences." (For the sake of simplicity of illustration, let us disregard the transmission of numerical symbols, punctuation marks, capital letters, etc.) Corresponding instructions would be given the receiving operator. Assuming sufficiently trained operators, little or no loss of signal strength, and the possibility of unerring discrimination between pulses of different lengths, faithful reproduction of any message written in the English alphabet would be assured. However, it requires little ingenuity to discover the relative inefficiency of this transmission method with respect to time and power consumption. The reader can easily verify for himself that the transmission of the abovementioned message would last for 133 seconds, with pulses on the line for 124 seconds.

Sooner or later somebody would come up with the suggestion of saving transmission time by assigning the pulse lengths to the letters not according to their position in the alphabet but according to their relative frequency in English. The result would be a new sheet of instructions in which the pulse length 1 would now be assigned to the most frequent English letter, "e", 2 to "t", and so on in the order: a, o, n, r, i, s, h, d, l, c, m, u, g, y, p, w, b, v, k, x, j, q, z, which is said to be the frequency rank order list of letters in literary English. (As a matter of fact, for telegraphy purposes, a slightly different list would have been adopted.) It is easy to compute that the transmission time for our particular message would now be 89 seconds, i.e. about 67% of the previous time. The saving is consequently about 33% in time. It will, of course, be somewhat different on the average.

Again, it is rather obvious that some ingenious engineer will in due time propose an even more economical transmission method, a different correlation of pulses, or sequences of such, with letters, or sequences of such, i.e. a different *code*. He will come to think that periods of silence could be used more efficiently, namely not only to indicate borderlines but also to identify letters, when suitably combined with pulses. He might propose, for instance, to use only two types of pulses, of one second and two seconds in length, respectively. For each letter, between one and four of these pulses would be used with silence periods of one second between any two pulses. Letter borderlines would now be indicated by, say, a silence period of two seconds, word borderlines by a silence period of three seconds, and sentences would be separated by a four-second interval. The letter "g" would be transmitted, say, as a 2-pulse, silence, 2-pulse, silence, 1-pulse signal, in short as "221". Assume that the following codebook, adopted from the International Morse Code, would be given the operator:

a 12	h 2222	o 222	v 1112
b 211	i 11	p 1221	w 122
c 2121	j 1222	q 2212	x 2112
d 2111	k 212	r 121	y 2122
e 1	l 1211	s 111	z 2211
f 1121	m 22	t 2	
g 221	n 21	u 112	

It is easy to compute that the transmission would now last for 67 seconds. Could greater savings be achieved? (For the purposes of our presentation, let us not take into consideration a reduction of the lengths of the pulses or the silence periods.) It seems rather likely that this should be possible, and even in various ways. One way would be to make still better use of the actual relative frequencies of the letters, a problem known to communication engineers as that of *most efficient coding*, as a result of which some very infrequent letters might get even longer code-correlates whereas some of the more frequent ones would get shorter code-correlates, with an additional saving on the average. Another way might consist in *encoding* units longer than letters, perhaps sequences of two letters, syllables, whole words, whole phrases, or even whole sentences. An intelligent encoding must result in additional savings in transmission time since the relative frequency of letter occurrences is not independent of their environments. The relative frequency of the *digram* "th" among all letter digrams is, for instance, much higher than the product of the relative frequencies of "t" and "h" among the letters separately, whereas the relative frequency of "ht" is very much smaller than this product. However, saving in transmission time is only one of many factors by which transmission efficiency is measured. Under the envisaged system, the saving in time would be accompanied by a considerable increase in the complexity of the encoding process. If left to a human operator, the encoding would require more extended training with probably a larger number of expected errors, etc. Leaving the commerical considerations aside, one point has been driven home, I hope: *A knowledge of the relative frequencies of the English letters, absolute, and conditional, or, equivalently, of the English letters and their sequences, is of importance for the telegraph engineer.* It turns out, for certain plausible reasons which shall not be discussed here, that a convenient quantitative concept to deal with the situation is not the relative frequency itself but rather the logarithm (to the base 2) of its reciprocal. If "$rf(s)$" denotes the relative frequency of the occurrences of the signal[1] (or signal sequence) s within a certain well-defined set of occurrences of signals (or signal sequences), assumed to be fixed once for all, then the function $\log_2 \dfrac{1}{rf(s)}$, which measures somehow the *rarity* of the occurrences of s, is of prime importance for the theory of telegraphy and even, since the situation is not much different for other means of communication, for the theory of communication in general.

Since most people, mathematicians and engineers included, are in the somewhat unfortunate habit of using the highly ambiguous expression "probability" instead of the relatively unambiguous "relative frequency", one will find in the usual presentations of communication theory expressions of the type "logarithm of the reciprocal of the probability of s" or, what amounts to the same thing, "negative logarithm of the probability of s"; in the corresponding symbols, "$\log \dfrac{1}{p(s)}$" and "$-\log p(s)$", "$p(s)$" is sometimes taken to mean exactly the same as "$rf(s)$", and at other times to stand rather for the *estimate* of $rf(s)$ for the whole set of signal transmissions, past, present, and future. The difference between these two conceptions is greater than one usually thinks, and disregarding it leads almost invariably to confusion.

Whereas the savings I have discussed so far are due mainly to the use of intelligence in encoding and the knowledge of English letter frequencies, other savings can be achieved on the basis of some psycho-linguistic facts. t s fr nstnc wll knwn tht lmst ll nglsh txts cn b mmdtl ndrstd b sffcntl ntllgnt rdrs vn f ll thr vwls r mttd, and this fact forms the basis of many stenographic systems. If no use is made of this fact in telegraphy, as I think it is not, it is probably due to the circumstance that in certain exceptional instances a unique reconstruction of the original message is impossible and that such a failure may cause the sender, or the receiver, greater harm than he is ready to risk. Another reason might be the cost of rewriting the original message in its vowelless form, a cost that might well reduce the savings considerably if not balance them.

Other psychological facts are however made use of. Knowing that most people are in the habit of sending rather stereotyped messages for certain recurring occasions, like Christmas or marriages, telegraph companies began suggesting to their customers that they indicate which of a list of, say, 37 long Christmas messages they would like to send, combining with this suggestion another one explaining that, by choosing one of these standard messages, the customers can save money. The companies would

---

[1] I am obviously using here "signal" as a class of equiform "occurrences" (or tokens) of this signal (-type).

not lose, of course, since they could now transmit, instead of the correlate of a long message of, say, 25 words, a short signal sequence corresponding to something like C29, to be *decoded* at the receiving end with the help of a code-book into a *replica* of the original message. Incidentally, this trick is, in principle, nothing more than another application of the general method of assigning short code correlates to frequent letters and letter sequences, extended this time to whole sentences or even longer units.

Other code systems frequently used are based on the fact that the messages sent for communication between members of certain professions, business-men, hotel managers, travel agents, meteorologists, pilots and control tower operators, can be rephrased, without appreciable loss, into one or another of a certain relatively restricted set of complete messages, which can then be suitably coded as such and quickly, as well as cheaply, trans-mitted.

Notice the expression "without appreciable loss" in the preceding para-graph. This is, of course, a rather vague term which is, in addition, highly subjective. Although a particular meteorologist may deplore the fact that the number of cloud formation terms at his disposal is so limited, meteor-ologists as a class believe that the existing set is sufficiently elaborate for most purposes and that a further elaboration would not yield returns comparable with the corresponding cost.

This drives home my second point, namely that *economies in time and cost can sometimes be achieved by permitting a certain deterioration in the rep-lication of the original message.* We must, however, distinguish clearly between various senses of "deterioration", all of which are relevant in our context. The deterioration involved in the reformulation of the original statement of the meteorologist from colloquial English into a highly stan-dardized statement of the meteorologists' specific technical language is of a *semantic-pragmatic* kind. The second statement is believed to preserve the content of the first statement, to a sufficiently high degree, inasmuch as this content is relevant for meteorological purposes. The loss may be im-portant for other considerations but it is regarded as relatively slight for the given restricted aim. The original statement is irretrievably lost, though one can make guesses about it, knowing, say, the poetic inclinations of a particular meteorological observer. The point is, however, that no other meteorologist is interested in the original statement. He is interested only in its functional reformulation.

The situation is different in the case of vowelless English. The deterio-ration involved in the omission of the vowels is tolerated, and tolerable, only because the receiver, if he knows English sufficiently well, will be able to replicate the original message either in full or at least to such a degree that no relevant semantic loss will result.

Whereas the first deterioration utilizes the fact that people often tend to say things which are irrelevant for certain purposes and, consequently, can be discarded by somebody interested in these purposes alone, the second form of deterioration is due to the existence of statistical dependencies between English letters which can be utilized by the encoder to shorten the original message and by the decoder to retrieve this message from its shortened version.

It has become customary to explain both kinds of intentional deteriorations in the transmissions of messages as an exploitation of the *redundancy* of natural languages. It should, however, be clear by now that this term covers at least two phenomena which are entirely different from, and independent of, each other, belonging to entirely different dimensions of language. One could, of course, distinguish easily between these phenomena by the use of qualifying adjectives. Grammatical redundancy, comprising morphological and syntactical redundancy, and semantic redundancy suggest themselves. In other contexts, phonemic redundancy might be a useful concept.[2] It is true that these various redundancies can be utilized for the same purpose, namely economies in transmission time and cost, but this is by no means a sufficient reason for disregarding their essential differences.

The intentional deterioration of the original message, matched to the specificities of the various redundancies of the language in which this message is formulated, is, as we saw, one of the means by which a communication engineer achieves major economies. However, every message undergoes some deterioration on its way from the sender to the receiver, in other words in its *channel*. Some of the distortions are theoretically trivial and eliminable through improved equipment—atmospherics, leaking insulation, interference of other sound waves are of this nature—others, however, are unavoidable because of the simple fact that any transmission of messages is performed by physical means, electrical pulses, as considered above, or sound waves, flag wavings, light ray emissions, etc., and each such physical process is susceptible to distortions originating in the constant (thermal) movement of all molecules. These distortions, which are unintentional and random, are known as *thermal* or *white noise*, the latter term being a metaphorical extension from the optical case.

The longer the distance between sender and receiver, the more, *ceteris paribus*, is the transmission of a message subject to noise distortions. In

---

2 This is not the place to go into an elaboration of these concepts. Some indications are given, e.g., by Miller [99: 102–111].

general, therefore, whatever arrives at the receiving end of the communication channel is not an exact replica of the signal sequence that was sent. However, from a knowledge of the *absolute probabilities* of the sent sequences $s_1, s_2,..., s_i,..., s_n$, of the absolute probabilities of the received sequences $r_1, r_2,..., r_j..., r_m$, and of the *conditional probabilities* of the r_j's being received given that the s_i have been sent—the set of which is nothing but what the mathematicizing communication engineer would call the *noise function*—, the receiver is able to arrive at the conditional probabilities of the s_i's being sent given that an r_j has been received. The *posterior probabilities* of the s_i, after a certain r_j has been received, will, in general, be different from their *prior probabilities*; the posterior probability distribution will, in general, be sharper than the prior probability distribution, the situation will, therefore, in general become more specific, after the reception of a certain signal sequence. One of the main tasks of the communication engineer is to increase this specificity per cost.

A complete communication process can be described in the following form.

Let F stand for the operation of putting ordinary language into functional form,
let C stand for the operation of encoding into a symbol sequence,
let S stand for the operation of transforming a symbol sequence into a signal sequence,
let R stand for the operation of distorting a signal sequence during transmission,
let S^* stand for the operation of transforming a signal sequence into a symbol sequence,
let C^* stand for the operation of decoding a symbol sequence into functional language,
let F^* stand for the operation of putting functional language into ordinary form.

Instead of explaining the various operations at length, let me give an illustration, albeit a highly simplified one: A meteorological observer may have in his diary the following entry: "February 3, 1953, 11 A.M. Thank God, it's getting warmer, but it's still only 17.4°F". Let this statement be m. Then $F(m)$ will be, say ,"The outside temperature on February 3rd, 1953, at 11 A.M., on top of Mount Washington, N. H., is 17.4°F". The meteorologist will then encode this statement (which only a beginner will have to write out as such) into, say, "050203110010174", where "05" stands for message form no. 5, i.e. that referring to temperatures, "02" for the second month, "03" for the third day, "11" for the time in hours, "00" for the time in minutes, "1" for plus, "017" for degrees Fahrenheit in units, "4" for degrees in tenths. This is $CF(m)$. He will next teletype this symbol sequence into a signal sequence, say, by digit-for-digit transformation into sequences of short and long pulses. This is $SCF(m)$. We shall not write down the standard indication of these pulse sequences. The teletypewriter at the meteorological center of the U.S.A. will receive a pulse sequence, $RSCF(m)$, which will in general be slightly different from the sent one, and transform it into the symbol sequence $S^*RSCF(m)$. For certain purposes, this symbol sequence will have to be decoded into a functional form $C*S*RSCF(m)$ (and if one of the officers at the central meteorological bureau has sufficient imagination and poetic inclination, he might even try to put this functional statement into a full-blooded form $F*C*S*RSCF(m)$). If the meteorologist, or his clerk, made no mistakes in either functionalizing, symbolizing, or teletyping, and the distortion in the channel was only slight so that $RSCF(m)$ turned out to be not appreciably different from $SCF(m)$, then $S*RSCF(m)$ will be identical with $CF(m)$ and $C*S*RSCF(m)$ identical with $F(m)$. (Only by extreme luck and empathy will $F*C*S*RSCF(m)$ turn out to be identical with m, but no meteorologist cares.) If, however, there was considerable noise in the channel, then $RSCF(m)$ might be sufficiently different from $SCF(m)$ to be transformed by $S*$ into a symbol sequence different from the sent one. Some such distortions will be immediately recognizable as such by resulting in logically impossible sequences as when, for instance, the third digit is printed out as "2". Others will be rather unlikely, whether by themselves or in view of prior reports from the same station and/or simultaneous reports from neighboring stations. A twelfth digit of "1" would be very unlikely by itself. A thirteenth digit of "2" is unlikely if the corresponding digit in the weather report issued one hour ago was "8", or if neighboring weather stations give "8" for the same position in simultaneous reports. *Reduction of errors in transmission, and their automatic or semi-automatic recognition is another aim of communication engineers to be achieved either by improved equipment or by improved coding or by both.* This aim is closely related to that of increasing the specificity, in fact not much more than a restatement of this aim in another form.

Notice that, perhaps by using a little force, the transformations $C, S, S*$, and $C*$ can be regarded in our illustration as one-one, and that $S*$ is the inverse of S, $C*$ the inverse of C. Consequently, if only R is, in a given case, an identity transformation, $C*S*RSC$ will be an identity transformation, too, leaving its argument $F(m)$ unchanged. F is many-one, $F*$ is one-many, and R, unfortunately, many-many, in general. We can now rephrase the major aim of communication engineering as being that of combatting the damaging influence of R by judicious choices of F, C, and S. One of the most interesting theorems of recent statistical communication theory states, in essence, that for any given R, there are F, C, S, not necessarily any more one-one but perhaps rather one-many (hence $S*$ and $C*$ many-one), such that the effect of R can be theoretically overcome (at the expense, if necessary, of increased time lags and storage capacity, hence of increased cost). Since the cost of (nearly) distortionless communication is usually prohibitive, compromises attempting to maximize the utility, i.e. the overall balance of gain and loss, are generally made that often require high ingenuity. The various modulation systems for transmission of electrical pulses are such compromises, each having certain advantages and disadvantages, according to the specific conditions.

II

The statistical theory of communication is a recent development, not more than 25 years old, with its major presentations dating only from 1948 onwards. Its impact on the understanding of the processes connected with transmission of signals has been tremendous, so great indeed that many people have come to believe that its achievement should be brought to use also in other fields connected somehow with "communication". Now, analogical reasoning is certainly legitimate, but also dangerous and misleading, especially if no attempt at disciplined thinking is made. It is my opinion that the early and somewhat dramatic achievements of statistical communication theory have given rise to speculations which are far beyond the legitimately tolerable. I believe, in addition, that this mushrooming development is due mainly to the misfortune of introducing from the beginning a highly ambiguous term to denote the basic function of the theory, i.e.

$\log \dfrac{1}{p(s)}$, or its weighted average $\Sigma p(s_i) \log \dfrac{1}{p(s_i)}$.

R. V. L. Hartley, in his classical paper [66], stated that his aim was "to set up a quantitative measure whereby the capacities of various systems [in electrical communication] to transmit information may be compared" [66:535]. Such attempts had been made before. Hartley's new insight, however, was that the measure he was looking for had to be dependent upon "the frequency relations involved in electrical communication" [66:536]. The phrase, "to transmit information", used by Hartley is highly ambiguous, but in this context, the term "information" has certainly nothing to do with what we might call the *semantic content* of the signals transmitted. Hartley is aware of the ambiguities of "information" and insists that "as commonly used, information is a very elastic term, and it will first be necessary to set up for it a more specific meaning as applied to the present discussion" [66:536]. He closes up by saying that "it is desirable therefore to eliminate the psychological factors involved and to establish a measure of information in terms of purely physical quantities" [66:536]. We might add that not only psychological but also semantic factors are eliminated by the procedure envisaged by Hartley. When he speaks of the "measure of information", or of the "amount of information" [66:540], or of the "information content" [66:541] of a signal sequence, he has nothing else in mind than a certain function of the relative frequency of this sequence among the set of all possible signal sequences of the same length.[3]

Hartley goes on to assume silently that all possible signal sequences are *equipossible*, i.e. are to be expected, before the accumulation of relevant evidence, to occur with equal relative frequencies (in the long run), and is thereby led to consider the number of these sequences itself as a possible measure of information of any specific sequence. Indeed, the larger this number, the rarer the occurrence of each sequence. However, for good, though admittedly somewhat arbitrary, reasons he finally decides "to take as our practical measure of information the logarithm of the number of possible symbol sequences" [66 :540]. Therefore, the measure of information of a certain symbol sequence s, when the set of all (equi-)possible sequences of the same length contains n members, is log n. The "probability" of s, $p(s)$, is then, of course, just $1/n$, hence $n = 1/p(s)$, and we arrive at the function mentioned above, log $1/p(s)$, which is now christened as "the measure of information (amount of information, information content) of s".

This christening turned out to be a continuous source of misunderstandings, the more so since it sounds so plausible that "when we speak of the capacity of a system to transmit information we imply some sort of quantitative measure of information" [66:536]. However, it is psychologically almost impossible not to make the shift from the one sense of information, for which this argument is indeed plausible, i.e. information = signal sequence, to the other sense, information = what is expressed by the signal sequence, for which the argument loses all its persuasiveness. And this shift is the less avoidable since it is hardly good English to talk about "measure of signal sequences" or "amount of signal". Therefore, we see over and over again that, in spite of the official disavowal of the interpretation of "information" as "what is conveyed by a signal sequence", "amount of information", officially meant to be a measure of the rarity of kinds of transmissions of signal sequences, acquires also, and sometimes predominantly, the connotation of a measure (of the rarity or improba-

---

3 It seems that Hartley did not distinguish to a sufficient degree between the relative frequency of a class of signal-sequence types among the class of all possible signal-sequence types and the corresponding conception with tokens (or occurrences) instead of types. Assume that there are 1000 three-letter English words (types), then the relative frequency of the unit-class comprising the word-type "the" as its only member among this class is 0.001. The relative frequency of the class of the tokens of "the" in a given text among the class of all tokens of three-letter words will be much higher, perhaps 0.1 or more. It is the estimate of the relative frequency in the second sense which is the only concern of the communication engineer.

The vital distinction seems to have been missed by many other information theoreticians. And not sufficient thought has been given to an exact determination of the reference class in the second case. Far too often the rather naive assumption was made that the observed relative frequencies were identical with the estimates, or expectation-values, of the relative frequencies in future samples.

bility) of the kinds of facts (events, states) designated by these signal sequences. And since this last concept is certainly a highly interesting one— we shall have to say more about it later—, it turned out to be humanly impossible not to believe that one has got some hold of this important and doubtless rather difficult concept on the basis of such a simple procedure as, say, counting frequencies of letter occurrences in English.

Frankly, I am not sure that this confusion is only a *result* of an unfortunate terminology. To a certain degree, at least, it seems that the confusion was rather the *cause* of the misleading terminology. This can be seen in Hartley's paper itself. At one point, he points out the important connection between his measure of information and certain *processes of selection*. The larger the set of signals from which the sender chooses the specific signal he is going to transmit, the more complex the process of selection. "At each selection there are *eliminated all of the other symbols* which might have been chosen [italics mine]. As the selections proceed, more and more possible symbol sequences are eliminated, and we say that the information becomes more precise. For example, in the sentence, "Apples are red", the first word *eliminates other kinds of fruit* [italics mine] and all other objects in general. The second directs attention to some property or condition of apples, and the third eliminates other possible colors" [66:536]. Notice again how slight, almost imperceptible transformations lead from truisms to interesting conclusions, which are, however, wholly unjustified and simply false. By selecting a certain symbol one "eliminates" (i.e. does not select) all other possible symbols—how true! By proceeding with the selections, other symbol sequences are eliminated—how obvious! But now comes the crucial shift from the elimination of other symbols to the elimination of "other kinds of fruit". Hartley must have succumbed to the illusion, not uncommon among linguistically unsophisticated scientists and even among the sophisticated ones in unguarded moments, that by not using a certain word, say "apples", at a certain moment one is not dealing with the entity or entities denoted by this word at this very same moment. The fallacy in this reasoning, if it has to be pointed out at all, is obvious from the simple fact that by using "apples" at a certain moment, one is not using any other word or phrase for apples at this moment and is, consequently, not dealing with apples at this moment.

The fallaciousness of the argument is not reduced by the obscurity of the statement that by proceeding with the selections, the information becomes more precise. "Apples are red" carries indeed (relatively) precise information, in the commonsensical sense of this expression. But in this sense, the information carried by "Apples are" is not less precise but nonexistent. Nothing short of a statement conveys information, and this information is not built up piecemeal from an accumulation of the information carried by each signal, if only for the truistic reason that non-sentential signals do not carry information in this sense. It is true, on the other hand, that common-sense has the vague feeling that the *meaning* of a statement is a function (perhaps even a kind of accumulative one) of the meanings of its constituents. But whatever the explication of this feeling will turn out to be in a full-fledged *semantics*, its only function in our context is to increase the confusion. I wonder how Hartley would have treated the increase of "preciseness", had he chosen as his illustration rather "Apples are not blue". I can explain the confusions only by assuming that Hartley felt that his measure of information could give him a measure of what would ordinarily, though vaguely, be called "the information content" of "Apples are red", though he decided later, as if for technical reasons, not to deal with this aspect and to "ignore the question of interpretation" [66:538].

Let us put it in different terms: It is quite customary to compare statements, in ordinary language, with respect to the information they convey. It makes full sense to say, for instance, that a report "The enemy attacked at dawn" conveys less information than "The enemy attacked in battallion strength at 5:30 A.M.", and it is also perfectly clear that the second statement is more precise than the first. It is therefore sensible to ask whether one could not refine the comparative evaluation into a quantitative one and tell *how much more information* is conveyed by the second report over that conveyed by the first one. Communication engineers, on the other hand, will be interested in the comparative rarity of reports of this kind expected to come from a certain source and would therefore like to have a quantitative measure of these rarities. But it must be perfectly clear that *there is no logical connection whatsoever between these two measures, i.e. the amount of (semantic) information conveyed by a statement*[4] *and the measure of rarity of kinds of symbol sequences*, even if these symbol sequences are typographically identical with this statement. The event of transmission of a certain statement[4] and the event expressed by this statement are, in general, entirely different events, and the logical probabilities assigned to these events, relative to certain evidences, will be as different as will be the frequencies with which events of these kinds will occur relative to certain reference classes. I admit that the temptation to identify these measures is great and almost irresistible when the "information" terminology is used. But the identifi-

---

[4] Or of the proposition (event) expressed by this statement. Ordinary usage is highly ambiguous with respect to the logical type of the entities that "convey information". Nor is it of prime logical importance whether these entities are regarded, for a systematic explication of this term, to be propositions or statements. The corresponding question with regard to logical probability has been treated at length by Carnap [28: § 52], who also discussed the problems connected with the proposition-event terminology [28: 34–35].

cation is still a mistake, and the fact that this mistake was made by many competent thinkers only increases its seriousness and the necessity of a complete clarification of the situation.

Notice that *the concept of semantic information has intrinsically nothing to do with communication.* If an explication for this concept can be found, then the proposition that all apples are red will carry a certain amount of information entirely independently of whether a statement to this effect is ever transmitted. The event itself may, of course, be that of transmitting a statement, but even then its semantic information would be independent of whether a statement saying that a certain statement has been transmitted is transmitted. Events of transmission of statements expressing events are of special interest for theoreticians interested in semantic information only as potential (and actual) sources of confusion.

Though there is no general logical connection between the two above-mentioned functions, as we tried to say so emphatically before, certain psychological connections exist in special cases. It seems worthwhile to point this out, since it is possible that this type of connection might have facilitated the confusions and made their detection more difficult. Let us assume that a census has to be taken in a certain village. Let the inhabitants of the village be a, b,... The census is interested only in the sex and age (young or old, suitably defined) of the inhabitants. The censer is expected to report to which of the categories Male, Female, Young, and Old each inhabitant belongs in series of symbol sequences, each having the form '—.', where the dash is to be replaced by one of the letters 'M', 'F', 'Y', and 'O', and the dot by small Roman letters denoting the inhabitants. Let us assume, for the sake of simplicity, that each such symbol sequence carries one unit of information both by itself and relative to any other symbol sequence of this set (except the one which is its contradictory)—let us not stop here to inquire into the basic assumptions from which this could be derived—, and that the measure of expected rarity of the classes of symbol sequences starting with any Capital letter is such as to assign to each such class approximately the same number (which would be a reasonable assumption if the censers are known to be reliable, the evidence being that in the U.S. the number of males equals approximately the number of females and that the number of young people equals approximately the number of old people). Under these assumptions there exists indeed a proportionality —and, through suitable choice of units, even a numerical identity—between the amount of information of (the logical conjunctions of) the symbol sequences and certain measures of rarity.

In this special case, we would indeed be entitled to infer from the length of a received report—leaving aside distortion—the amount of information conveyed by this report. If we receive a message of 20 letters in length, we can immediately compute that the amount of information conveyed by this message is 10, since we know that every two letters form a statement. Notice, however, that this exceptionally close correspondence is achieved only through a rigid determination of the code that the censers are instructed to use, and through the psychological *assumption* of the reliability of observing and reporting.

At some time between 1928 and 1948, American engineers and mathematicians began to talk about "Theory of Information" and "Information Theory", understanding by these terms approximately and vaguely a theory for which Hartley's "amount of information" is a basic concept. I have been unable to find out when and by whom these names were first used. Hartley himself does not use them nor does he employ the term "Theory of Transmission of Information", from which the two other shorter terms presumably were derived. It seems that Norbert Wiener and Claude Shannon were using them in the Mid-Forties. It would be of some interest to find out more about this terminological development and the semantic changes accompanying it. Let it only be remarked that the terminology used in Great Britain developed in an opposite direction. Whereas the term "Theory of Information" came to be used in the United States, at least as from 1948 (probably due to the impact of Wiener's **Cybernetics** [151]), as a certain not too well defined subscience of Communication Theory, the British usage of this term moved away from Communication and brought it into close contact with general scientific methodology. It seems that, for this development, MacKay [93] was the driving factor.

In view of what we said above, one cannot but deplore the terminological development in the States. "Theory of Transmission of Information" is still tolerable, though "Theory of Signal Transmission" would fit much better the subject matter that is of interest to communication engineers, but "Theory of Information" could not fail to stimulate the illusion that finally a radically new solution of some of the age-old puzzles connected with the concept of meaning has been found, and this on the basis of certain relatively simple and straightforward technological conceptions. Wiener himself, for instance, deliberately treats as synonyms "amount of information" and "amount of meaning". He says, "The amount of meaning can be measured. It turns out that the less probable a message is, the more meaning it carries, which is entirely reasonable from the standpoint of common sense" [150:8]. We see here very clearly the fusion of the improbability of (the event of transmission of) a message with the improbability of the event expressed by the message. Wiener's statement is resonable only in the second interpretation, which is, however, as said before, independent of any communication process. The term "message", on the other hand, indicates that the first interpretation is (also) considered. For this interpretation, however, the argument is far from reasonable and no connection whatsoever with any meaning of "meaning" is in sight.

What Wiener asserted explicitly and deliberately was as explicitly and deliberately denied by others. Shannon, for instance, who in general carefully avoids the term "theory of information", though he uses freely "amount of information", insists that "these semantic aspects of communication are irrelevant to the engineering problem" [136:3], to which alone he dedicates his attention. And he manages to steer clear of the pitfalls which the use of "amount of information" invites. However, his co-author, Warren Weaver, though insisting over and over again that "information must not be confused with meaning" [136:99] and though often fully aware of these pitfalls [136:106] is still convinced that the Mathematical Theory of Communication, as presented by Shannon, is of deep significance not only for the fact that a treatment of the communication process on a semantic or pragmatic level "can make use only of those signal occurrences which turn out to be possible when analyzed at" the signal level—this contention is highly plausible indeed and indicates an important hierarchical relationship between signal level and semantic level—but also for the fact that the analysis at the signal level discloses that "this level overlaps the other levels more than one could possibly naively suspect... I hope that the succeeding parts of this memorandum will illuminate and justify these last remarks" [136:97–98], and "that the interrelation of the three levels is so considerable that one's final conclusion may be that the separation into the three levels is really artificial and undesirable" [136:114].

I am fully sympathetic with Weaver's uneasiness about the exact relationship between the treatment of messages as signal sequences and as content-bearing entities, between the outright insistence not to confuse information with meaning and the expression of "the vague feeling that information and meaning may prove to be something like a pair of canonically conjugated variables in quantum theory" [136:117]. But I do not think that the later parts of his memorandum justify his hopes of illuminating his remarks formulating this relationship. Weaver's remarks about the Semantic Receiver who "subjugates the [received] message to a second decoding, the demand on this being that it must match the statistical *semantic* characteristics of the message to the statistical semantic capacities of the totality of receivers" [136:115] are far too concise and rely far too heavily on entirely undefined and hardly immediately comprehensible notions like "statistical semantic characteristic of a message" to carry much persuasion with them. Weaver may have had a better intuitive and imaginative understanding of the relationship than many other information theoreticians, but I cannot admit that he justified his claim "that this analysis [of Shannon] has so penetratingly cleared the air that one is now, perhaps for the first time, ready for a real theory of meaning" [136:116].

An explicit denial of the relevance of information theory for semantics has, as a matter of fact, been standard procedure with most writers in this field. Feeling rightfully that everybody will take "information" as a semantical term, they were usually in a hurry to exclude this interpretation. In the by far best presentation of the development of information theory, E. Colin Cherry [31] states, not as his personal opinion, but as an expression of a general attitude: "It is important to emphasize, at the start, that we are not concerned with the meaning or the truth of messages; semantics lies outside the scope of mathematical information theory" [31:383]. There is no reason to disbelieve the sincerity of this statement. However, Cherry himself cannot help being deceived by this unfortunate term "information". And, so he says later: "... when we solve a set of simultaneous equations we do not really obtain new information; the various steps and the final solution represent transformations (or "codings") of the information which was contained implicitly in the original equation" [31:389]. The information contained in the original equations has surely nothing to do with the rarity of these equations among the set of all possible equations (of the same length). What Cherry has in mind is the important, though certainly not new, observation that the solution of a set of simultaneous equations does not carry semantic information in excess to that carried by this set itself, since the solution is logically derivable from these equations, and this in spite of the fact that it carries excess psychological information, in the sense that not everyone who gets the equations is able to solve them instantaneously if at all. It is obvious that Cherry uses here "information" in one or more of those senses which he tried to exclude from his investigation. The temptation must have been too strong.[5]

The problem of the exact relationship between a (statistical) theory of signal transmission and a theory of semantic information is indeed a highly interesting and urgent one. However, it could not be treated effectively as long as no theory of semantic information was in existence. By now, an outline of such a theory has been created (Chapter 15), and we are now in a position to say more about this topic. The simple fusion of these theories, which has been customary until now, though often unconsciously and in spite of overt declarations, could result only in confusion.

---

[5] Compare also the long list given by Miller [100: 3] of what "information", in the technical sense it got in Information Theory, is *not* intended to mean.

III

Before I attempt to describe the relationship between the communication engineer's theory of information and the semanticist's theory of information, let me first rechristen these theories, in order to get rid as far as possible of disturbing associations connected with the ambiguous term 'information', the (statistical) Theory of Signal Transmission and the Theory of Semantical Content, respectively. I would now say that both these theories can be regarded as different interpretations of a common formal system, the Calculus of Information. This calculus consists, reduced to its simplest terms, of two sets of numbers: $S = \{s_1, s_2, ..., s_n\}$ and $R = \{r_1, r_2, ..., r_m\}$, fulfilling the conditions

$$\sum_{i=1}^{n} s_i = 1 \quad \text{and} \quad \sum_{j=1}^{m} r_j = 1,$$

and two functions, $f(s_i, r_j)$ and $g(s_i, r_j)$, each of two variables ranging over the sets S and R respectively, fulfilling the conditions

$$\sum_{j=1}^{m} f(s_i, r_j) = s_i \quad \text{and} \quad \sum_{i=1}^{n} g(s_i, r_j) = r_j.$$

In this calculus, the properties and relations of the negative logarithms of the numbers $s_i, r_j, f(s_i, r_j)$, and $g(s_i, r_j)$, i.e. of $- \log s_i$, $- \log r_j$, $- \log f(s_i, r_j)$, $- \log g(s_i, r_j)$, of various weighted means of these numbers such as $\sum_i s_i(- \log s_i)$, $\sum_{i,j} f(s_i, r_j)[- \log f(s_i, r_j)]$, of the limits to which these means tend, when either n or m, or both, go to infinity, etc., are developed.

The founders of the statistical theory of signal transmission succeeded in driving home the importance of this calculus for communication engineering. They interpreted s_i as the relative frequency of the set of emissions of the i-th signal (or signal-sequence) within the set of emissions of all signals (or signal-sequences) from a certain source, r_j as the relative frequency of the set of all receptions of the j-th signal (or...) within the set of receptions of all m signals (or...) at a certain target, $f(s_i, r_j)$ and $g(s_i, r_j)$ as certain conditional relative frequencies, into the details of which there is no need to go here.

But it should be quite obvious that the Information Calculus can be given many more interpretations, some of which are of much greater generality and likely to be of equal, if not greater, importance in their fields. Let, for instance, $H = \{h_1, ..., h_n\}$ and $K = \{k_1, ..., k_m\}$ be exhaustive systems of events (for a given evidence e) i.e. systems of events such that (on the given evidence e) exactly one of the n h_i and exactly one of the m k_i must occur.[6]

---

[6] For a less loose way of describing this interpretation, see Section 11 of Chapter 15.

It can then be shown that, interpreting now the s_i as the degrees of confirmation (or inductive, or logical, probabilities) of the events h_i on the evidence e and the r_j as the degrees of confirmation of the events k_j on e, $-\log s_i$ may be taken as a measure of (at least a certain aspect of) the content of h_i, $\Sigma_i \, s_i(- \log s_i)$ as a measure of the average content of the events h_i, etc. (Chapter 15). (This is not to say that a theory of semantic content must rely on the mentioned calculus. It has been shown that quite different measures seem to have some significance.)

These considerations lead up to the result that the Theory of Signal Transmission and the Theory of Semantic Content have a certain calculus in common. This is much, but not too much. Since these two theories are formally analogous, one is entitled to assume that the counterparts of the important concepts and theorems in any of these theories might be of importance in the other theory. Certain concepts of the Theory of Semantic Content have indeed been deliberately formed in analogy to existing concepts in the Theory of Signal Transmission. It is not improbable, e.g., that concepts like *semantic noise, efficiency* and *redundancy of a conceptual framework*, etc., coined in analogy with *channel noise, code-efficiency* and *code-redundancy*, should prove to be quite as useful for semantic analysis as are their counterparts for communication engineering.

Information-theoretical concepts are nowadays being used everywhere. Papers on applications of Information Theory in psychology, linguistics, sociology, anthropology, physics, etc. appear in rapidly increasing numbers. It might be helpful to point out that, in most cases, it is rather the *information calculus* that is applied and not at all its communication engineering interpretation. The information calculus can indeed be usefully and powerfully applied in psychology, say, in test theory, because the r_j may be interpreted, for instance, as the relative frequency of the members of a certain population showing the i-th trait, the s_i as the relative frequency of the members of this population showing the j-th mark in an intelligence test, $f(s_i, r_j)$ as the relative frequency of the people showing the i-th trait within the subpopulation of the people obtaining the j-th mark, etc.

Disregarding the distinction between a calculus and its interpretations, together with the unfortunate term 'information', has led in this case, as in so many others, to misunderstandings and futile discussions. One is astonished to read that Brillouin, an authority in the field of communication engineering, seriously raises the question wherefrom the information contained in a certain book is obtained, since the author of this book does not, in general, "lose" this information [18:595] and whether this information, by the simple process of printing, is not multiplied out of nothing. And I am sure that Cherry and MacKay do not necessarily contradict each other, in spite of appearances, when the first states that "a calculatory machine cannot create information" [31:383] and the second speculates how such machines can do just this [94]. It is only that the term 'information' is used by these authors in these contexts in different ways, though the exact usages are not easily determinable.

The term 'information' is, of course, also used as a psychological term. Locutions like "This message was loaded with information for A, but was meaningless for B" point to this concept, which is obviously of paramount importance for psychologists, teachers, etc. Whether the information calculus, in its present development, is the appropriate tool to handle this field is at least highly doubtful. It might, however, be possible, under certain conditions, to replace the statement, "The message m carries much information for X", which seems to involve the concept of psychological information, by another statement that involves the semantical concept only. We shall not go into this interesting possibility here.

The application of information theory has been considerably encouraged by the identification "amount of information" with "*uncertainty*", though— as we shall see—there are also other versions of their relationship. This identification originated probably from looking at the process of signal transmission through the eyes of the receiver. He may be awaiting news about which horse won a certain race and may even have assigned probabilities to the various possible outcomes. He is therefore in a certain state of uncertainty about the result of the race. Having received the message "Golden Horn has won", his uncertainty is resolved (if he has no reason to believe that this message is faked), and this due to the "information" contained in this message. The greater his uncertainty about the outcome, i.e., roughly speaking, the nearer to the rectangular his subjective probability distribution of the chances of the horses to win the race, the greater the expectation value of the amount of the information of the message before he receives it. Hence we get: uncertainty = amount of information (though some would argue for the necessity of introducing a minus sign at one side of the equation).

Notice that I formulated the situation as involving uncertainty about race-results, i.e., non-linguistic events, hence again about something with which official information theory is committed not to deal. In this case, however, it would cause no difficulty to rephrase the situation in terms of messages and signals alone. The nervous bettor is awaiting the arrival of a certain message out of a set of possible messages. To each of these messages he assigns, ideally, certain a priori probabilities—which have, of course, nothing to do with the relative frequencies of such messages in the English language—, his uncertainty about which particular message is going to be transmitted is, consequently, a certain function of these probabilities. Any received undistorted message will eliminate this uncertainty by providing the receiver with a certain amount of information.

But here we run into additional trouble, perhaps only of a terminological nature, though it may also indicate additional confusion. *Any* received message will eliminate the same uncertainty, but, in general, each of these messages conveys a different "amount of information". In fact, the uncertainty can be reasonably assumed to be a weighted mean of the amounts of information which the various possible messages, say $s_1, s_2, ..., s_n$, convey, hence is equal to

$$-\sum_{i=1}^{n} p(s_i) \log p(s_i).$$

The amount of information conveyed by a particular s_i is, however, simply $-\log p(s_i)$ which may be equal to $-\sum p(s_i) \log p(s)_i$ but will in general be either larger or smaller. If we follow up consistently our way of talking, we must say that the bettor may sometimes receive an amount of information which is greater than his uncertainty.

However, instead of realizing that this counterintuitive result shows that their choice of the psychologistic term "uncertainty" is apt to backfire, at least in certain situations, some information theoreticians decided—though not only for this reason—to use the term "amount of information conveyed by s_i" not for $-\log p(s_i)$ but rather for $-\sum p(s_i) \log p(s_i)$. This solves our prior puzzle rather neatly. Everybody sees immediately and trivially that uncertainty is now exactly equal to amount of information. But now another puzzle arises, I would say, an even more disturbing one. Any two messages of the same set, whether their probabilities are the same or not, carry the same amount of information! By receiving any of these messages we gain the same amount of information! Indeed, there are textbooks of information theory in which the amount of information contained in a book or in the Sunday issue of the New York Times is determined simply as a function of the number of characters used. It is extremely difficult to understand what the authors can gain by calling this function, whatever its merits otherwise are, "amount of information". Any attempt to rationalize this deplorable result of a bad terminology must result in obscurity and uneasiness. Weaver has it this way: "To be sure, this word information in communication theory relates not so much to what you *do* say, as to what you *could* say. That is, information is a measure of one's freedom of choice when one selects a message... Note that it is misleading (although often convenient) to say that one or the other message conveys unit information. The concept of information applies not to the individual messages (as the concept of meaning would), but rather to the situation as a whole..." [136:100]. D. Gabor [56] repeatedly tried to point out this confusion and ridicule questions of the type "What is the amount of information in the telegram just received?", if "amount of information" is understood in the Shannon sense, but his continued use of "amount of information" for this concept somewhat vitiates his criticism.

As soon as one rids oneself of the inconsistent psychologistic web in which many information theoreticians have involved themselves—due more to their laudable intention to present their theory in a fashion palatable to the general educated public than to any intrinsic necessities—, the situation becomes clear; communication engineers have no use for $- \log p(s_i)$ as such but only, at most, as a stepping stone to $- \Sigma\ p(s_i) \log p(s_i)$. That both of these functions, and many others too, were called "amount of information" "beautifully illustrates", to quote a dictum by Weaver himself used in another connection, "the semantic trap into which one can fall if he does not remember that "information" is used here with a special meaning" [136:109].

The full communication process, as illustrated in our meteorological example, can be split up, for specialized study, in various ways. Some communication engineers like to confine themselves to the investigation of the operations S, R, and S^* mentioned there, i.e. to what I have proposed to call Theory of Signal Transmission. Others, realizing that the overall effectiveness of communication depends also on the coding, would like to include C and C^* and would hence be led to investigate also what we might call *Theory of Coding (and Decoding)*. Still others might insist that the process of functionalizing ordinary language is of relevance and bring into the scope of their interest also F and F^* and might therefore be called *language engineers* or *language technologists* and their field perhaps *language engineering*. Language engineers will, of course, soon realize that they must know something about the messages m themselves in order to transform them efficiently into $F(m)$ and will, therefore, be induced to study theoretical *linguistics, logic,* and *semantics,* all of which are subfields of the general *theory of signs* or *semiotics,* or, at least, to cooperate with those scientists who are specializing in these fields. And, finally, to ensure, say, an efficient communication system between pilots and control tower operators, *aviation* must be known by at least some of the designers of the system, and to increase the efficiency of sales reporting in department stores, *management* and *business administration* are necessary, etc. Communication starts from events that are, in general, extra-linguistic, and goes through their verbalizing, reverbalizing, encoding, sending, distorting, receiving, decoding, expanding, understanding, and acting upon. One may prefer to deal with this process in all its generality or one may dedicate oneself to one or more of the partial processes involved. It may be disastrous to employ prematurely in one subfield a terminology that is fitting in another subfield or the whole field, and though nobody should be discouraged from looking for analogies between the subfields, precautions have to be taken against being misled by presumed analogies, among them, of course, the precaution not to call from the beginning by the same name entities whose identity one hopes to establish in the course of the investigation.

Even more important than the change of name from Information Theory to Theory of Signal Transmission (plus, perhaps, Theory of Coding) would be to discard the use of the term "information" within this theory, with all its ambiguities and semantic traps. It is up to the engineers to revise their terminology, not in order to please some overpedantic philosopher or logician but in order to save themselves futile discussions and to discourage others from ill-advised "applications".

Let me conclude this section by pointing out that a terminological clean-up is also required for the use (in order to avoid the misuse) of such more general terms as *sign, message, word, symbol, signal, code, code element, elementary symbol, signal sequence, symbol sequence*, etc. Though I think that this debabelization should not turn out to be too difficult, I have no intention to undertake it here.

IV

In the preceding sections, I tried to outline to the philosophically interested reader a picture of a new science, the so-called Theory of Information. I hope to have made it clear that, contrary to some claims, no direct impact on Semantics is to be expected from this new science, though the calculus employed in it may very well turn out to be a powerful tool also in other fields including (Inductive) Semantics. Let me add immediately that in my opinion the great new insghts into the process of communication, which have been achieved recently, partly with the help of the information calculus, will be of paramount importance for Semantics. But just in order to utilize these insights to their full extent, a clarification of certain basic misconceptions which have crept into the foundations of Information Theory is necessary. This task has been undertaken here only to a limited extent, due mainly to lack of space. I did not even attempt to discuss here the highly exciting implications of the observation that certain central functions of the Information Calculus occur also in those parts of thermodynamics and statistical mechanics which center around the *entropy* concept. I must also refrain from dealing with the contributions of the European school of information theoreticians, MacKay, Gabor, Cherry, and others. In order to combat constantly recurring misunderstandings, let me conclude by again pointing out that in the British usage, Information Theory is not identical with Theory of Signal Transmission but is a much more comprehensive science, apparently more related to Semantics than to Communication Engineering, though no exact delimitation seems to have been achieved as yet.

Semantic Information and its Measures* | 17

The following presentation will be confined mainly to the theory of semantic information as it was developed in Chapter 15. Also it will be concerned with the relation of this concept to the concept of amount of information, as developed by C. E. Shannon [136], and an attempt will be made to show that the two are not in competition. The presentation will occasionally touch upon the relationship between thermodynamic entropy and amount of information, emphasizing both the positive connections and the nonidentity; and it will also touch upon the distinction between statistical probability and inductive probability.

Information Theory, in the sense in which this expression is used in the United States, namely, Theory of Information Transmission, is not generally spoken of as dealing with the content of the messages transmitted, and hence it is regarded as a discipline having no connection with semantics [31].

However, few could resist falling into the semantical trap laid by the use of the word "information" and not assume sooner or later that this field of interest is applicable to semantics and does reveal certain aspects of meaning. Claude Shannon is, to my knowledge, the only major information theoretician who consistently refrained from drawing illicit inferences.

The theory, an outline of which is presented here, is meant overtly and exclusively to deal with the concept of semantic information conveyed by a statement, or the semantic content of a statement, and various measures for this concept.

Many would not consider this a worthwhile aim. They would insist that it is sensible to talk about information in the communicational sense and, as a next step, about information in the full-blooded pragmatical sense, i.e., about how much information a certain statement carries for someone in a given state of knowledge. This latter concept is obviously of greatest concern to psychologists, teachers. and other people involved in transmission of information or in the study of this transmission process. But they would

* First appeared in **Transactions of the Tenth Conference on Cybernetics,** Josiah Macy, Jr. Foundation, New York 1952, pp. 33–48.

deny that the intermediate concept of semantical information—which is pragmatics-free, abstracts from the users of language and deals only with the relationships between linguistic entities and what they stand for, or designate, or denote — is of any importance. I believe that this view is mistaken. However, instead of starting a polemic, I shall present merely the outline of the theory and allow you to decide whether or not it can be fruitfully applied.

To repeat, the following is a systematic *explicatum* of what is meant by the content of a statement, or the information carried by a statement, or when it is said that the information conveyed by statement *j* is greater than that conveyed by statement *i*. Only statements that convey or carry information are being used as arguments. This is done deliberately. Not that I want to deny that there are other entities that are said, in ordinary discourse, to carry information. Communication theoreticians assign amounts of information to all kinds of signs or symbols, and scientists talk about the information conveyed by the outcome of an observation or an experiment, or by any other kind of event, in general. I shall not at this time go into the interesting technical question of to what degree these usages are reducible to information carried by statements. What regards assignment of information to events, i.e., entities expressible by statements, I shall adopt this usage as an alternative to my regular usage, whenever this proves profitable. Though there are some interesting philosophico-logical questions involved in this, I shall not discuss them here.

Let me then give you immediately what seems to Dr. Carnap and me to be a reasonable *explicatum* for the presystematic concept of information, in its semantical sense. We call it *content* and denote it by "Cont," with a capital "C." According to the scholastic dictum, *omnis determinatio est negatio*, we take *the content of a statement* to be the *class of those possible states of the universe which are excluded by this statement*, that is, the class of those states whose being the case is incompatible with the truth of the statement.

For technical reasons, however, we prefer to talk about *state-descriptions* instead of states. The final definition for the content of a statement is, consequently, *the class of all state-descriptions excluded by this statement*. One of the advantages of the shift to state-descriptions is that this forces us to relativize our treatment with respect to given languages. Unfortunately, however, we are able so far to present reasonably adequate definitions for rather restricted language systems only, namely for what is known in the profession as *applied first-order language-systems with identity*. These languages are certainly too restricted to serve as languages adequate for all science. Their major drawback is the absence of functors for quantities such as mass, temperature, etc. This drawback is admittedly serious, and attempts are being made to extend the impact of our theory to richer languages [77]. For the time being, however, I beg you to keep this restriction of scope in mind.

To illustrate the concepts I am going to introduce, I shall use a specimen language, and this will help you to visualize their applicability. The specimen language has the following structure. It contains, in addition to the customary connectives, "$\sim$," "$\vee$," "$\&$," "$\supset$" and "$\equiv$," being, respectively, the signs for negation, disjunction, conjunction, (material) implication, and (material) equivalence, three individual-signs, "a," "b," and "c", and two primitive predicates, "M," and "Y." The interpretation is as follows: A census has to be taken in a small hamlet of three inhabitants. The census is of a very restricted scope. The census taker is required to find out only whether the inhabitants are male or female and young or old (defined, respectively, as being under 35 years of age, or otherwise). The three individual-signs denote, then, the inhabitants of the hamlet, in a certain fixed order, and the two primitive predicates the properties Male and Young. For "$\sim M$" and "$\sim Y$," denoting, respectively, the properties Not-Male, or Female, and Not-Young or Old, we shall use the abbreviations "F" and "O."

Any sequence of one of the letters "M," "F," "Y," and "O" and one of the letters "a," "b," and "c" is called a *basic statement*. "Ma," for instance, is a basic statement signifying that a is male. All the statements of our language consist of the twelve basic statements and the statements formed out of them with the help of the connectives.

Our specimen language is extremely poor. What it loses thereby will, I hope, be outbalanced by the perspicuity of the applicability of the rather abstract concepts to be introduced presently.

An example of a state-description in our language is as follows: Since such a state-description denotes a possible state of the universe dealt with in this language, it tells us, for each individual, whether this individual is male or female, young or old. It consists, consequently, altogether of a conjunction of six basic statements. "$Ma \& Ya \& Fb \& Yb \& Mc \& Oc$," for instance, is a state-description telling that a is male and young, b female and young, c male and old. This conjunction describes our universe completely. As soon as I add a basic statement which is not identical with any of the six components of this conjunction, this basic statement can only be the negation of one of these components so that the resulting conjunction will be self-contradictory. We conclude, then, that any statement which logically implies, or is stronger than, a state-description is self-contradictory. In this sense, a state-description is a strongest synthetic statement in its language.

We take as the *explicatum* for the information conveyed by a given statement the class of the state-descriptions excluded by that statement. Each statement in our specimen language excludes, then, none, one, or more (up to 2^6, or 64, which is the number of all state-descriptions) of the state-descriptions. An analytic, or logically true, statement, such as "$Ma \lor Fa$," excludes none; a self-contradictory, or logically false, statement, such as "$Ma \& Fa$," excludes all; a synthetic, or logically indeterminate, statement excludes some, but not all, state-descriptions. An analytic statement has minimum content, and a self-contradictory statement maximum content. This is not surprising. A self-contradictory statement tells too much, it excludes too much, and is incompatible with any state of the universe, whereas an analytic statement excludes nothing whatsoever and is compatible with everything.

A state-description itself, as a strongest synthetic statement, excludes all other state-descriptions. We shall deal somewhat later with its counterpart, a weakest synthetic statement, that excludes just one state-description.

Notice that we have so far explicated only the notion of information itself. On one occasion Shannon mentioned that he did not define the concept of information itself and was not interested in it. He wanted to define only the concept of amount-of-information, with undeletable hyphens. To my knowledge he never uses the notion of information as such in any essential way, nor is there any reason why a communication engineer should do so. We offer an explication for information itself, in its semantical sense, for whatever it is worth. Whether Cont is a good *explicatum*, remains to be seen.

Our next problem is now to define *measures of content* to serve as *explicata* for amount-of-information, in the semantical sense. So long as we are talking only about content itself, the most we can say is that a certain statement has a larger content than another one, and this in case that the class of state-descriptions excluded by the first statement includes the class of state-descriptions excluded by the second one as a proper part. Thus we would say that

$$\text{Cont}(``Ma") \supset \text{Cont}(``Ma \lor Yb"),$$

since the class of state-descriptions excluded by "Ma" (theie are 32 of them) contains the class of state-descriptions excluded by "$Ma \lor Ya$" (there are 16 of them) as a proper part. But if two contents are exclusive, i.e., have no member in common, or overlapping, i.e., have some but not all members in common, we can say no more about the statements whose contents they are, although we certainly would like to be able to say, and justify, that "Ma" has a larger content, conveys more information, than "$Mb \lor Yb$".

In order to do just this, we must go over to the stage of talking about measures of content, to define—as the mathematicians would say—a measure-function ranging over the set of contents. Fortunately, we do not have to start from the beginning. Carnap [28] has developed a rather extensive theory of measure-functions ranging over, not, to wit, contents, but something very similar to them, namely, what he calls *ranges*. (The range of a statement is the class of those stato-descriptions that logically imply that statement.) These measure-functions, which he calls *m-functions*, are meant to explicate the presystematic concept of *logical* or *inductive probability*.

Now, since a measure-theory of ranges has already been developed, we can clearly make full use of it and define our content measure-functions on the basis of Carnap's *m*-functions. For each such *m*-function, a corresponding function can be defined in some way that will measure the content of any given statement.

Let *m* be a measure-function of ranges. What kind of function of *m* shall we take as a measure for contents? We have a multiplicity of choices. But all choices will have to fulfil the following condition that seems clearly indicated for any adequate explication of amount of information: *the greater the logical probability of a statement, the smaller its content measure.* The fulfilment of this inverse relationship will be the guiding requirement for our choices.

The mathematically simplest relationship that fulfills this requirement is the complement to 1. Let $m(i)$ be the logical probability of the statement *i*. Then $1 - m(i)$ can be taken as a plausible measure for the content of *i*. We call this measure simply the *content measure* of *i* and denote it by "cont(*i*)" with a lower case "c," in distinction to the upper-case "Cont" standing for content. The formal definition, is then,

$$\text{cont}(i) =_{df} 1 - m(i).$$

It can easily be seen that cont fulfills, in addition to the aforementioned condition of adequacy, other requirements of an adequate explication of amount of information, *but not all*. It fails to fulfil a certain requirement of additivity, the counterpart of which plays a great role in Shannon's theory. This requirement, in our case, would be that the content measure of two statements that are *inductively independent*—meaning thereby roughly that the logical probability of either statement should not be changed by being given the other statement—should be equal to the sum of the content measures of each of them taken separately. But, it is not the case, in general, that if *i* and *j* are inductively independent, then $\text{cont}(i\&j) = \text{cont}(i) + \text{cont}(j)$. There is, indeed, an additivity theorem for cont, but the condition under which it holds, is not that *i* and *j* should be inductively independent but rather that they should be *content-exclusive*, i.e., that there should be no state-description excluded by both i and j. This additivity condition makes sense though it is at odds with the more customary one of inductive independence. It makes sense to say that the content measure of the conjunction of two statements should be equal to the sum of their content measures if, and only if, they are content-exclusive. Then cont has certain plausible properties though it lacks certain other properties which are equally plausible. Since, however, no concept can have both these plausible properties simultaneously, we are led to the idea—and there are many other arguments pointing in the same direction—that we do not have in our mind *one* clearcut, unique, presystematic concept of amount of information but at least two of them (and both still in the semantic dimension). This is not so strange. On the contrary, it is a rather common phenomenon that two related but different concepts are regarded as being identical although con tradictory properties are required for their *explicata*.

Though cont seems to be a very natural and simple systematic correlate for the presystematic concept of amount of semantical information, neither it nor, what is perhaps somewhat more surprising, its statistical counterpart have been discussed much so far. On second thought, however, it is perhaps not difficult to account for this neglect. It seems that in communication engineering, the requirement of additivity under the statistical counterpart of inductive independence is much more important and practical than such a requirement under the counterpart of content exclusiveness, and it is doubtful whether this condition makes sense there at all. Another reason will be given further on in the presentation.

At this point, it will probably be of some help to present a pair of content-exclusive statements in our specimen-language:

$$\text{``}Ma\text{'' and ``}Ma \supset Fb.\text{''}$$

You can easily see that the contents of these two statements do not overlap if you transform the second statement, according to the rules of the ordinary propositional calculus, into "$Fa \lor Fb$." More generally, any two statements, one of which is an implication statement having the other as its antecedent, are content-exclusive.

I already mentioned that we chose the roundabout way of introducing the concept of content measure *via* the m-functions only because an extensive theory of these functions stood at our disposal. For those unacquainted with that theory, it would probably have been pedagogically wiser to base the whole thing not on state-descriptions but on their "dual," which we call *content-elements*. You get the "dual" of a state-description if you replace the " & "-signs by " $\lor$ "-signs and each capital letter by its complement. The dual, for instance, of the state-description, I mentioned before for illustrative purposes is:

$$Fa \lor Oa \lor Mb \lor Ob \lor Fc \lor Yc.$$

Just as the state-descriptions are the strongest synthetic statements, so the content-elements are the weakest synthetic statements. I could then have defined the content of i as the class of all content-elements logically implied by i. I could then finally have defined cont(i) as a measure-function of contents dually analogous to Carnap's definition of m-function.

Since cont is not additive under inductive independence, we need another *explicatum* for amount of information that will have this property, and will assign to "Ma & Yb," for instance, an information measure that is equal to the sum of the information measures of "Ma" and "Yb" since these two statements are inductively independent for any adequate m-function I can think of. Being given the information that a is male, the logical probability of b's being young should not be affected. This seems rather obvious. Under a certain normalization, the information-measure of each of these two statements turns out to be *one* (bit). We would then like the information measure of their conjunction to be 2. But this does not hold for cont. The cont-value of the conjunction is smaller than the cont-value of the components, since these two statements are certainly not content-exclusive: They both imply, for instance, the statement "$Ma \lor Yb$." Since a synthetic statement is logically implied by both statements, their contents cannot be exclusive.

Insisting on additiveness on condition of inductive independence we obtain another set of measures for amount of information which we call this time *information measures* and denote by "inf." We can define "inf" either with the help of "cont" as

$$\inf(i) =_{df} \log_2 \frac{1}{1 - \text{cont}(i)}$$

or else directly on the basis of m as

$$\inf(i) =_{df} \log_2 \frac{1}{m(i)} \quad (= -\log_2 m(i)),$$

which immediately recalls the standard definition given by many people, though not by Shannon himself, for the amount of information carried by a single signal i. We have only to replace "$m(i)$" by "$p(i)$" for this purpose.

It can easily be shown that inf, as defined by either of these definitions, fulfills the above-mentioned requirement.

There is another requirement which causes dissension among people looking for an explication of amount of information. Some would insist that the amount of information of *any* two statements should always be at most equal to the sum of the amounts of information of these statements;

others would not want to commit themselves on this point. It can be shown that cont fulfills this requirement, i.e., that for any i and j,

$$\text{cont}(i\&j) \leqq \text{cont}(i) + \text{cont}(j),$$

whereas between inf $(i\&j)$ and the sum of inf(i) and inf(i) all three possible relationships of magnitude may subsist.

One standard objection, to be found among those who believe that an explication of the semantical sense of information is of little or no use, is that the concept of information, as ordinarily used, is essentially subjective. The statement, "Johnny is hungry," carries no information for someone who already knows that Johnny is hungry, a moderate amount of information for someone who is ignorant about Johnny's state in this respect, and a very large amount of information for him who believes that Johnny is not hungry.

In analogy to the situation with respect to probability—and this analogy is, of course, no accident in view of the close relation between probability and amount of information — this objection must be split up into two quite different parts, only one of which points to an essential subjectiveness. This part is only the relatively trivial one in which the same statement can be said to carry different amounts of information even for two people with the same beliefs. Admitting this, we admit no more than we were ready to do long before, namely, that there is a concept of pragmatical information which is badly in need of explication. But the other part, based upon the fact that different people may have different sets of beliefs, need not necessarily be interpreted as pointing to *subjectiveness* but can better be interpreted as pointing toward *relativity*, toward the fact that the same statement might carry different informations, *objectively* different semantic informations *relative* to other statements, taken as objective evidence. With regard to our illustrations, we would prefer to formulate the situation by saying that the statement, "Johny is hungry," carries different informations when taken relative to the statement, "Johnny is hungry," as evidence, when taken absolutely, and when taken relative to the statement, "Johnny is not hungry," as evidence. This points only to the necessity of distinguishing clearly between the information carried by a statement absolutely, taken by itself, and the information carried by it relative to other statements. This we do, of course, and distinguish Cont(i/j) — the content of i relative to, or given, or on the evidence of, or simply on, j — from Cont(i), cont(i/j) from cont(i), inf(i/j) from inf(i). The definitions look alike, that of inf(i/j) is, for instance, as one would probably predict,

$$\text{inf}(i/j) =_{df} \text{inf}(i\&j) - \text{inf}(j).$$

Denoting any analytic statement by "t," we find that

$$\text{inf}(i/t) = \text{inf}(i),$$

an equation that would have allowed us to define inf(i) in terms of inf(i/j), i.e., the absolute information measure in terms of the relative information measure, instead of the other way round.

Here the question arises: What are the relations of the relative content and information measures to the relative, or conditional, probability measures? Defining $m(i/j)$, i.e., the inductive probability of i given j, in the customary fashion as

$$m(i/j) =_{df} \frac{m(i\&j)}{m(j)}$$

we arrive at the remarkable result that

$$\text{inf}(i/j) = - \log_2 m(i/j),$$

in complete analogy to

$$\text{inf}(i) = - \log_2 m(i).$$

There is no corresponding theorem for cont, i.e., it is not the case that

$$\text{cont}(i/j) = 1 - m(i/j).$$

This is then the other reason, intimated previously, for the preference given in communication theory, and everywhere else, to the correlate of inf. It seems that many authors take it for granted, more or less, that the amount of information of i relative to j should be the same function of the probability of i given j as the absolute amount of information of i of the absolute probability of i. The fulfillment of this requirement leads indeed to a log type of function.

I claimed previously that the fact that both cont and inf exhibit plausible properties indicates that the presystematic concept of amount of semantic information is ambiguous and apparently an amalgam of at least two different concepts, one of which is explicated by cont, the other by inf. (In addition to this, the vital distinction between the absolute and the relative concepts is often not made, thereby still increasing the confusion.) To prove this once more: A moment ago, a property of inf was pointed out which many regard as essential for an amount of information function. I am going to point now at a property that characterizes cont but not inf, which is considered by many as a *desideratum* for an amount of information function. When I asked people what they regard as the appropriate relation between the absolute amount of information of a given statement i and its amount of information relative to any j, most of them were very positive that no increase in the evidence should increase the amount of information, though it might not necessarily decrease it. It can, however, easily be shown that whereas indeed

$$\text{cont}(i/j) \leqq \text{cont}(i),$$

the corresponding statement for inf does not hold.

I shall show this for our specimen language. For any adequate m-function, $m(\text{``}Ma\text{''}/\text{``}Fb\text{''})$ will be less than $m(\text{``}Ma\text{''})$, since, according to the *principle of instantial relevance*, the instance "$Fb$" is negatively relevant to "$Ma$." Therefore $- \log_2 m(\text{``}Ma\text{''}/\text{``}Fb\text{''})$ will be greater than $- \log_2 m$ ("Ma"), hence

$$\text{inf}(\text{``}Ma\text{''}/\text{``}Fb\text{''}) > \text{inf}(\text{``}Ma\text{''}), \text{q.e.d.}$$

It is perhaps not too far from the point if we regard cont as a measure of the *substantial aspect* of a piece of information, and inf as a measure of its *surprise value*. When the census taker learns that Ma, when he first comes to the hamlet, he learns that the universe he is interested in is not in any of certain 32 states out of the 64 states it could possibly have been in. If this is the second thing he learns, having learned first thing that Fb, the substantial increase of his knowledge about that universe is less, since "Ma" tells him now only that the universe is not in any of 16 states out of the 32 it could still have been in, these 16 states forming a subclass of the class of 32 states, in the first case. But though his knowledge increases less substantially, he is (or should be) now more surprised than he was in the first case. Knowing nothing, he expects a to be M as much as F, but having observed that b is F first, he then expects a to be F rather than M—it is important to remember that this is *all* he knows, in our fictitious situations; *he* knows nothing about attraction of sexes and all the other many things *we* know and which are relevant to the census — and is therefore rightfully surprised when a turns out to be M after all.

By illustrating in psychologistic terms, I am afraid I created more puzzle than enlightenment. In order not to fall into the trap laid thereby, it might perhaps be preferable to speak of inf as a measure of (objective) *unexpectedness* rather than of surprise.

Though inf is a monotonic transform of cont, it is not a linear transform. Consequently, not only are the cont-values and inf-values in general different, but so are the cont and inf ratios. It will, therefore, in general make a difference whether, in a given practical situation, one is going to use the cont or inf measure.

This can be illustrated by means of the following story, inspired by the title of a book by Agatha Christie entitled **Bridge Murder Case**. There was a bridge party in A's villa, with B, C, D, and E participating; A was the host and only kibitzed. When the last rubber was finished and the guests were looking for A to take leave of him, they found him murdered in the garden. Every one of the four players had been the dummy at one time or another and had left the room for refreshments. Each one had, on the available evidence, an equal opportunity for murdering A. A reward was promised to those who could forward information leading to the identification of the murderer.

A day later, X came and produced evidence sufficient to prove that B could not have been the murderer. The next day Y showed, to the district attorney's satisfaction, that C was innocent. The following day, Z did the same for D. Whereupon E was duly convicted and electrocuted.

The problem now for the district attorney was how the reward should be distributed; he had to adopt some numerical proportion. He could evaluate the information given by the three informants according to the absolute cont value of their statements, or according to their absolute inf value, or according to their measures, relative to the information he received, or according to any explicit function whatsoever. I believe that American law does not require him to justify his method of distribution.

I asked six friends at MIT how they would have handled the situation. I received six different answers. One, a newcomer to MIT, with little previous contact with Information Theory, would have distributed the reward equally between X, Y, and Z. Another claimed that the information supplied by Y was worth more than that supplied by X, since X's testimony excluded one suspect out of four, whereas Y's testimony eliminated one out of three, and similarly for Z. He was in favor of distributing the reward according to the proportion 1/4 : 1/3 : 1/2. A third agreed with the second's evaluation of the situation but argued for a distribution of the reward according to a logarithmic scale. A fourth wanted to give all of it to Z, since he alone achieved the identification of the murderer. A fifth, an Iranian, was sure that if the story had happened in his country some years ago, the attorney would have kept the reward for himself, which is probably exaggerated; and I have forgotten what the sixth had to say.

The story could be usefully elaborated in many different directions: I shall not do this here, but I hope I have made one point clear: A numerical measure of information content is of interest not only for science but even for everyday situations.

The next concept we introduce is the *estimate of the amount of information* conveyed by a statement. Consider, for instance, that we are about to perform an experiment with so many possible outcomes and that these outcomes form what we call an *exhaustive system*, so that one and only one outcome must occur. Under these conditions, it makes sense to ask: What is the amount of information which the outcome of this experiment can be expected to carry?

Let H be the exhaustive system, and $h_1, h_2, ..., h_n$ the n possible outcomes.

Let $p_1, p_2, ..., p_n$ be their respective logical probabilities with $\sum_i p_i = 1$. We define now *the estimate of the amount of information carried by* (the members of) H as the weighted average of the information carried by each h_i, with the probabilities serving as the weights. In symbols:

$$\text{est}(\text{in}, H) =_{df} \sum_i p_i \times \text{in}(i)$$

(where "in" stands for any amount-of-information function). For the specific inf function, we have

$$\text{est}(\text{inf}, H) = -\sum_i p \times \log_2 p_i.$$

If there are, for instance, 16 possible outcomes and these outcomes are equiprobable, then each of these outcomes will carry four units of information according to inf, and the expectation-value will then, of course, be also four. But if the probabilities are not equal, the estimate will be less than four, with the difference depending upon the specific distribution.

We then go on to define even more complex notions like *amount of specification* and *estimate of amount of specification*. I shall not go into a discussion of them at this time. May I point out, however, that the whole theory now takes on an aspect which should be very familiar to those who are acquainted with current (communicational) Information Theory. The task of thoroughly comparing these two theories is still before us, though many preliminary attempts have been made. Pointing out that they deal with entirely different subject matters in a manner that shows very far-reaching formal analogies is a good start but certainly not all that could and must be said. But no more will be said at this time.

Many of you are acquainted with the considerations, not to say speculations, that accompany another formal analogy subsisting between the basic formulas of Information Theory and mechanical statistics, and the concepts of entropy and negentropy have popped up in discussions more than once. Some of our best thinkers have expressed the view that this analogy is much more than just any analogy, and statements identifying thermodynamics and communicational information theory, requiring a revision of the second principle of thermodynamics, and even statements identifying thermodynamics with logic have been made recently. I believe that these declarations were more than an attempt to explode old-fashioned ways of thinking and to force people to go deeper into the foundations of thermodynamics than they did so far. But, perhaps for the first time in my life, I find myself on the side of the scientific conservatives. I find it utterly unacceptable that the concept of physical entropy, hence an empirical concept, should be identified with the concept of amount of semantic information, which is a logical concept, and this in spite of the recent attacks by excellent logicians on the logical-empirical dichotomy [126].

I think that my initial attitude will carry more weight if it is shown what might have brought about this identification, in addition to the formal analogy. One source of this mistake lies in the fact that many physicists are accustomed to say that entropy—physical, thermodynamic entropy—is a concept that depends upon the state of knowledge of the observer, so that if someone is going to compute the entropy of a given system, for example, a container of gas, he will have to do this relative to his state of knowledge. If this were so, then it turns out that the entropy concept in physics is becoming a psychological concept, which is at least as disturbing as saying that it is becoming a logical concept (and probably behind this latter statement). This is, of course, not the first time that physical functions have been described as being dependent on the state of the observer, including his state of knowledge. It has even become a kind of fashion, probably originating with certain expositions of relativity theory, to introduce everywhere such dependencies. However, this talk about a physical function being dependent upon the state of knowledge of the observer can hardly be taken seriously. It is probably no more than what Carnap has termed "qualified psychologism," i.e., formulations from which the psychological terminology can be eliminated without loss. It may be of some didactical importance to present certain arguments in terms of the observer, but one can do without then. The introduction of the observer is only a *façon de parler*.

Not being a physicist, what I am about to say now in conclusion may well be pure nonsense, but I feel that it is necessary to say this in order to provoke clarification of the prevailing situation by those who are more qualified to do so than I.

As I see it, the entropy of a system is a determinate quantity. However, being fallible human beings, we are unable to determine this quantity, at least in general. If the outcome of some action of ours is a function of the entropy of a system, then we would like to act on our knowledge of the *true* value of this quantity. However, all we can do is to act on our *estimate* of this value. This is utterly trivial and no different from, for example, the case of the length of a table. This quantity is, of course, uniquely determinate, though in order to act, we have to rely on estimates of this length derived, for instance, from certain measurements through averaging operations. Now, of course, estimates are relative to the available evidence, hence in a sense to the state of knowledge of the estimator. Someone's estimate of the entropy of a given system depends upon his state of knowledge. I would urge not to formulate this situation by saying that the entropy of the system depends upon his state of knowledge. The treatment of estimate functions of entropies, of lengths, or of any other quantities, belongs to (inductive) logic, but this does not mean, of course, that the treatment of entropies belongs to logic.

PART V
Mechanization of Information Retrieval

A Logician's Reaction to Theorizing on Information Search Systems* | 18

1. INTRODUCTION

There seems to be almost universal agreement that the traditional methods of storing and searching for information are not efficient enough at the present time and will become less so in the future. Many proposals for changing these methods have been made in the last decade, and some of these have already proved to be of considerable practical value. Nevertheless, it is my conviction that most of the theoretical thinking behind these practical innovations is marred by several fallacies. It is the purport of this chapter to expose and criticize these fallacies.

The fact that no simple and universally acceptable solution to the various problems connected with information searching has been forthcoming, in spite of the effort put into this task by many gifted and authoritative thinkers, has had some unfortunate repercussions. There were those who despaired of the whole task; I understand that Professor Norbert Wiener, who should be sympathetic to attempts at modernizing information search systems, reacted in a rather skeptical manner. He stressed that when he is investigating a problem, he knows all the authors whose work he is going to consult and therefore, at the most, he needs nothing beyond the traditional author catalogue. On the other hand, there are those who reached the conclusion that there is something deeply wrong with the handling of this whole problem and that the task of solving it should be presented to more fundamental disciplines: structural linguistics, semantics, symbolic logic, the mathematical theory of communication (or information theory), theory of games, and so forth. Although there is a grain of soundness in both attitudes, it seems to me that they are still intrinsically wrong and based upon an insufficient analysis of existing needs. I would not deny that for a man of Professor Wiener's caliber and for the purpose of some general, theoretical investigation the best policy might well be to consult the works of major thinkers in the field and then to sit back and reflect upon their contents.

* First appeared in **American Documentation**, vol. 3 (1957), pp. 103–113.

The saving in time, achieved by not reading the output of the minor thinkers, may well, on the average, more than balance the time spent in redeveloping something that had already been found and published by one of these lesser stars; and the occasional failure to obtain an important result, because of not noticing the existence of a certain auxiliary technique that might be described in one of the minor publications, might often carry less weight than the fruits of unrestricted and unguided originality.

But this can hardly be regarded in our time as the typical situation for the research worker, and it is certainly completely atypical for common situations where mainly, or even exclusively, detailed factual information, rather than general theories or methods, is required. To make light of the need for quick and reliable access to all kinds of stored information, just because a few geniuses can obtain their results without recourse to it, would surely be a gross misevaluation of the present over-all requirements of research work.

But even more misguided, it seems to me, is the attitude of those who pass the burden of making progress in the information search field completely onto the basic theoretical disciplines, though I personally am much more interested in them than in many more practical matters and believe that every research project in these fields should be encouraged and might turn out to be, in due time, of more than purely theoretical interest. But the arguments for placing much hope in the practical consequences of the theoretical results of future research in these sciences for a solution of our problem have been extremely vague and unconvincing; and they might have had the unfortunate and partly unintended side-effect of discouraging any efforts to improve the present situation by going over the existing methods critically and carefully, eliminating some of the outmoded waste carried along by sheer conservatism and inertia, combining certain features that by themselves were perhaps not too efficient into a more potent whole, and utilizing already existing achievements in the basic disciplines to a higher degree. More will be said about this matter at the end of this chapter.

Some research workers who arrived at the conclusion that more work in the fundamental disciplines is required in order to modernize information search were not quite ready to sit back and wait for results to pour in from the professionals working in those fields. (Incidentally, to my knowledge, not a single first-rate logician, linguist, or information-theoretician has so far been sufficiently attracted to the problem of information search to want to spend much of his time on it.) They decided, therefore, to undertake this work themselves, and there seems indeed to be no other way out for those who are most concerned with the present state of the art, mostly librarians and documentalists, but to take their fate in their own hands and try to master the required fundamental sciences. Although I do not think there could be any objection in principle to any specialist's meddling in a neighbor specialist's field—as a matter of fact, this is what I am doing now—, this endeavor seems to have met in our case with almost complete failure, due on the one hand to the fact that the quest for foundations was based upon nothing better than unclear vision and insufficient analysis of the situation, and on the other hand to the fact that the people who undertook the job just did not quite manage to master the new fields.

The inclination to seek a remedy for the present unsatisfactory situation of information searching by "going to the fundamentals" seems to have been reinforced by the use of certain fashionable phrases and slogans that sound appealing enough as long as their inherent vagueness and lack of clarity is not exposed. I am referring to such catch words as "semantic" and "structure," to such statements as "information retrieval systems should not concern themselves with *words* but with *concepts*," and to the invocation of Boolean Algebra and Symbolic Logic. In one sense or other, it is doubtless correct to state that the information retrieved need not be identical to the information originally stored but only *semantically* equivalent to it, that in some information storage systems the *structure* of the original information is lost and can therefore not be mechanically retrieved, that in some indexing systems the indexes are not necessarily *words* occurring in the original document but rather signs for *concepts* dealt with in these documents, that many information storage and indexing systems rely on a classification of the subject matter and that therefore *Boolean Algebra* qua Calculus of Classes should be relevant, and that *Symbolic Logic* is nowadays regarded as a useful tool in all kinds of symbol-handling systems, so that it should be a useful tool for information searching systems, too.

It is equally correct to say that this is valuable at most as an extremely tentative and indefinite indication of the possible existence of some relationships and applications, as an expression of a vaguely felt hope that somehow or other a future theory of information searching will utilize these concepts, but so far no good reasons for these indications and hopes have been given. Worse than that, a thorough checking of the pertinent literature will easily show that the invocation of these fashionable phrases has often served only to becloud the issue and that on the few occasions when the authors left the realm of platitudinuous generalities and tried to show the impact of, let us say, Symbolic Logic, on the theory of information searching in some more detailed fashion, these attempts quickly ended in failure. A partial justification of this harsh judgement through some illustrative criticism will be given below.

2. THE CONFUSION OF INFORMATION RETRIEVAL WITH LITERATURE SEARCH

A scientist engaged in some kind of research becomes, almost without exception, involved in two infcrmation search situations which, though connected, have to be kept separate if confusion is to be avoided. He will be interested in getting so many detailed answers to certain specific questions, such as "How reliable is such and such an electronic component under such and such conditions?" or "Is such and such an electronic component commercially produced, and if so, who produces it?" or "What is the address of the author of a certain paper?" But he will also want to have access to all the literature that contains material relevant to his problem. In order to distinguish between these two facets of information searching, let us call the first *information retrieval* (narrowing thereby the customary connotation of this expression) and the second *literature search*. The answer to an information retrieval question will have the form of one or more declarative statements that might sometimes, of course, consist of no more than "Yes," "No", or "Sorry, we couldn't find out that one. Maybe, you should try...". The answer to a literature search question will take the form of a reference list, with or without annotation, with or without abstracts of the listed items, with or without copies of the relevant literature items themselves.

In view of this divergence, it might seem strange, on first sight, that these two facets were not always clearly distinguished. The explanation, however, is not hard to find. First, it is well known that requests of the information retrieval type will often be answered after an auxiliary literature search, i.e., by first finding out which documents do contain the relevant information and then looking up these items on the right page, access to which is obtained through some kind of index. Indeed, the answer to a certain ticklish request will be accompanied by a reference to the source of this information item, thereby enabling the requester to judge the reliability of the answer. Second, it is doubtless correct to say that sometimes a literature search is conducted only because no good direct information retrieval system is available, literature searching being under these circumstances a kind of poor substitute for a nonexistent efficient information retrieval system.

In spite of these observations, it should still be clear that in general no information retrieval system, and be it as detailed and encyclopedic as can be, will be able to replace reading the original literature, a procedure the value of which consists mostly in the stimulation it provides through its general line of argumentation and method rather than its wealth of factual material. All this is a truism that surely needs no further elaboration.

We are badly in need of improving both the information retrieval and the literature search systems, but to assume from the beginning that these two problems could be solved by the same methods is unwarranted and harmful. This does not imply that certain methods devised to improve one of these systems might not turn out to be useful as such, or after some adaptation, also for the other, or that theoretical thinking relevant to the one is totally irrelevant to the other.

To repeat, the output of an information retrieval system is a set of one or more detailed, factual statements, that of a literature search system—a list of documents. Both systems are necessary, each for its own purposes—which overlap quite often—, both can be mechanized to a certain degree today and, in order to increase their efficiency, will have to be mechanized to a higher degree in the future. But the setup of each, in order to be efficient, has to be quite different, and the processing of documents for information retrieval and for literature search must proceed along different lines, even though part of the way may be common.

For information retrieval systems, a set of statements is correlated with the document, and these statements preserve all the factual information-content of the original document, or as much of it as is considered to be of interest and value in the system, usually in some standardized and easily encodable form. This is then a kind of abstract, although ordinary abstracts often contain metalinguistic statements about the results obtained in the original document rather than a summary of the results themselves.

For literature search systems, a set of symbols is correlated with the document, and the one and only function of these symbols is to provide the literature searcher with a clue to the pertinence of the document. Though is is not inappropriate to say that these symbols, be they single words, whole phrases, subject-headings, Descriptors, Uniterms, and so forth (the term 'index' will be used from now on as a generic name for them) somehow *indicate* the information content of the document, it is rather misleading to say, as is often said it, that they themselves *contain* part of the information content of the document, let us say, in condensed form. This form of expression is partly a cause, partly an effect, of the confusion between information retrieval and literature search. An abstract is indeed, in a relatively clear sense, a condensation of the original document, but an index set is not a further condensation. It is a mistake[1] to assume that a word, or a phrase, contains information in the same sense in which a statement does. In spite of its *prima facie* appeal, the information content of a statement is not the sum, or combination, of the information contents of its

---

[1] Of the kind known in the lingo of analytic philosophy as "a (logical) category-mistake" and treated at length in [133:16 ff].

constituent phrases, and the locution "the information content of a (non-sentential) phrase" had better be avoided altogether.

An index set is a tool whereby a document is to be caught whenever it is pertinent to a certain topic and should be judged accordingly. The hook whereby a fish is caught is not, in general, supposed to be a miniature or condensed fish. (Though this may occasionally be the case, I am told.) There is no intrinsic reason why an index should be a miniature, or condensed document. That an index, in the sense in which this term is used here, is often, but by no means always, a word or phrase occurring in the document or in its title is probably only a transitory phenomenon, the result more of convenience and conservatism, than of any inherent reason. (That this practice does not break down as often as could be expected is perhaps due to the fact that in many document libraries the writers and requesters of documents have had similar scientific training and tend therefore to use the same terminology.) But even when an index is a phrase occurring in the document, it does not thereby carry part of the information content of that document. I have dwelt much on this point, perhaps with tedious repetition, because I regard the inherent confusion as a major obstacle in the way of clarification of the methodological issues in information searching systems.

At this stage, it is probably in order to leave the generalities and come to the specific illustrations I promised above. Let me insist that these illustrations form an almost random sample out of a rather large population, the partial criterion for their selection being, for the most part, the prestige and influence of the authors whose views I am about to criticize. This criticism should by no means be understood to be a general deprecation of their contribution to the theory of information searching. On the contrary, just because some of their work is so good and stimulating, it is mandatory to weed out the weaker points as quickly as possible.

3.   ILLUSTRATIONS

a.   *Abstracts and Indexes*

Let me start with an illustration of my last general point, the confusion between information retrieval and literature search. I refer to the "Report of the Committee on the Inventory of Methods and Devices for Analysis, Storage, and Retrieval", published by the School of Library Sciences at Western Reserve University, Cleveland, Ohio, on December 28, 1955, as Pre-Conference Paper No. 6 for the Conference on the Practical Utilization of Recorded Knowledge—Past and Future.

Figure 1 of this report exhibits the way in which the authors envisage the result of a typical processing of a paper on chemistry for machine retrieval purposes. The paper is first abstracted in a standardized way. The abstract, as well as the title, name of the author, and so on, are then coded and finally translated into a series of holes on standard punched cards by the use of a standard punching machine. So far, so good. But the coded abstracts, in what the authors call "a typical search", are not used in order to retrieve some factual piece of information but rather as hooks to catch the abstracts themselves. In a typical search of this kind, someone is looking for "all abstracts pertaining to the use of an Al_2O_3 catalyst". And this is to be achieved by searching for the occurrence of the phrase 'Al_2O_3 catalyst,' or rather its coded equivalent, in the *coded abstract*.

We have before us a proposal to do away with indexing altogether and to use the scheme of scanning an abstract for the occurrence of certain phrases as a means of deciding whether a more careful reading of the abstract would be worthwhile. Now, this is admittedly the procedure one sometimes follows when no good indexing system is available. The authors apparently believe that the obvious inefficiency of such a procedure could be overcome by having the scanning done mechanically instead of by the interested research worker himself. But the authors do not seem to be fully aware of the extremely problematic nature of this proposal. It is true that by scanning an abstract an expert human reader will generally be able to decide to a high degree of fidelity that the abstract is worth reading *in extenso*, or that possibly the original paper should be consulted, but it is very doubtful whether machine scanning would be as reliable, in view of the fact that the purpose of preparing the abstract was not specifically the facilitation of a literature search.

The fundamental difference between the information-preserving function of an abstract and the clue-providing function of an index set seems to have been masked by the decision of the authors to use telegraphic style abbreviations in the abstracts. Instead of "The maximum yield is 97% at high temperatures," they have "maximum yield 97% at high temperatures", and this looks like an index phrase. On second thought, however, it should become clear that not only is this sequence of words not a well-formed phrase, for grammatical reasons, but—and this is the decisive point—it is almost completely useless as a possible clue. That the maximum yield is 97% under certain conditions is a potentially important piece of information, but the phrase '97%' will practically never be used in a literature search process; a request for the literature dealing, say, with dehydrations whose maximum yield is 97% is almost unthinkable.

It is true that the authors are careful in the formulation of their proposals and guard it by a frequent use of 'may'. So they say [italics mine]: "The literary form of such abstracts *may* be designed to meet varying require-ments. Also, telegraphic style abstracts *may* simultaneously serve such purposes as preparation of alphabetized indexes, encoding for machine searching and publication of an abstract bulletin to provide current aware-ness of recent advances." Perhaps my imputation of confusion was too harsh, and we have before us only a tentative proposal for a fusion of the abstracting and indexing processes. However, this proposal is backed by nothing more than the statement, correct as such, that such a fusion would "enable a variety of documentation services to be provided at a minimum cost." Certainly the cost factor can never be neglected. But no arguments have been given so far to show the the proposed preparation of an encoded abstract to be mechanically searched, even if it is more economical than the preparation of a standard abstract and a separate index set, would not result in a serious deterioration of the literature-search efficiency of the system. Moreover, this deterioration might not be balanced by the greater speed achieved through a mechanization of the scanning process. Trading the slow preparation of an adequate bibliography for the quick preparation of an inadequate one might be bad business.

b.   *Abstraction Ladders and Semantic Factors*

The statement, "All dogs are mammals", is not only true but, as some philosophers and logicians say, analytically, or logically, so. Aristotle was very much impressed by the existence of statements the truth of which is somehow compulsory, that cannot help being true, as against statements like 'Socrates was condemned to death' which, although true, are so by accident. Leibniz was even more impressed by the *truths of reason*, in fact so much so that he tried, at least for a time, to show that the *truths of fact* have this characteristic only because of the inadequacy of human minds, whereas to God, Who knows the true character of everything, all truths are truths of reason only. To God-like creatures, in a dispute on the truth of some statement, one would never have to invoke observation or experi-ment but pure reason alone. Such creatures would only have to exhibit the *semantic factors* of the concepts treated in a controversial statement and then, by simple logical operations on these factors, decide who was right. As a matter of fact, Leibniz himself took this factoring very seriously. He regarded each concept, unless simple itself, as a conjunct of many simple concepts, so that by assigning to each simple concept a certain prime number, he could assign to each compound concept a certain compound number in a bi-unique way. As soon as this was achieved, said Leibniz, all controversy would end in sitting down at a round table and performing some simple calculations.

At about the same time, at the end of the seventeenth century, Dalgarno and Bishop Wilkins dreamed up universal languages, some of which were built around the prime-number principle or around some kind of consonant-vowel-sequence pattern that would make the resulting symbols utterable. Dalgarno, for instance, classified all knowledge into seventeen basic, and a number of derivative, categories. If, then, a concept fell, in an Aristotelian hierarchical classification scheme, into family G, genus E, and species M, its symbol would be 'GEM'.

Why do I retell this all-too-familiar story? Because strangely similar conceptions have popped up in recent theoretical literature on information search systems, such as in the writings of Perry and Associates on abstraction ladders and semantic factors. They do not seem to be fully aware that their attempts to reduce all concepts to conjuncts of simple concepts have had such an illustrious history; they seem to be even less aware of the devastating criticisms that were raised against Leibniz' and Dalgarno's attempts. But be the general philosophical or epistemological significance of such reductionist attempts whatever it may be, it should be perfectly clear that for purposes of literature search, and especially for the coding of indexes, this reduction is at most of secondary and auxiliary importance—in those limited cases where it is possible at all—and that over-playing it is definitely harmful. Since so much ado has been made about this topic, it might be worthwhile to go into more detail.

One of the most bothersome problems in literature search—it bothered me, at least, a great deal—is the problem to what degree one should be concerned with literature that deals not with the specific topic of interest but with related ones. If someone wants to study the development of French foreign trade from 1950 to 1955, he wants first of all to road all the documents that deal exactly with this topic, but documents dealing with French foreign trade after World War II, with the first five years of EPU, with the export of wine from France to England, with the French economy in the twentieth century, or with the economic recovery of Europe after 1945, might all be of importance, some perhaps of decisive importance, for him. It would be desirable to have some scheme by which the attention of the reader could be directed to these documents in spite of the fact that their topic does not coincide with the searcher's topic. In many indexing systems, this is done by some sort of cross-indexing and 'see also' notices. These systems might not provide the perfect solution, and the problem of how to instruct a machine to follow up these indications might very well be a tricky one.

At any rate, the widespread belief that exhibiting somehow in the code chosen for France that France is part of Europe and in the code chosen for foreign trade that foreign trade is an aspect of economics, for instance, by coding 'France' as 'EUFR', as Perry would have done in some of his schemes, is—in spite of some initial attractiveness—definitely mistaken. This is so for many reasons: not only because it is in general by no means clear what should be the 'next higher' index to a given one, but also, and even more importantly, because it is by no means always the case that if a certain topic is denoted by the phrase A containing the word 'France', then a document dealing with the topic whose description B results from A through the replacement of 'France' by 'Europe' will be highly, or even at all, pertinent to the original topic. It is quite conceivable that a document dealing with European foreign trade in 1950–1955 will contain no useful information whatsoever for our investigator, if the foreign trade of Europe is not split up into countries, as might well be the case.

I do not wish to deny that in practice the replacement of 'France' by 'Europe' in a certain index phrase might lead to useful documents, but so would the replacement to 'France' by 'Western Europe', by 'EPU', by 'NATO Countries', by 'Normandy', by 'Paris', and so forth. It is generally impossible to foretell which of these replacements will prove more helpful for a certain literature search, and it might happen that none would be. There seems, therefore, to be little point in having the codes for one of these terms form part of the code for 'France'. That France is related to Europe, to NATO, etc. in a fashion that might conceivably be interesting, is better indicated by a cross-reference—or its mechanical counterpart—which can either be followed up mechanically or left to the option of the searcher.

A wealth of interesting problems center about the organization of an efficient cross-reference system. Their solution is hindered more than helped by over-emphasizing semantical factoring. This emphasis, incidentally, is caused by, among other things, a method of logical misconception that is none the less serious for being very common. Far too often, people believe that the interesting concepts, hence those that would be denoted by indexesf are class-concepts for which the idea of being described as products o, simpler class-concepts has at least some initial appeal. I shall not try again to trace the history of this misconception. Let us note only that in the topic taken above as an illustration, viz., French foreign trade from 1950–1955, none of the concepts one might want to choose as bases for indexes, viz., Trade, Foreign Trade, French Foreign Trade, France, 1950–1955, is a class-concept[2]; also, whatever sense abstraction-ladders and semantic

---

[2] At least, as ordinarily treated, some of the concepts are individual concepts, others are relational or functional concepts. Logicians, of course, know all kinds of tricks by which they can treat these concepts, in an appropriate artificial language-system, as class-concepts, and it is conceivable that it might be worthwhile to follow this lead.

factors might still make with respect to class-concepts is either completely lost with respect to other concepts or else watered down to a rather meaningless metaphor.

c. *Classification, Classes, and the Class-Calculus*

Let D be a given collection of documents, I its total index set, 'a', 'b', etc., the indexes belonging to I. Let A be the class of all those documents of D the index set of which contains 'a'; similarly for B and 'b'. Then the class of documents (of D) the index set of which contains both 'a' and 'b' is, according to the customary terminology, the meet (intersection, or product) of classes A and B, in symbols: $A \cap B$, and the class of documents whose index set contains either 'a' or 'b' (or both) is the join (union, or sum) of the classes A and B, in symbols: $A \cup B$. Finally, the class of documents whose index set does not contain 'a' is the complement of A, in symbols: A'. D and its subclasses form then a Boolean Algebra with respect to the operations of complementing, intersecting, and joining. All this is well known to any advanced student in either mathematics or logic.

This simple fact has been much overplayed and even misused during the last decade and a great number of confusions have arisen in this context. Perhaps the worst confusion appears in the assertion that the document class $A \cap B$ deals with the "logical product" of 'a' and 'b' (or rather with the logical product of the a and b). Herein a series of blunders is committed simultaneously. First, as mentioned above, not all indexes—perhaps only a minority—denote classes at all. If the index set of a certain document contains, for instance, the indexes 'Fauna' and 'Newfoundland',[3] then 'Newfoundland' does not denote a class. 'Newfoundland Fauna' is synonymous with the 'Fauna of Newfoundland' and denotes the fauna of Newfoundland and not the product of the classes Newfoundland and fauna, i.e., the class of entities which are both fauna and Newfoundland, in contradistinction to 'Red Houses', which denotes indeed the product of the classes red and house, i.e., the class of entities that are both red and houses. Second, even if the indexes 'a' and 'b' are class-terms, if, for instance, they stand for fish and food, respectively, their concatenations 'a'⌢'b'[4] and 'b'⌢'a', even in case they are class-terms at all, by no means denote always the meet of the denoted classes; in our illustration, the concatenation of 'fish' and 'food', i.e., 'fish food', does not denote the meet of the classes fish and food, i.e., the class of entities that are simultaneously fish and food, and the concatenation of 'food' and 'fish', i.e., 'food fish' is hardly significant at all. Third, even if a concatenation of two class-terms does denote a class, it is

---

3 For this example, see [140: vol. 2, 23–24].
4 i.e. the sequence of the term 'a' followed by 'b'.

by no means necessary, though occasionally likely, that a document the index set of which contains these two class-terms deal with the class denoted by their concatenation.

All these blunders are facilitated by the persistent use of the time-honored term 'classification' by most workers in the field of literature search. Though it must have been pointed out many times that classification, in the way librarians use this term, has little to do with classes, time and again the superstition that sub-dividing a topic means splitting a class into sub-classes has prevailed, with disastrous consequences. Only a detailed investigation of the history of methodology, for which there is no space here, would explain the origin and perpetuation of this superstition.

d.   *Use and Mention of Signs*

Another confusion that comes up consistently in discussions of information search systems is well known in modern methodology of logic as "the confusion between use and mention of signs". (It has been popularized by general semanticists as the confusion between symbols and the entities symbolized.) This confusion is probably partly responsible for the widespread contention that in order to group documents—such a grouping might be an important step in many systems of storage or retrieval—it is necessary to classify their combined subject-matter, presumably the total field of knowledge. But it is also responsible for dozens of less spectacular blunders.

If someone writes "Any system of names or related facts can be considered or used as a category" [140: vol. 1, 29], this means of expression which seems to regard names as facts may perhaps be excused as a slip of the pen. But if he also talks of ideas being logical products of terms and terms being logical products of letters [140: vol. 2, 53], the confusions can no longer be explained away and, indeed, they immediately breed pseudo-problems such as how 'rat' and 'tar' could be different words if they are both "logical products" of the same letters. The actual situation is, of course, rather simple and can be described in standard logical terminology; some ideas, namely classes, are logical products (meets, or intersections) of other ideas (but, of course, *not* of terms), and printed terms (words) are sequences (or concatenates but, of course, *not* logical products) of letters and not just sets of letters.

The confusion between the symbol and symbolized entity lies also behind the often repeated slogan that information search systems should operate not on words (signs, or symbols), or phrases, but on ideas (or concepts). Understood literally, this is again plain nonsense. The entities that are operated upon (usually the operation is just matching) in information search systems are *always* physical patterns that serve as symbols for something else and never ideas (which are certainly non-material, whatever else they are supposed to be by the users of this term). If author X does not want, for some reason, term 'a' to be an index for a certain document, he cannot replace it by an idea, but only by some other index, belonging perhaps to a different kind of index. If author Y insists upon using as indexes only terms that occur either in the title of the document or in the document itself, and author Z regards this procedure as bad—for good reason, for bad reason, or for no reason—then Z's own index set will not consist of concepts but again of words (or other symbols) which, however, may not all occur in the original document but instead may be taken from some preconceived terminological framework. I am not arguing now for or against an exclusive adherence to the terms used in the document in the choice of the index set, I only maintain that the customary way of putting this issue is confused and tends to becloud it for others.

I could easily go on *ad infinitum* in the same vein, but this would be rather pointless and hardly more than an exciting exercise.

e. *Getting Something for Nothing*

Many authors of proposals for information search systems claim that their system enables the searcher to get out of the system more than has been put into it, or, in terms of one recent reviewer, "to conduct searches by generating as needed new combinations of terms, i.e., combinations not preformed in the system" [16:138]. These claims are totally without foundation. Surely, if a requester looks for all the documents the index set of which contains, say, the indexes 'a', 'b' and 'c' (and perhaps others also), then he will simply get none, if no document has been indexed by these three indexes. The claim that "in the system of bibliographic coordination, by combining various terms, we may get information, which although implicit in the system, was never explicitly recognized" [140: vol. 1, 29], in addition to its lack of any basis, is clearly another instance of the confusion between information retrieval and literature search.

Underlying this claim to being able to get something for nothing is the following situation, which I shall present by giving an example rather than by a general discussion. If a document deals with diseases of dogs, then in some indexing systems its index set will contain 'dogs' and 'diseases' but not 'animals'. In some literature search systems, this may result in the fact that this document will not be listed in the reference list that is supplied to a requester asking for a complete bibliography on diseases of animals, whereas it might conceivably be pertinent to this request. Other indexing systems would have 'animal' as an additional index, even though this word does not occur in the document, and a literature search in this system for the same request would yield this document. I am not discussing here the question, which by itself is of extreme importance, whether or not this fact proves the superiority of such an indexing system, nor am I suggesting that this beneficial result might not also have been attained by another, perhaps better, approach. I am only saying that making the claim for the superiority of a system that exhibits the mentioned features in terms of "getting more information out than was put in" is misformulated and confusing.

f. *Guilt by Association*

The laudable desire of constructing an indexing system that would overcome the restrictions imposed by the traditional classification and subjectheading systems upon the transition from a given topic to related ones and allow for a mechanization of this transition has recently come to strange fruition. Based upon remarks by Dr. Vannevar Bush [20], that certainly show a great deal of vision, but are also unfortunately rather vague and indefinite, a proposal was made by Dr. Mortimer Taube and Associates to supplement the indexing system by deriving from it a *dictionary of associations* that would be of great value not only for literature search purposes but also for operational research purposes. These authors believe [140: vol. 2, 79], for instance, that the achievement of an operations research worker, who pointed out during World War II that, even though enemy planes were not shot down by them, anti-aircraft guns were valuable because they decreased the accuracy of the enemy planes enough to lessen the chance that they would sink merchant vessels, could also have been obtained by means of a mechanized association dictionary, in which "the relevant information had been properly indexed or associated", so that the association of accuracy of bombing with the arming of ships would produce an automatic result.

Unfortunately, it turns out that the proposed association machine is nothing more than a pair-list of co-occurring indexes, i.e., a list of all the pairs of indexes that belong to the same index set of some document. It can easily be verified that this relation of co-occurrence between indexes is reflexive, symmetrical, and nontransitive, hence a *similarity relation*. Its *ancestral*, i.e., the relation that holds between two indexes 'a' and 'b' when there exists a chain of n (≥ 0) indexes 'c_1', c_2',... 'c_n', such that 'a' co-occurs with 'c_1', 'c_1' with 'c_2' ... and 'c_n' with 'b', is reflexive, symmetrical, and transitive, hence an *equivalence relation*. The logic of similarity and equivalence relations is a well-developed chapter in modern symbolic logic and the definitions and theorems of this chapter could profitably be applied in our case[5]. It seems, however, that Taube and Associates are unaware

---

[5] An application of this chapter of logic to linguistics was given in Chapter 1.

of this, and their own attempt to develop the logic of what they call mis-
leadingly (once more, because of confusing symbols and symbolized entities)
"association of ideas" is marred by many blunders as well as by inadequate
symbolism and terminology.

Aside from the treatment given this relationship of co-occurrence between indexes by Taube himself, what is the value of such a co-occurrence
list? Knowing that 'a' and 'b' co-occur, i.e., that there exists a document X
to the index set of which both belong, and that 'b' and 'c' co-occur, i.e.,
that there exists a document Y (not necessarily different from X) to the
index set of which they belong, what do we know about the connection
between the "ideas" a and c? Clearly, nothing definite whatsoever; not even
that any connection of importance exists between them. When interested
in the documents the index set of which contain both 'a' and 'b', should I
also read the documents the index sets of which contain 'a' and 'c' but
not 'b'? Maybe. Would following up the leads provided by a co-occurrence
list of indexes be an efficient procedure for research workers or for literature
searchers? Almost definitely not. The whole idea of approximating the
association-chain of ideas in the human brain by a co-occurrence chain of
indexes, to be traced by a machine, whatever its initial appeal in an age
where so many so-called mental operations are successfully imitated, or at
least approximated, by mechanical devices, seems on second thought to
hold very little promise.

4.   A COUNSEL OF DESPAIR

Let me stress again, before I proceed, that the six issues treated in the
previous section at some length were chosen only for illustrative purposes.
I hope that this discussion will have provided some justification for the dim
view I take of the present state of information search theory. This view
is shared by others. The urgent need for improving existing literature
search procedures has caused some of them to offer "practical" suggestions
for improvement which, although they are not based on faulty theory,
since they are not based on any theory, still seem to lead into a blind alley.
A colleague of mine, a well-known expert on information theory, proposed
recently, as a useful tool for literature search, the compiling of pair-lists
of documents that are requested together by users of libraries. He even
suggested, if I understood him rightly, that the frequency of such co-requests
might conceivably serve as an indicator of the degree of relatedness of the
topics treated in these documents.

I believe that this proposal should be treated with the greatest reserve.
Although much less ambitious than Taube's proposal of an association
dictionary, it is in many respects strikingly analogous to it and shares its

shortcomings. The fact that a co-requestedness chain of documents can be easily followed up by a machine is not in itself a sufficient reason for making the assumption that this relation might be a useful approximation to the important relation of dealing-with-related-topics between documents. And one can think of many other easily establishable relationships between documents that stand a better chance of being a useful approximation, e.g., co-occurrence of their references in reference lists printed at the end of many documents, co-quotation, and so on. It would be a pity if despair of constructing in the near future an adequate theory of information search should lead to the undertaking of "practical" experimental research, the only justification of which would be "maybe it will give us some results".

5. CONCLUSION

It is time to sum up and implement my criticisms by some more constructive proposals. My treatment of the problem of information search has been sketchy, and no attempt was made to cover the ground or to present my critical remarks in a very systematic fashion. It is my definite feeling at this time, however, that since money for research projects in information searching seems to be easily forthcoming and, therefore, the danger of wasting this money and valuable research time is considerable, a critical approach to our problem is mandatory and blind alleys should be avoided as soon as possible. When a few basic widespread confusions are understood and eliminated, the road for definite progress will be cleared.

It is also my belief that a clear understanding of the distinction between information retrieval systems, the function of which is to make detailed, factual information available, quickly, cheaply, and reliably, and literature search systems, the function of which is to provide a bibliography of documents for the use of the investigator of a specific problem, and of the related distinction between the information-condensing function of the abstract and the clue-providing function of an index, is necessary for progress in information searching[6].

The construction of efficient information retrieval or literature search systems is doubtless a very difficult task, and no miraculous shortcuts through the invocation of certain fashionable disciplines should be seriously expected. The traditional methods of literature searching have their shortcomings but this does not imply that they should be totally disregarded. Modern methods avoid some of these shortcomings but have faults of

---

[6] This distinction is made in [16], but not in a sufficiently pregnant form. It is also stressed in [102].

their own. A judicious combination of the better features of these methods should lead to immediate practical improvements, without theoretical revolutions. A thoroughly planned interplay of the modern methods of clue-providing by short-phrase index sets with streamlined and mechanizable tracing of leads through cross-references, seems to me to be definitely superior to any existent method. The resulting system will still have its shortcomings. One of them stems from the fact that reliance on short-phrase indexes must result in the frequent appearance of a certain number of irrelevant references in a bibliography supplied by this system. As long as the index set of a document dealing with the export of wine from France to Germany in 1955 consists, let us say, of the indexes 'Export', 'Wine', 'France', 'Germany', '1955', (and perhaps additional ones) and the request for the literature on this topic is handled as a request for a list of documents with index sets containing these indexes, a reference to this document will surely occur in the bibliography supplied to the man looking for literature on the export of wine from Germany to France in 1955. How serious a failure this is, must still be determined. And whether it can be overcome, should it turn out to be serious, by relatively simple modifications of existing schemes, or whether some radical alteration, perhaps the return to the use of long-phrase indexes, is indicated, remains to be seen. All these are problems that have so far hardly been touched[7]. For their solution, experimentation, perhaps even large-scale, costly experimentation, seems to be unavoidable.

---

[7] The remarks made on various occasions by Mooers, Perry, and Taube on this problem have been so far too sketchy to carry much real weight; in addition, no factual evidence was provided by them.

Theoretical Aspects of the Mechanization of Literature Searching* | 19

1. INTRODUCTION

The present article is meant to be almost exclusively critical; its specific aim is to scrutinize some of the theories that have recently been proffered in the field of literature searching. It will be shown that these theories are often based on naive and crude conceptions of linguistics and semantics and apply a mathematical terminology to no special avail. Not being a documentalist, and having only a user's interest in the mode of operation of a library or documentation room, it is not my business to evaluate documentation systems with regard to their substance. I am, however, vitally concerned that the much needed research into improving the techniques of recording and processing knowledge for subsequent retrieval, and especially into the mechanization of these techniques, should not be directed into blind alleys. The theories to be criticized could lead—and occasionally have already led—in this direction. Should some constructive suggestions be derivable from my animadversions, this will be an incidental though certainly welcome side-effect.

2. THE PROBLEM

There are innumerable situations in human life whose rational and effective handling requires a mastery, at least to some degree, of the accumulated knowledge pertinent to these kinds of situations. Since this knowledge will only in very exceptional cases be stored in the memory of him who needs it on a certain occasion, he will have, in general, to obtain access to it by other means. I am interested here only in the problem of how to retrieve knowledge that has already been recorded in some form or other at the time it is needed, say, for the sake of simplicity, in optically accessible form. This simplification will not matter for the logical and methodological aspects of our problem, which are the only aspects which I intend to discuss here. I shall not deal here with the many highly interesting questions of where and how to store this knowledge, how to translate it into a language the user understands, etc., but exclusively with the following situation: **Assuming that there exists somewhere a body of recorded knowledge—in technical terms, a collection of documents—and assuming that someone has a certain problem for the solution of which this collection might contain pertinent material, how shall he decide whether there are in fact documents in this collection that contain such pertinent material, and, if so, how shall this material be brought to his attention?**

---

* First appeared in **Digitale Informationswandler** (W. Hoffman, ed.), Verlag Friedr. Vieweg & Sohn, Braunschweig 1962, pp. 406–443.

The recorded knowledge to be utilized might be of two kinds which should preferably be kept apart in spite of the fact that the borderline between them is vague and flexible. On the one hand, it may consist of the recording of one or more facts or data (where the question of what constitutes "facts" or "data" can safely be waived at the present level of discussion). On the other hand, it may have a much less definite form consisting, in addition to the recording of a rather indefinite body of facts, of a discussion of methods, arguments, critiques, background information, etc., the usual mixture making up the substance of the books, articles, reports and other standard forms of scientific and technical documentation.

If someone is, for whatever purpose, only interested in certain factual data, he would like to have these data "at his fingertips". If a project engineer has to know at a certain stage of his work, whether and by whom an electronic component with certain specific properties is produced, or if a staff officer at the headquarters of a certain army would like to know at what production stage a certain type of intercontinental ballistic missile is in a potential enemy country, their needs would, in theory, best be covered by a system that would allow the relevant information to be presented in a form of straightforward statements of the kind: "*Component... fulfills the requirements and is produced by — — —*", or "*Missile ... is already in operational production in — — —*", with the dots and dashes suitably filled in.

Information of this type is often stored in textbooks, reference books, handbooks, catalogues, classified documents, etc., and the question is where and how to locate it. As said above, I am not thinking now of the difficulties involved in getting copies of these documents, or in understanding them in case they are published in a language unknown to the user, but of the more theoretical difficulty of establishing just in what document or documents the required information is contained. This difficulty is well known, and has been extensively discussed. A great many proposals for overcoming it have been made during the ages, and a good part of the library sciences are dedicated to their treatment.

3. DATA-PROVIDING AND REFERENCE-PROVIDING SYSTEMS

The advent of punched-card equipment and, even more so, the recent invention of electronic digital computers has encouraged speculation on the possibility of establishing an automatic data-providing information system that would respond to a specific request for data with a specific answer providing just these data, all this in an entirely automatic fashion and with great speed. At the basis of these speculations lies the well-known ability of electronic digital computers to solve complicated computational problems in a fraction of the time it takes a human computer to solve them, mainly because of the much greater speed in which an electronic component such as a vacuum tube or a transistor is able to change its state in comparison with the relative slowness of human neurons, as well as to the great advances in the programming of machines for the automatic performance of long series of elementary operations. The existence of data-processing machines that not only store huge amounts of specific data, which they are able to display at a moment's notice, but also process these data in certain ways if programmed to do so, and hence are in a position to put out statements that were not stored in their memory as such but are rather logical consequences of the stored statements, has caused many people to think of machines that would constantly be fed with a flow of incoming recordings of facts, say, within a specific field such as electronic componentry or army intelligence, and would relentlessly draw all possible logical consequences of these facts and store them too, perhaps even draw inductive inferences from them, etc.

Though I like occasionally to speculate myself, and I am quite ready to discuss the fascinating theory of the mechanization of deductive and inductive inference, let it be very clearly stated that to my knowledge no automatic data-providing system is at present in actual operation or in production stage that goes beyond the extremely restricted and rigid capacities of the data-processing computers, where "processing" is not much more than performing certain computations upon numerical data. Certain steps in this direction were made in the past, and I understand that quite a few groups are at present working towards the construction of large-scale data-providing systems. But I am not aware of any theoretical investigations which would indicate that anyone has been making serious progress towards the achievement of this aim. For this reason I shall deal here no further with such systems.

The second type of retrieval systems is needed by someone who is not particularly concerned with certain specific facts, but would rather like to know the "state of the art" pertinent to some research project. He is then interested in a system whose output is a collection of documents that, ideally, would consist of copies of all and only those documents the knowledge of whose contents would help him in his project, and would contain no copies of documents the reading of which would be of no avail to him. Elsewhere [8], I have tried to show that no implementation of such an "ideal" system could exist, not only for practical reasons, but for the much deeper reason that it is based on contradictory requirements. In practice, one may then expect a host of *reference-providing systems*[1], each with some merits and

---

[1] I prefer this admittedly awkward term to others that have been suggested of late including the term "systems that store references" which has been adopted by at least one agency [108], which also uses "systems that store data" for my "data-providing systems". I think that the stress has to be laid on the form of the output of the system rather than on the form of its storage.

demerits. It also seems very unlikely that there should exist an effective theoretical procedure for their comparison so that the evaluation of such systems will have to be done according to almost exclusively practical considerations, with all the well-known difficulties inherent in such procedures.

The decisive factor is simply that of cost. This trivial point cannot be stressed enough. It is obvious that in an effective reference-providing system, the cost of the supplying of the literature suggested for reading must be commensurate with the cost of the whole research project. What has to be taken into account is, of course, not only the cost of setting up the reference-providing system and of procuring copies of the suggested reading material, but also the cost of not reading pertinent material because of imperfections n the system, plus many additional factors.

4. THE FOUR STAGES OF REFERENCE-PROVIDING

As long as not every piece of suggested reading is really pertinent—and this will in general happen even for the best possible reference-providing systems—, it might be more economical to have the system put out not copies of the documents suggested, but rather abstracts of these documents or perhaps their citations or even only their accession numbers, and leave to the user the decision whether to ask for the presumably more costly procurement of a full copy of a certain document. The most economical system might then perhaps consist of four stages: in the first stage, *accession numbers* are provided, which are used in the second stage to identify *citations*, from which the user will choose in the third stage the *abstracts*, after whose reading he will, in the last stage, ask for *copies* of those documents whose abstracts looked pertinent. The first two stages should preferably be combined, since the transition from accession number to citations is one-to-one and no further selection is indicated at this point.

That the most economical and, in this sense, most efficient reference-providing system should contain these four stages is not, of course, an original idea of mine, but just mirrors the existing situation. This is the way one often deals with literature, as every reader who has been doing some kind of research will agree out of his own experience. There exist to my knowledge no good reasons why this fourfold division should not be kept in mechanized or partly-mechanized reference-providing systems. Some of the better-known literature search systems such as the Rapid Selector, originally envisaged by VANNEVAR BUSH and RALPH SHAW, under current further development at the U.S. National Bureau of Standards, the Filmorex of SAMAIN, and the Kodak Minicard system—all of which have been described many times in the literature—excel by *not* keeping this division and rather providing a copy of the suggested document in one single step, but then the economic feasibility of these systems is still very much in question.

This point is important in view of the necessary imperfections of the reference-providing systems. A system that for every pertinent document supplies also ten irrelevant documents would be at the moment, in view of the relatively high cost involving in procuring copies of complete documents, a rather uneconomical one. A system that, for every relevant citation, supplies also ten irrelevant ones which are quickly discarded by the user might well be practically efficient; this view is also shared, e.g., by ESTRIN [50]. Avoidance of so-called "false drops" is indeed a serious problem for document-providing systems. It is less serious when abstracts are provided, and might turn out to be quite harmless in the case where the output consists of citations. I shall come back below (Section 21) to this problem of false drops. For my present purpose I shall waive it in favor of the much more pressing question, how to make sure that the reference list provided is as complete as possible where completeness is to be taken not in an absolute sense, i.e., relative to the totality of documents existing at that moment, but in a more restricted sense, i.e., relative to a given document collection. In other words, assuming that P has a research problem and that D is the collection of documents which in some sense (that need not be specified here) stands at his disposal, how can one make sure that the list of citations from D which is the output of (the stage of) the reference-providing system will be as complete as practically possible and economically feasible for P's purposes?

This is, of course, one of the many problems of library science in general, and perhaps the central problem of documentation in particular. Much thought has been devoted to its solution, and scores of reference-providing systems have been proposed to handle it.

The customary terms are, incidentally, 'information retrieval', 'information search', 'literature search' and similar ones. These terms, however, and especially the word 'information' occurring in some of them, might suggest that the output of the system dealt with is some actual piece of information, i.e., that we are dealing with data-providing systems. I am afraid that one of the reasons why these two kinds of systems have been so disastrously confused is the use of the fashionable term 'information' which I shall therefore try to avoid as much as possible.

Some of the reference-providing systems have been in actual use for many years, others are still in the experimental stage. Some seem to have been working quite efficiently and to the satisfaction of at least some of their users. Nevertheless, the traditional systems have been criticized lately, for instance by TAUBE and Associates [140], sometimes rather severely, and many more or less radical innovations have been proposed in their stead. Some of these have in their turn been operating for a few years now, and again to the satisfaction of some of their users. These new systems were often backed up by theories which seldom, however, went beyond the programmatic and outline stage. As stated in the introduction, most, if not all, of these theories of reference-providing have little substance and are often quite misleading. The following sections of this report will contain a critique of some of the more recent theories (while some older theories were criticized in Chapter 18).

5. THE UNAVOIDABILITY OF INDEXING

The obvious general solution to our main problem, **how to select out of a given collection of documents those documents that are relevant to a given topic**, and the only practical solution for manually operating reference-providing systems—we shall presently turn to the issue of mechanization—, it to assign to each document a clue, or rather a set of clues, and to assign likewise to each topic a set of topic-terms, in such a way that by comparing the set of topic-terms with the set of clues a decision as to the (probable or possible) relevance of the document can be reached. A large number of closely interwined questions arise as soon as this general solution has to be made specific in order to establish a definite system. It is here that the opinions of librarians, documentalists and information retrieval specialists diverge widely. There would be no point to discuss here this whole gamut of questions. There exists a vast literature on it, and in the bibliography we call attention to some of the more recent publications in the field. We shall restrict ourselves to discuss here, as implied by the title of our article, only some of the theoretical aspects of the problem.

Before we turn to this, however, let us first investigate whether general-purpose high-speed electronic computers or else specially designed automatic reference-providing machines could not be used in order to radically change the accustomed pattern of reference-providing. Could not the stage of clue assignment be completely skipped and the request topic be directly compared with the original documents? It is very natural that such a thought should have arisen, but it must be stressed that there is nothing in our knowledge of the workings of communication which would indicate that such a proposal is, or ever will be, practical. Since this is a point of capital importance for the problem of rational utilization of digital computers, it might be worthwhile to dwell on it at some length.

First, in view of current misleading formulations, let the rather trivial point be stressed that the comparison procedure mentioned above, if carried out by an automaton, could not be between the request *topic* and the documents but only between some *formulation* of this topic and the documents. A comparison can only be based upon matching some encoding of the formulation of the request topic with an encoding of the documents. Assuming that a suitable encoding of a set of documents is given—and it is not unlikely that future methods of printing will at no great extra cost provide such a machine-operable encoding each time a document is printed— there can be no doubt that digital computers could find out whether certain expressions, i.e., strings of words, do occur in these documents, even find out how often they occur and act in accordance with Boolean operations on these findings. For instance, if instructed to provide the references of all documents in the appropriate collection which contain the expression *electro-plating* at least three times and the expression *corrosion prevention* at least twice but do not contain the word *chromium* even once or else contain the expression *copper plating* at least once (notice that this formulation of the instruction in ordinary English is ambiguous, but that a non-ambiguous formulation can be easily achieved with the help of well-known symbolic methods), a digital computer could easily carry out this instruction. However, it is rather obvious that the reference list provided by this procedure will have little chance of being satisfactory. If what the requester was interested in was to get a list of all documents dealing with corrosion prevention through electro-plating, chromium plating excepted, or with copper plating in general, the lack of satisfactoriness will be due to a large number of much-discussed reasons. The first and immediately obvious one is that of language. Documents dealing with the mentioned topic but not written in English will not be caught. Second, among the documents written in English and dealing with this topic, an indeterminate number will not be referred to because they do not contain a sufficient number of times the expressions mentioned in the request formulation or contain an expression disallowed by this formulation. This may be because of any number of reasons. The author may be using synonyms, circumscriptions or even only such (for human beings) trivial deviations as having *prevention of corrosion* or *prevents corrosion* or *prevent corrosion* or *corrosion is prevented* or thousands of other formulations; on the other hand, to push the issue to its ridiculous extreme, the document may contain a sentence such as *in this paper we shall not deal with copper plating*. Thirdly, and even more seriously, the document, while still being highly pertinent to corrosion prevention through electro-plating, need not contain expressions which, in whatever extended sense of *synonymous*, are synonymous with the expressions occurring in the positive part of the request formulation. It might contain terms like *silver plating, brass plating, guilding, anticorrosive* and innumerably many others. The list of reasons could be almost indefinitely continued.

More sophisticated instructions could be envisaged which, at a cost, would improve the chances of the reference list's being satisfactory, and I shall mention one such method later on. But there exist so far no serious indications that the reference list obtained will ever be commensurate in quality with those obtained by competent humans at commensurate costs.

Though scientific and technological writers may not make full use of the theoretically unlimited number of ways of expressing their thoughts, put at their disposal by natural languages, they do make use of a large enough number to defeat any system based upon simple matching of expressions.

The situation would be different, of course, if scientists and technologists could be forced, or more or less gently persuaded, to use some rigidly standardized language for their publications. Everybody is free to discuss this issue, but unless the assumption of the universal use of a strictly regimented language of science is made, any scheme of directly comparing a request formulation with a straightforward one-to-one encoding of the original documents must be regarded as wholly utopian and unsubstantiated.

Though probably of purely theoretical interest, let it be stated that even the assumption of the enforced use of a completely standardized language for scientific and technological purpose will only solve some of the mentioned difficulties but by no means all of them. Though it is often assumed that such a language would not contain synonymous expressions, the assumption is demonstrably baseless. The most rigorous language system for the arithmetic of natural numbers, for instance,—surely a part of every language of science—contains for each natural number an infinite number of synonymous designations. The number 3, for example, can clearly be synonymously designated not only by "$2 + 1$", "$1 + 2$", "$1 + 1 + 1$" but also by "$4 - 1$", "$5 - 2$", ... ad infinitum, not to mention innumerably many other possible designations. In this specific case, incidentally, there does not even exist a decision procedure for determining whether two expressions designate the same number.

Somewhat less utopian is the idea to standardize, if not the language of the original papers, at least the language and form of the *abstracts*, e.g., by allowing as the only method of preparing the abstracts the filling out of a kind of questionnaire containing, say for chemical abstracts, a certain number of statement forms, with the abstractor entitled only to fill out these forms, according to certain rigid instructions, or to leave them empty. I brought up this idea during an informal meeting of the First Conference on Machine Translation which convened in June 1952, at the Massachusetts Institute of Technology—probably not for the first time, though I am not aware of any prior detailed proposals to this effect—, and it has since been taken up at various occasions, though never brought to any conclusive empirical testing. PERRY's "telegraphic abstracts" [114; 115] seem to be a kind of offshoot of this idea—PERRY participated in the mentioned conference—, but in their present form at least they are far from attaining the envisaged aim, in addition to their various shortcomings pointed out in Chapter 18. Here, however, is an interesting field for further theoretica¹ and experimental investigations and one of the few subjects in literature searching where the collaboration of a symbolic logician could be of use, at least in the negative sense of helping to avoid the exploration of blind alleys.

6. CRITIQUE OF AUTOMATIC INDEXING

Short of comparing the request formulation with the original document, one could think of comparing this formulation with a set of clues obtained from the documents by some mechanical procedure. Such procedures have come to be known as *automatic indexing.* (The abbreviation *auto-indexing—* introduced by LUHN [90], together with the term *auto-abstracting* discussed in the following section—is not to be recommended since *auto* will usually be understood as being a whole word by itself meaning *self* rather than an abbreviation for *automatic.*) However, the chances that thereby a satisfactory set of clues will be obtained are again rather slim. There can be no doubt but that computers are in a position to select out of the words or word-strings occurring in the encoded form of the original document those words or strings which fulfill certain formal, statistical conditions such as occurring more than five times, occurring with a relative frequency at least double the relative frequency in English in general² — on condition, of course, that such a general relative frequency distribution is presented to the machine in a consultable form,— etc. However, it is again rather unlikely that the set obtained thereby will be of a quality commensurate with that obtained by a competent indexer, for various, though not always the same reasons. First, there will be serious difficulties as to what is to be regarded as instances of the same word. Though this difficulty is recognized by some proponents of this method [90], it is not clear how they intend to meet it or why they believe that it can be met at all. In one example [90] it is indicated that such words as *differ, differentiate, differently, difference, differential* are to be regarded as instances of the same word, though it should be rather clear that this procedure would quite often result in including in the index set an index which should not be there and thereby perhaps excluding an index which should have been there, if the instructions are such

---

² For the idea of using the ratio of the relative frequency of a word in a given document to its relative frequency in the language in general as a measure of "significance" of this word in the document, rather than using the absolute frequency of this word in the document, see [8].

that there exists an absolute cut-off for the number of index terms to selected. Second, there arises again the problem of synonyms. Third, and most important, this procedure will yield at its best a set of words and word strings exclusively taken from the document itself. The efficiency of such an index set will then be equal to that of a set of uniterms obtained by a crude application of the uniterm system of indexing[3]. It would therefore share the major disadvantage of this indexing system, viz., that complex and costly measures will have to be taken in order to ensure an efficient matching of the request formulation with these index sets.

The cost of indexing as such is only a small part of the cost of reference providing by the uniterm method. It is very likely that manual uniterm indexing by cheap clerical labor will still, on the average, be qualitatively superior to any kind of automatic indexing, and it is very unlikely that the cost of automatic indexing will ever be less than this kind of manual uniterm indexing, unless the automatic indexing is to be of such a low quality as to totally defeat its purpose.

7. CRITIQUE OF AUTOMATIC EXTRACTION

Almost the same methods which have been proposed for automatic indexing could also be used for *automatic extraction* or *condensation*[4]. One can think of innumerably many methods of obtaining in a purely formal way, hence in a way performable by a computer, "significance numbers" of all the sentences of a given document and then to select out of the highest ranking sentences, again by innumerably many methods, a certain subset of the total set of sentences of the original document. This subset, arranged in the order in which its members appear in the original document, is doubtless a kind of *extract* of the document. It is quite natural to think that it could serve some of the purposes a manually prepared *abstract* is meant to fulfil. It is unlikely, though no longer so completely out of question, that extracts prepared in some mechanical way relying mostly on counting of frequencies (with all kinds of additional sophistications such as giving words occurring in titles additional weights, etc.) will be of the same average quality as manually prepared extracts of the same length. Even if *averages* should turn out to be commensurate, it seems likely that mechanical extraction will sometimes yield rather inferior products and might therefore occasionally cause considerable damage to their users, unless this procedure is complemented by other abstracting methods or unless some *mechanical*

---

[3] For a description of this system, see [140].

[4] The term used by the inventor of this notion [90] is auto-abstracting, which is doubly unfortunate since in this term the second component is misleading too, the "abstraction" being of an extremely restricted kind.

method can be found by which these failures can be identified. No proposals to this last effect seem to have been made so far, and it is not clear what direction they could possibly take.

The major question, however, is probably of what use extracts, even if prepared by expert humans, could be. It is rather obvious that they would not be up to the standards of ordinary abstracts, not even of the so-called indicative type[5]. There exists some serious concern as to the degree of practical usefulness of even the best manually prepared *abstracts*, and it should therefore be closely investigated as to what, if any, use can be made of *extracts*. The needed experimentation could profitably be made with extracts that were manually prepared. Only if such extracts should prove to have some value would it be worth while to continue investigation into mechanical extraction.

Should it turn out, contrary to my present guess, that an extract could fulfil some useful purposes, it is still likely that an author's extract would in general be at least as good as a mechanically prepared extract and often much better. Preparing an extract, in fulfillment of certain specified conditions as to its length, should be such a simple procedure for an author that it is extremely hard to envisage how it could be beaten cost-wise by any machine.

The discussion as to the worthwhileness of having an author supply his own *abstract* at the time he submits an article for publication is still going on. Opinions are sharply divided, and understandably so, since there are good reasons both for and against this procedure. But the argument intending to show that authors' abstracts are inferior to abstracts prepared by some other persons does not hold against authors' *extracts*, and I can hardly believe that it could be denied that an author's extract would in general be at least as good as an extract prepared by another human, in addition to its being much simpler to provide since the author will expend less effort than anyone else in rereading his own article for the purpose of marking those sentences he wants to have incorporated in the extract. Machine abstracting, if only it could ever reach the quality of an impartial expert human abstractor's output, with commensurate cost, would be something worthwhile to aim at since there would then be some good reasons to suppose that it would be of a quality commensurate with the author's abstract and perhaps even better. But this condition is totally counterfactual and there have, to my knowledge, been no serious attempts to implement it. Machine extracts, on the other hand, will in all likelihood always be inferior in quality to, and more expensive than, authors' extracts, However, it might be argued that it is usually not under the control of the user to have an author

---

[5] For a more elaborate critique, see Chapter 18.

supply him with an extract of his article, whereas having it extracted by a machine at his disposal is under his control. This is indeed true and certainly a point in favor of attempts at machine extracting, should the usefulness of extracts ever be convincingly demonstrated. But even so, the point loses some of its cogency if we take into consideration that machine extracting could be economical, if at all, only when the machine can be supplied at no or very little extra cost with a machine-searchable version of the original text. Otherwise, preparing this machine-readable version itself would probably cost more than the human preparation of an extract. This is likely, however, only if the printer of the article is ready, or can be persuaded, to cooperate with the potential extractor. If, now, such a degree of cooperation can be attained, the degree of cooperation needed for having this article augmented by an author's extract is only slightly higher and would therefore still probably be a simpler thing to aim at than improving the mechanization of extracting.

8. AUTOMATIC ABSTRACTING THROUGH TRANSFORMATIONAL ANALYSIS

A different technique for automatic abstracting based upon a method of linguistic analysis called *discourse analysis* by its inventor has been recently discussed by HARRIS [65], though only in a rather tentative way. It is therefore rather difficult to judge its value, and still more so its economical feasibility. To give just one example of what an application of this method could perhaps achieve: It is a well-known stylistic feature of scientific writing to use in the first sentence of a paragraph a noun-phrase consisting, say, of an adjective and a noun—for instance, *linguistic structure*—and to use in the following sentences of the same paragraph the noun only—*structure*, in our illustration—instead of the noun-phrase, without introducing this abbreviation in some formal way. Every occurrence of *structure* in these sentences should then be regarded as a synonym of *linguistic structure* for further treatment, say of the frequency-counting kind mentioned before. Whether discourse analysis will be able to give a set of valid rules for the determination of the formal conditions in which a noun occurring without an adjective before it in the second sentence of a paragraph will be regarded as an abbreviatory synonym of a noun-phrase consisting of the same noun preceded by an adjective in the first sentence of this paragraph, remains to be seen.

In addition to valid insights, the outline of this method contains, however, also various statements which are, literally understood, quite definitely wrong. It is envisaged that by the use of so-called *transformational analysis*, which is a preparatory step for discourse analysis but again so far exists only in outline, a complete text, say a paper, would be "reduced" to a sequence of sentences having a rather simple structure, so-called *kernel sentences*, with some kernel sentences occurring many times. By omitting repetitions—understood in a rather broad way, based upon a determination of text-dependent synonymities such as indicated above—, a shorter set of simple sentences is obtained which, so it is tentatively surmised, might serve as an adequate abstract of the document. This however, taken at its face value, is patently wrong: a sentence of the form "*A is not soluble in B*" would be kernelized into "*A is soluble in B*" and a sentence of the form "*If q then p*" would be processed into the sequence of the two sentences q and p, with possibly disastrous effects. Though these objections are surely well-known to the author of this method, it is not clear how exactly he intends to meet them. And it is, of course, not the question of how to meet every single one of them separately, which can always be attained by some *ad hoc* procedure, but how to get around the whole indefinitely large set of similar shortcomings.

It is again possible that this last method would be more effective for indexing than for abstracting. The above objections, for instance, clearly do not hold with regard to indexing, but even so it is still highly doubtful whether it can ever be refined into an economically feasible method with an output commensurate with that of competent human indexing. One could think of this technique also as being applied together with the above-mentioned frequency-counting one, improving the shortcomings of that technique in regard to synonymities, but it should be rather obvious that, at least for the time being, utilization of this combination of methods would now become so costly as to lose its competitiveness.

9.   RESTATING THE PROBLEM

The idea of using machines for abstracting or indexing is a relatively new one and has still very much to prove its mettle. There are, however, other operations in the total information retrieval process which appear to be more easily amenable to mechanization and have indeed already been mechanized in many information systems. The use of punched-cards for selecting citations (and occasionally also abstracts) of documents whose index set comprises the set of topic terms or stands in some more complicated relationship to it, if this relationship is still expressible by Boolean functions, with both indexing and assignment of topic terms done by humans, has already proved its economical feasibility for document collections of a size of a few thousand, and will not be discussed here, especially since there exists an up to-date exhaustive treatment of the issue [108].

The question to be discussed here is: **Can digital-computer-like devices be profitably used for reference-providing purposes and what are the relations**

between such a use and the methods of human indexing employed preliminarily to this use?

The only features of digital computers which have so far been taken into account in the various schemes offered for their utilization in reference-providing, leaving aside science-fiction-type proposals with no substantial basis at the moment[6], are the high speed with which they can perform matching and their large memory devices. This makes it rather likely that reference-providing machines, if and when they become commercial devices, will be special-purpose machines stressing these two features rather than general-purpose computers. Nevertheless, just for the sake of simplicity of expression, I shall use the term *"digital computers"* instead of, say, *"electronic reference-providing machines"*.

10. THE SCOPE OF MECHANIZATION IN LITERATURE SEARCHING

In order to have a specific situation before our eyes, let us assume that some outfit has a library of a million documents and that this outfit is ready to sell a certain service, say the provision of a list of references pertinent to a certain request topic, for $100, its mode of operation being either manual or including punched-card devices. The reference list provided by this outfit will usually have certain defects, both by containing irrelevant references and, perhaps more importantly, by not containing some pertinent references. Could a system be envisaged which, based upon this very same collection and starting from scratch, through the use of digital computers in suitable stages of the whole reference-providing process, would be in a position to compete commercially with the established system? The competition would consist in undertaking to supply either a reference list of approximately the same quality for a smaller sum, or a list of better quality for the same or even a higher sum, but still lower than the limit the requester would be willing to pay, or a list which, though of lower quality, would be supplied for such a low price that the requester would still be ready to pay that much for this service. This is an eminently practical question to which a satisfactory answer can be given only by an extremely detailed investigation of thousands of different particular items which we have no intention at all of doing here. We shall from here turn our attention only to the questions of principle involved.

A skilled reference librarian, when asked for a list of documents pertinent to a certain topic—and notice again that what this means is that a certain, quite

---

6 MOOERS' readable and stimulating piece of ball-gazing [105] suffers from a heavy reliance on "inductive inference machines", about which there exists, however, nothing so far but very obscure remarks.

definite formulation (of this topic) is submitted to him—, will, out of his knowledge of the specific way in which the document collection at his disposal is indexed, assign to the request what is in effect a certain Boolean function over
some of the index terms[7] and thereafter, in an obvious fashion, arrive at a
first approximation of a reference list. A first approximation because the list
arrived at by this simple operation will often be far from satisfactory,
especially in the sense of not containing all or even a sufficiently large part
of the relevant references. By either changing the topic terms with the help
of *see* and *see also* indications which he will find in the subject catalogue—
or with the help of analogous indications in other indexing systems—and/or
by using a different Boolean function, he will arrive at additional references
which he will add to the first list. No fast rules exist for this whole procedure,
and the quality of the final reference list will mainly depend upon the understanding and skill of the particular reference librarian. Occasionally, the
requester, if dissatisfied with the provided list, perhaps out of his feeling
or even knowledge that references pertinent to his topic have been omitted,
will himself change the formulation and thereby initiate a second round of
this process.

Let it be immediately stressed that out of the processes described above,
neither the assignment of topic terms to a given request, nor the reformulation of a given request are processes which could conceivably be adequately
mechanized, contrary to some speculations in this direction, though they
could be aided by some mechanical devices in a way we shall discuss immediately. It seems, therefore, that **the only steps of the literature search
process which are amenable to performance by a digital computer are those
steps which follow the assignment of the Boolean function over the topic terms,
up to and including the printing of the reference list.** These steps, after human
intervention, may be iterated several times to yield the final reference list.

None of these operations are such that they could not be in principle
performed by a human being, though their performance might take him a
longer, perhaps much longer time. The quality of the final output is wholly
determined by the system of indexing and the skills of the requester and
librarian in formulating and reformulating the request. It would not be
entirely right, however, to conclude from this that the problem of employing
digital computers for reference-providing is an exclusively practical one,
raising no theoretical problems additional to those raised by conventional
indexing in general. Due to the enormous speed and large storage capacity
of digital computers, it is definitely conceivable that methods of indexing
which would be utterly impractical for human operators and which therefore

---

[7] This is a loose way of characterizing a process whose exact description would have
to be rather tedious.

have not been seriously investigated in the past will turn out to be practical for these computers. As a matter of fact the availability of computers has not only given additional impetus to the investigation of certain extant indexing methods, but has also instigated the investigation of entirely new indexing methods, such as the one known as KWIC (Keyword-in-Context) Index [91], which, however, has yet to prove its economical value even for the restricted aim of *current awareness* for which it is meant.

It is likely that mechanization will play a greater role in information systems whose task is to call the attention of industrial research workers to recent developments of possible pertinence to their current work than in systems meant to service scientific research proper. When speed is more important than care and accuracy, a mechanically prepared *dissemination index* might indeed be more appropriate than a manually or semi-automatically prepared retrieval index.

11. COMPARISON OF INDEXING SYSTEMS

The next seven sections will deal with some general theoretical problems involved in reference providing, after an introductory comparison of indexing systems. These problems are not specifically related to mechanization. However, they must be satisfactorily solved before even those stages in the whole literature search process that are at all amenable to mechanization can be delegated to the uninterrupted operation of a computer.

The discussions as to the relative value of the various indexing systems are still going strong and show no tendency of subsiding. Since *a priori* reasons are more and more being regarded with suspicion, one has lately turned to experimental comparison. Interestingly enough, but perhaps not surprisingly, the first results have been rather inconclusive. Since the scope of these experiments has, however, been rather restricted, it is better not to rely too much at this stage on this inconclusiveness and to wait for the outcome of more extensive experimentation on the way, such as the ASLIB Cranfield Research Project conducted by CLEVERDON [42]. Each of the extant indexing systems seems to have its advantages and drawbacks and it is perhaps not unlikely that they should, in the grand average, turn out to be more or less equal in their efficiency though they might still show considerable differences in this respect with regard to particular document collections. But in spite of various and occasionally heated claims to the contrary, no convincing case has so far been made for the definite superiority of any indexing system over the others even in such well-determined situations. True enough, for a small industrial company with a few dozen prospective users of the document collection and a collection size of a few thousand, a descriptor-type indexing system such as Zatocoding [102] appears to have some definite advantages and has been working satisfactorily in some such companies [17]. But it also seems that even then the advantages are only temporary and are apt to be lost as soon as the company grows beyond a certain size, both as to the size of its document collection and to the number of its members, as DE GROLIER [60] rather dramatically found out for himself. Similar remarks could be made for every other indexing system.

Whenever a new indexing system is proposed, there exists an understandable tendency on behalf of its proponents to claim great theoretical and practical advantages for the system, usually combining this claim with a harsh criticism of the other systems. The criticism is in general valid, though often stated in a highly exaggerated manner, but most of the time the positive claims cannot be substantiated in their theoretical aspects and must await substantiation as to their practicality. A relatively detailed critique of the theorizing behind some of the recently proposed indexing systems, especially by workers in the United States, has been given elsewhere (Chapter 18) and shall, in general, not be repeated. I shall rather turn my attention to some still more recent proposals.

12. LATTICE THEORY AND DISTANCE MEASURES BETWEEN TOPICS

In another publication (Chapter 18), I have already had an opportunity to deplore the tendency of some innovators to back up their practical proposals by invoking such fashionable and prestige-carrying disciplines as *structural linguistics, symbolic logic, theory of information, theory of games,* etc. Since then, some of these claims have been repeated by the same and other authors, but no additional substantiation has come to my attention so that no additional refutation is required. On the other hand, new claims have been made and backed up by reference to other disciplines, more especially of a mathematical nature such as *lattice theory* [51; 52;104;146;145; 96], *topology* [104] and others. Now, sets of documents are sets and therefore, as all other sets, form a lattice with respect to the inclusion relation, and the assignment of indexes to documents can be regarded as a mapping of the document "space" into the "space" of the subsets of the total index set. But to my knowledge, nothing of any importance has so far been obtained by this "application" of lattice theory and topology to the theory of indexing. MOOERS' claim [104] of having laid "*the foundations for a unified mathematical theory for the language symbols of retrieval*" must be definitely rejected. With regard to his paper, and to many others of the kind, one can only say, following LEES but with a slight twist, that the information retrieval "*literature is peppered with mathematical and quasi-mathematical treatments; a few are of interest, but the vast majority are vacuous, if not just wrong*" [87: 271] and that in order to be of any avail *"the mathematical system serving as a model must yield theorems whose interpretation affords some deeper insight or knowledge"* [87: 300]. Unfortunately, I cannot but agree with FOSKETT [54] when he criticizes proponents of certain recent schemes of literature searching as *"attempts to disguise (their) commonplace notions in weird and sometimes self-invented pseudoscientific jargon, supported, albeit unnecessarily, by masses of impressive mathematical diagrams and calculations"*. Whether the use of a lattice-theoretical or topological terminology might have a clarifying effect on the ways of thinking of librarians and documentalists who are not used to it is a moot question which I see no way of answering at this point.

However, lattice structures are supposed to come up also on other occasions. One decisive question, we recall, was how to change the assignment of topic terms to a request or *"how to make perturbations of the initial selection of search terms"*, in ESTRIN'S [50] formulation, if the first reference list one gets by matching the first set of topic terms with the set of indexes is not satisfactory. I have already said that usually this is done with the help of the *see* and *see also* remarks accompanying the indexes in the catalogue, or corresponding similar devices. An indexing system might well stand or fall with the quality of these cross-references. Leaving aside that function of cross-references which consists of calling attention to synonyms, what they usually do, or are supposed to do, is to call the attention of the user to the possibility of changing the formulation of his request to a more or less closely related one, with the expectation that the new reference list thereby obtained will contain material relevant not only to the changed topic but also to the original one. If someone is interested in getting a list of all documents (in a given collection) relevant to the topic *Diseases of Animals in South America*, it is likely that he would find interest in reading documents that treat the topic *Diseases of Dogs in Argentina*, which he would obtain by a suitable change in the original set of topic terms to a new one. A similar likelihood exists in the inverse direction, and perhaps a lesser likelihood that a document dealing with *Diseases of Cats in Brazil* would be relevant to the topic *Diseases of Dogs in Argentina*. Now the class of Dogs, as well as the class of Cats, is a subclass of the class of Animals, and therefore these two classes, together with all the other subclasses of the class of animals, form again a lattice with respect to the inclusion relation. Similarly, Argentina and Brazil are parts of South America and therefore form together with all the other parts of South America a lattice with regard to the Being-Part-Of relation (on condition that we are ready to work with the notion of a *null-area* which is a part of every area). All this is certainly true and even rather trivially so except that not distinguishing the Inclusion relation between classes from the Part relation between physical entities occasionally causes a certain amount of confusion. Assuming now that a certain classification of all animals is fixed, e.g., one of the standard biological classifications, the class of Dogs and the class of Cats will occupy certain fixed positions in the resulting *tree*. (Notice that under this assumption we get a tree structure rather than a lattice structure, because biologists do not like to work with null-classes as well as because the biological classification is assumed to be both exhaustive and exclusive.) Between these two classes, and any two classes occurring in the tree, there will be a path of shortest length combining them and we could measure their *distance* by the number of nodes between them (or rather by this number plus one, for obvious reasons) —as is intimated, e.g., by BERNIER and HEUMANN [13]—or perhaps by some monotone function of these numbers. Similarly, by assuming some division of South America into non-overlapping but together exhaustive parts, e.g., a political division into countries, and of a similar division of these parts into subparts, e.g., an administrative division into provinces, etc., we could arrive at another tree whose nodes would be occupied by South America and its various parts, subparts, etc., and could then again easily define a distance measure function (not to be confused, of course, with the average geographic distance of such two parts).

For the purposes of the following remark we shall keep the term *diseases* fixed. (Defining a tree in which this term would occupy a certain position would be possible but difficult and space consuming.) Assume now that being interested in the topic of *Diseases of Dogs in Argentina* we have reasons, good or bad, to be dissatisfied with the first reference list obtained from our system. To fix the idea, let us assume that the system uses some kind of so-called coordinate indexes, uniterms, descriptors or the like. Assume further that the topic terms assigned to our topic are just *Disease(s)*, *Dogs* and *Argentina*. We might then be inclined to change our topic in the hope that thereby additional documents would be called to our attention which might well satisfy our needs. It is rather natural to think of changing our topic in small steps, as it were, first to very closely related ones, then—if necessary —to rather closely related ones, to remotely related ones, etc. It is again rather natural to believe that the above-mentioned distance measures would be the means of doing this. For instance, we could think of defining the distance of two 3-membered index sets whose indexes occur pairwise in the same trees as the sum of the distances between these pairs and then define the distance between two topics as the distance between their index sets. Assuming, for instance, that the distance between *Argentina and South America* in the geography tree (cf. Figure 1) is 1, the distance between *Argentina* and (the province of) *Mendoza* is 1, between *Brazil* and *South*

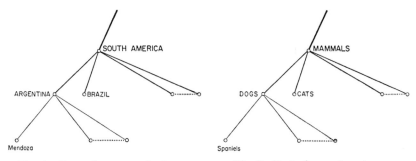

Fig. 1.   Part of a geography tree   Fig. 2   Part of a zoology tree

America 1, hence between *Argentina* and *Brazil* 2, and that the distance in the zoology tree (cf. Figure 2) between *Dogs* and *Mammals*, between *Dogs* and *Spaniels*, between *Cats* and *Mammals* is 1, etc., then, according to the mentioned definition, topics with a minimum distance of 1 from the topic *Diseases of Dogs in Argentina* would be *Diseases of Dogs in South America*, *Diseases of Dogs in Mendoza*, *Diseases of Mammals in Argentina*, *Diseases of Spaniels in Argentina*; topics with distance 2 from the original topic would be, e.g., *Diseases of Dogs in Brazil*, *Diseases of Spaniels in South America*, *Diseases of Mammals in Mendoza*; *Diseases of Cats in Brazil* would have distance 4. One could then think, and has perhaps even vaguely thought, of having a reference-providing system where you would on the first push of the button get a list of all documents dealing, inasmuch as their indexing can be trusted, with the very request topic itself, on the second push of the button all those documents dealing with topics once removed from the original topic, on the third push the documents twice removed, etc.

However, it is quite obvious that this whole schema floats in thin air. The "mathematics" of it is as impeccable as it is simple and trivial, involving nothing but counting and adding, but the practical utility of the outcome of these operations is more than doubtful. There seems to exist but a strenuous and ill-determined relationship between the "distance" measures obtained by these operations and either our intuitive feelings about topic-relatedness or the practical usefulness of the additional reference lists. To give but a trivial counter-example: The term *Domestic Animals* would not appear at all in a scientific Biology tree; it is nevertheless rather likely that a document dealing with *Diseases of Domestic Animals in Argentina* would be relevant to the requester. So would, in all probability, a document on *Diseases of Dogs in Temperate Zones*. A distance according to some such schema as the mentioned one would not be defined at all between the original topic and such a topic as *Bacteria Living in Dogs* or *Life Cycle of Insect X* (which insect, let us suppose, may cause a disease in the dogs of Argentina), but nevertheless documents dealing with these and an innumerable number of other topics with no distance defined between them and the original topic might be no less relevant than documents dealing with topics of defined distances. Nor is there a serious reason to suppose that documents with distance n will necessarily be more relevant than documents with distance m, where n is smaller than m, nor even that this is likely to be so. Is it, for instance, really likely to be the case that a document dealing with *Diseases of Dogs in Brazil* will be less relevant than a document dealing with *Diseases of Spaniels in Argentina*?

BERNIER-HEUMANN, FAIRTHORNE, MOOERS and VICKERY—among others— are fully aware of the decisive importance of defining an adequate distance measure between topics. But their efforts must be regarded, in my opinion, as complete failures. BERNIER and HEUMANN [13] are talking of a rather shapeless, multifaceted qualitative concept of semantic relatedness, but later go on to give some hints on a kind of measure of degree of relatedness and are ready to state, in all seriousness, that "there is an eleventh-order relationship between 'beta-d-glucose' and 'thing' ", because in a certain chemistry tree they have in mind there are 10 nodes between the two corresponding nodes, giving no hint of their awareness of the utter accidentality of these numbers. It turns out that all "semantemes" of a given science are related.

Why only of a given science? Presumably the biology tree(s) and the geography tree(s), too, have "thing" as their apex, thereby creating a relatedness between the "semantemes" of these trees. Finally, all "semantemes" will turn out to be related, a result that should not be too surprising.

And then the semantemes of a science are *"pictured as a large, very irregular ball made up of layers with the most abstract terms near the center."* It would be pointless to go on quoting.

FAIRTHORNE [52], after having stated rather surprisingly that *"distance, in any context, is based on the idea of 'difference' "*, quickly wanders off into irrelevant technicalities of non-Boolean operations. MOOERS [103] is concerned with distance measures between documents rather than between topics. Having defined one such "measure", he goes on to prove neatly that this "measure" does not fulfill the so-called triangle inequality, i.e., that according to his measure it is quite possible that the distance between documents A and B should be m, the distance between B and C should be n, and the distance between A and C greater than $m + n$! I did not understand why, having established this result on p. 9, he goes on for another 32 pages.

VICKERY [146] — who in another publication [145] rightfully stresses that *"relation between terms is the central semantic problem of subject indexing"*—does not attempt to define a metric for relatedness, but even his qualitative treatment is marred by oversights and inaccuracies. After having defined the relation of coordinateness between two terms as holding when they have *"meanings which are included in that of the next term"*—but forgetting already on the next page to draw a broken line indicating coordinateness between B and A in his illustrative figure

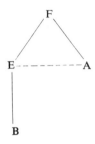

(and calling this figure a "lattice", for some reason) —, he goes on to talk about coordinateness of subjects (topics) without apparently being aware that it is by no means obvious how the transition between coordinateness of terms to coordinateness of topics works.

This failure completely vitiates VICKERY's talk [145] about "levels of discrimination". It is not clear at all what he has in mind when mentioning the possibility that *"the machine is programmed so that, requested to search for subject S at Level L, it will retrieve all items marked S and those at levels $L + 1, L + 2, L + 3, L - 1$ and $L - 2$ related to S"*. At best, he might there be groping for a distance measure of the kind I have just discussed and found wanting. Incidentally, in the closing sentence of the paragraph, VICKERY makes a deplorable bow to fashionable ways of speech when he says that *"the machine might even re-programme itself"*.

The failures of these attempts, I would say, are not due to the insufficient stature of those who made them, but rather to the fact that they attempted the (almost) impossible. I do not hesitate at all to state that one of the aims of Area 6 of ICSI, i.e., the establishment of a concept of *"relatedness or connectivity of documents in a collection along with a suitable metric to define the degree of relatedness"*, as stated in the introduction to the papers published in this Area [123: 1273], is either unattainable at all or at least a devilishly difficult task, no approach being in view that has any chance of leading to a function that will give us a useful measure of distance between topics, and still less between documents.

13. THE METHOD OF DECREASING TOPIC TERM SETS

A somewhat different, less ambitious and therefore more promising approach to get at more satisfactory reference lists in case the first list is not satisfactory is the following, illustrated again by a descriptor-type indexing. Assume that to a certain request topic a set of n topic terms is assigned, and that the list of all those documents whose index set includes this topic-term set as a subset is not satisfactory. The reference librarian could then be instructed to obtain a list of all those documents whose index set comprises any $n-1$ out of the original n topic terms. The reference list thereby obtained would in general be more comprehensive than the criginal one, perhaps even much more so, and might therefore be more satisfactory, in spite of the fact that it would now probably contain a good amount of references of little or no relevance to the original topic. If necessary, this procedure could be repeated with $n-2$, etc. It is known that this procedure has been partly successful in actual operation, the rationale behind it being rather obvious. However, it would again be a mistake, albeit an attractive one, to think that every document whose index set comprises m out of the n original topic terms is necessarily at least as relevant to the original request as every document whose index set comprises only $m-1$ topic terms. There is, for instance, no reason to assume that a document whose index set comprises *Diseases* and *Argentina* but not *Dogs* is more relevant to the requester's topic then a document whose index set comprises *Dogs* but neither *Diseases* nor *Argentina*. There are some vague and indefinite plausibility considerations involved here which may account for the relative practical success of this method, but it is very implausible that any theory can be built around these considerations.   The technique of decreasing topic term sets has been in use in the systems advocated by MOOERS, PERRY and others.

14. DEGREE OF RELEVANCE OF DOCUMENTS TO TOPICS

So far we have stressed the difficulties of arriving at a reliable estimate of the probability of a document's containing material pertinent to a given request topic, from the characterization of the document by a set of indexes and the characterization of the request topic by a set of index terms. However, the situation is in reality even worse. In our discussion we assumed that a document is either relevant to a given research topic or irrelevant, i.e., we worked with the so-called *classificatory concept* of relevance. In fact, however, it is rather the degree of the document's relevance which is important. Vaguely speaking, a document is worth the time spent on its reading if and only if its degree of relevance is higher than a certain point; very roughly speaking again, the estimate of the gain to be obtained from the perusal of a document should be higher than the utility of the effort spent in its reading. So far this is all rather trivial, but only because all the concepts employed in this remark are so vague and indeterminate. Leaving aside all well-known difficulties with regard to the measurement of utilities, the point I would like to stress now is how difficult, if not simply impossible, it is to arrive at an adequate explication of this *quantitative concept* of degree or relevance of document to topic. This explication is certainly a more difficult task than that of explicating the qualitative concept. The concept of degree of relevance, incidentally, should be distinguished from that of the *probability of being relevant* though, intuitively, there might exist some ill-determined connections between them. There exists, to my knowledge, only one serious attempt in this direction [95] (in which the just mentioned distinction is not yet made) but even this attempt has at most some exploratory value and raises, in addition to the theoretical questions of its adequacy, the practical question of the economical worthwhileness of the effort put into the determination of the relevance measures. In short, the essence of this proposal consists of assigning—so far in a rather arbitrary-looking way—weights to the index terms, whereas in the usual indexing systems an index term is just either included in or excluded from the index set of a given document.

15. THE APPEAL TO SYMBOLIC LOGIC

In Chapter 18, I have already had an opportunity to complain about the fact that some proponents of new indexing systems found it necessary to claim that their proposals were based on the findings of *symbolic logic*, thereby apparently intending to strengthen their proposals by an appeal to the high prestige which this discipline enjoys to a measure which seems inversely proportional to the degree of acquaintance with it. I shall not repeat here the argument to the effect that this appeal was utterly unjustified. How important it is to dispel the illusions that have been created in this respect emerges, for instance, from the fact that METCALFE [98] pays far too much respect to the claim that certain recent schemes for literature searching are based upon modern symbolic logic, whereas the old classification indexing systems are based upon old-fashioned traditional logic. I hold no special brief for the traditional theory of definition and even less for the metaphysics which goes with it, but a critique of this theory is completely independent of what is done in modern symbolic logic. As a matter of fact, the theory of definition is a rather neglected part of symbolic logic with sometimes rather serious repercussions for this discipline. Old-fashioned scientific methodology is to be overcome and improved upon not by symbolic logic but rather by a modern methodology of science and a better understanding of the theory and concept formation. This better understanding will indeed be helped by a better knowledge of symbolic logic (to a much higher degree than that shown by the proponents of the new indexing systems), but is not a simple consequence of this knowledge. Modern methodology might be sufficient to show that the methodological foundations of classificational indexing are shaky, but does nothing, as far as I can see, to show that the new systems are any better. Unfortunately, the appeal to symbolic logic manifests itself in nothing beyond the use of EULER circles, VENN diagrams and ample mentioning of *logical products* and *logical sums*, quite often in the wrong context, and the use of the most elementary symbolism of propositional and class calculi, again not at all always with adequate skill, whereas the probably much more relevant (but also much more difficult) logic of relations is hardly mentioned and never employed.

The feud between, say, coordinate indexing and classificational indexing has absolutely nothing to do with the issue, or rather pseudo-issue, between symbolic logic and traditional logic. Any reference to this issue is misleading and just another instance of the well-known fallacy of Appeal to Authority.

16. THE APPEAL TO SEMANTICS

Another theory to which appeal is often made is semantics, the study of the meaning and reference of signs. However, there are few signs in the recent publications of any serious knowledge of the considerable insights which semanticists have given us into the workings of language or of a mastery of the conceptual and terminological framework which they have erected. A recent publication [113] by authors who make heavy use of the term *semantics* and its various derivatives contains a definition of *degree of synonymity* (p. 24) according to which two terms have the degree of synonymity 1 if they apply to the same objects. This definition forms part of a "mathematical model" which they construct in the belief that it would be helpful for the theory of information retrieval. They show awareness of the difficulties of extrapolation from what holds in their model to what holds in actual situations, but do not seem to be aware that there are good reasons to suppose that nothing at all can be extrapolated. Though the definition of degree of synonymity just mentioned may have some value for this model, it is absolutely useless in any adequate theory of indexing. What they do define is rather the concept *degree of co-extension*. Whatever the importance of this concept in the theory of reference, one of the two major branches of logical semantics, within the theory of meaning one has to work with the concept *degree of co-intension* or rather just with the qualitative concept *co-intensional*, as it is clearly this concept which is involved in indexing[8].

The lack of semantic understanding, not even of a highly sophisticated level, by many otherwise thoughtful workers in information retrieval is

_____

[8] For all these concepts, see, e. g., Chapter 2, where further references are given. The whole "mathematical model", incidentally, is not much more than a pointless

distressing. In spite of earlier warnings (Chapter 17), one can still find in an important recent article [86: 1224] a statement such as: *"Suppose one wants to find all articles on the application of nuclear theory, i.e., all articles each of which is associated with* all *of the following given words*: *application, nuclear, theory.*" So long as the adherents of uniterm indexing systems do not realize how problematic this transition, so innocently indicated by "i.e.", will be in general, their theorizing will remain baseless: Not all documents dealing with Applications of Nuclear Theory will be indexed by *applications, nuclear* and *theory*, and not all documents indexed by these terms will deal with Applications of Nuclear Theory.

17. THE THESAURUS APPROACH

Some recent attempts at attacking the problem of topic-distance have made considerable use of the term *thesaurus* [90; 52; 104; 96; 13]. Now a thesaurus like ROGET's is a kind of glorified synonym dictionary combined with a universal classification scheme. To the degree that such a thesaurus is based upon competent and shrewd observation, there can be no doubt that it might be helpful to someone who is in search of a reformulation of his original topic when a literature search based on the original formulation did not yield satisfactory results. It is again therefore rather natural to think of mechanizing these transitions, of having, at the push of a button, the original index terms replaced one after the other by those terms which a specific consulted thesaurus indicated as synonyms or quasi-synonyms, and of repeating the literature search with the index set thus obtained. However, there is no reason to assume that a satisfactory theory for this method can be found, any more than for the other methods discussed before. I do not see any possibility of quantitative control as to the relevancy of the additional documents whose references are supplied by this method. There will surely be documents that will be more or less relevant to the original topic and there will be others that will not. Since the practicality of this method will depend among other things upon the ratio of the numbers of these two kinds of documents, or perhaps some other function of these numbers, and as there does not seem to be any way of predicting something useful about

mathematization of purely commonsensical qualitative remarks as to the various cost factors that are involved in various indexing systems. Writing down some 27 linear equations, where linearity is only assumed for the sake of being able to write down such equations, with summations and integrations interspersed for good measure, is only apt to create bad feelings against mathematical treatment in general, since documentalists who are the likely readers of such books might easily get the impression that this is all that mathematics can do.

It seems that this whole pseudo-mathematical effort was made in order to create a favorable background for the proposal of its initiators to use automatic equipment for information retrieval. In fact, however, nothing at all follows from the model, not only because it is so patently inadequate, but also because no indications are given of how to arrive at the numerical determination of the 27 constants which occur in it.

this ratio, there exists no other way to evaluate this proposal but to test it experimentally in comparison with other methods. However, even such an experimental test will tell very little of any general importance, Sould it, for instance, turn out that a literature search method based upon ROGET's Thesaurus would not be worth its cost, one could still go on believing that some other thesaurus would do better.

Quite often however, the concept of a thesaurus has been watered down by workers in information retrieval to such a degree that it is no longer clear whether it is at all different from the cross-reference systems so well known to the librarians. It may be hoped that the somewhat mystical aura which has been spread around the use of thesauri in literature searching, whether on purpose or by misunderstandings, will be dispersed in order to make room for a sober and down-to-earth discussion of the issue.

18. ANALYSIS OF CUSTOMARY LITERATURE SEARCH PROCEDURES

Altogether, time has perhaps come to ask oneself the fundamental question what exactly it is that one expects an automatic literature search system to perform. When embarking upon a new research program, one would usually be interested in getting a reliable view of the state of the art in order not to spend time on thinking through issues which have already been satisfactorily discussed by others or in performing experiments which have already been done by others and the results of which have already been published. In addition, of course, one would like to know whether sufficiently related issues have not been discussed before, and whether similar experiments have not been performed before from whose set-up and/or outcome one could learn. Usually there is no very great hurry for this process of getting to know the literature, and it is certainly not necessary at all to have a complete reference list at one's disposal before one starts reading the documents. The usual procedure is rather to start reading some documents which one regards as containing relevant material and to which one is led either by memory or by advice from a colleague or by the use of some existing literature search system. The reading of these documents itself then suggests the reading of additional documents through references, footnotes, etc., and these additional references are obtained rather cheaply as an almost automatic by-product of the reading itself. It is difficult to see how any other method, manual or automatic, could possibly be more efficient in this provision of additional references, However, what could of course happen, and does happen, probably quite often, is that this acquisition of additional references will not be sufficient to uncover all important references containing relevant material, if only for the obvious reason that the additional references will usually[9] have been published at a date preceding that of the primary reference. In addition, of course, the secondary, tertiary, etc., references one will get by this customary procedure might still not cover the whole ground since it is conceivable and even likely that, when starting this process with a narrow primary reference list, the whole sequence of references obtained will converge only to a subset of the total set of relevant documents, whether because of a tendency to quote literature written in a certain language, or published in a certain country or for very many other reasons. Experience teaches that by this traditional method valuable material is often not caught, with occasionally rather detrimental consequences. Without here going into the details of the information gathering habits of scientists, it is clear that the major trouble of literature searching is how to get hold of very recent and/or out-of-the-way references. Whereas a lead provided by a footnote in an article one reads in preparation for his research will usually yield only older references belonging to a relatively restricted circle, the leads one will obtain by "disturbing" the original index set "impartially" will yield both older and more recent material, stemming from similar or totally different sources written in the same or in different languages. Unfortunately, however, we have already seen that a "purely-mechanical" (now using this term in its customary derogatory connotation) perusal of this method will not necessarily be satisfactory, either.

19. A HETERODOX CONCEPTION OF THE USE OF COMPUTERS IN INFORMATION RETRIEVAL

It might therefore be worthwhile to think of a literature search system that, while utilizing the high speed and the large memory capacities of the modern electronic computers, would not fall into the traps of their "mechanical" use. When the computer is used for computing, it is clearly best, for economical reasons, to program the solutions of a problem and to have the computer work on it without any human intervention until the final solution is printed out. It seems that the rule: *Interrupt the work of a computer as little as possible,* has been too readily taken for granted also for non-computational uses. It might very well turn out that the best way to make human use of an electronic computer for such non-computational purposes and information retrieval (or machine translation, for that matter[10]), would be exactly this kind of intermittent employment which is still so much

---

[9] I say "usually" because often useful leads will be obtained from footnotes calling attention to documents yet to be published.

[10] In general, "the analogy between machine translation and literary search" [96; 152] has been greatly exaggerated. It is true enough that many people, including myself, have dealt with both fields—after all they are both non-numerical applications of digital computers—, but this personal union proves nothing about the existence of useful analo-

shunned. The actual descision as to the changes to be made in the original set of topic terms in order to get additional references would not be left to the computer. Whether a new search should be conducted on an index set obtained from the original one by omitting one of the topic terms, by substituting for one of the topic terms some other term, or whether the request is to be replaced altogether, all this is probably best decided upon by the human requester, perhaps in collaboration with the reference librarian. Some kind of simple mechanical device might conceivably be useful for obtaining suggestions as to the changes to be introduced, but it is highly doubtful whether the use of an electronic computer for this purpose could ever be economically justified. It is possible, however, that an electronic computer (or rather a special-purpose device constructed with more or less the same components as an electronic computer but in different proportions and costing much less per hour) could be usefully employed for printing out the additional reference lists. This in such a way that whenever a new reference list is printed out, the machine would turn to some other literature search problem waiting for it and would come back to the original one only if especially instructed to do so. The requester would do this if he is not satisfied with the list, having checked through the titles of the suggested documents, perhaps having read some abstracts or even some of these documents themselves. In other words, what I am suggesting here is to find out whether for such purposes as information retrieval, electronic computer-like devices might not be better used as slaves to many masters, always doing only short runs of routine work, though with a rather inhuman capacity of instantaneously switching from job to job, rather than as almost autonomous units working prolongedly and uninterruptedly on some one job till its completion, when provided with one final set of instructions. I believe that this "conversing with the machine" is a more promising way of utilizing the capacities of digital computers than letting the machine carry on a "monologue" by continuously working on a series of questions propounded at the beginning, contrary to the view of KOLLER et al. [80: 339]. However, I do not believe that present-day computers could be economically put to work along the indicated line. I understand that work is already in progress to construct computers that would be adapted to such kind of work. This means, of course, a much less ambitious use of computers for information retrieval than has been envisaged and talked about by many recent workers in the field. The only stages in a complete litera-

---

gies, and I for one have so far been unable to profit from them in my own investigations. Nor is it very difficult to exhibit the sources of this prejudice as I have done elsewhere [10]. One such source is the customary, fashionable, loose and thoughtless usage of such terms as 'information', 'translation', 'transformation', and the like.

ture search which I can see as being usefully turned over to computers are

(1) the storage of the references and their index sets,

(2) the matching of some Boolean function over a given set of topic terms with the various stored index sets,

(3) the printing out of reference lists corresponding to these matchings.

On the other hand, I do not believe that one should delegate to computers

(1) decisions as to the changes to be made in a literature search program when the output of the original program is not satisfactory,

(2) indexing and abstracting.

I also do not believe that it makes any sense at present to talk about computers learning to make literature searches and improving their performances in time. I do not think I should say here more about this last topic since nothing beyond non-committal talk exists on this subject until now.

The specific kind of man-machine partnership I am suggesting here is perfectly commonplace as such; it is only that this type has so for been shunned when the machine-partner was a digital computer with a salary of hundreds of dollars per hour. SAMAIN who heads the section on bibliographic research of the Documentation center of the French National Center for Scientific Research has recently introduced an experimental service in which the requester is sent the copies of the abstracts selected by the original search which was conducted in accordance with the original formulation of his request, plus a list of associated terms which may suggest to him further useful searches. The decision whether and how to reformulate the request is left to the user, with some aid given to him by the list of associated terms. However, no indication is given as to the method of arriving at this list. Presumably, it is just commonsense that is used for this purpose.

20. THE OUTLOOK

The outlook for the possible use of computers in information retrieval is thus far from clear. Existent claims for their far-reaching use in this field have not been substantiated either in theory or in practice. Partial uses whose feasibility seems plausible in theory have not yet been seriously tested as to their economical practicality, and might well, in addition, require the construction of special-purpose devices whose mode of operation differs rather radically from the one generally accepted at present as being most efficient. This point will have to be very closely studied. In the best study on the use of electronic computers for information retrieval that has come to my attention, OPLER and BAIRD [111] arrive at the conclusion that for very large systems which require frequent reference to logically complex comparisons, commercially available large electronic data processing machines are well suited, whereas smaller computers are of only marginal usefulness. This conclusion is reached from *experience* and not from theorizing. Their final evaluation is somewhat equivocal. Whereas in the opening Thesis they state simply that their *"experiences have shown that the use of electronic computers provides fast, convenient, accurate, and inexpensive retrieval"*, the remainder of the paper cannot but seriously qualify this statement, so that in the closing Conclusion their claim has been toned down to saying that *"only the experience to be gained in the years ahead can fully justify"* the widespread adoption of electronic computers in the information retrieval field. They have nothing to say on the use of special-purpose machines, perhaps because they believe that in *"only a few highly specialized cases could the installation of a large computer solely for searching be justified. These exceptional situations warise here very large files must be frequently searched (e.g., U.S. Patent Office, Chemical Abstracts, etc.),"* in addition to the fact that they just had no personal experience with such machines.

The prospects for efficient use of computers for information retrieval have so far been greatly hampered by inept theorizing, by pointless attempts to "apply" prestige-carrying scientific, and especially mathematical disciplines, by letting imagination roam freely and by greatly underestimating the intellectual effort required to arrive at a good abstract, a good index set, and a good judgement as to the closeness of topics. This underestimation may partly be explained by the great crudeness of the semantical views exhibited by many information retrieval specialists. Greater sophistication in this respect, though leading to a negative appraisal of many existing attempts at the automation of literature seraching, will unfortunately not necessarily lead to more promising attempts and is therefore often regarded as being purely destructive, hence rather useless. I would not agree with this last turn of the argument. I am afraid that the present paper, as some of my earlier ones, is indeed almost purely destructive (though the suggestions as to the change in policy of using computers given above are constructive in a sense). But I would not want to agree that this paper is therefore useless. On the contrary, should it fulfill its purpose of discouraging information retrieval workers from futile theorizing and from working towards the realization of hopeless schemes, thereby freeing their time for more promising investigations, the destructive force of my arguments could, at least indirectly, have definite constructive implications. I know, of course, that innumerably many times claims as to the futility or impossibility of certain approaches have been proved false in time so that the proponents of these claims were then regarded as reactionaries and stumbling blocks in the progress of science. But I also know that equally innumerably many times such warnings have been effective in redirecting research effort that was in danger of being wasted on futile projects into more profitable directions. The fact that I might prove to be wrong does not, I think, justify my shunning the risk. The issue is not an emotional one, that of being optimistic or pessimistic (as it has often been put by some of my colleagues and opponents) but, so I hope, a purely intellectual one. I have tried to present arguments for my "pessimistic" view, and I have tried to show that no good arguments have been given for the "optimistic" view cherished by others. I would like my criticism to be judged by the quality of its argument and not by its emotional appeal or its conforming or nonconforming to vested interests. I might be proved wrong, perhaps even very soon so, and, to be frank, I would not be too sorry about it; emotionally, if I am allowed to analyze myself for a moment, I have rather great expectations for the use of electronic computers and would be glad to see them do more than I can rationally justify at the present.

APPENDIX

In this appendix, I intend to discuss various issues which do not look so important to me as they do to others. I therefore did not deal with them at all in the main text, or only somewhat perfunctorily. But since many would feel that I omitted treating important theoretical aspects of the literature search problem, I feel obliged to present these issues as I see them.

21. FALSE DROPS

It is unavoidable that a reference list, even when based upon the best of all possible indexing systems, provided in response to a certain request, will occasionally contain references which are of little or no relevance to this request. I shall here take this unavoidability as a simple empirical fact rather than try to deduce it from the theory of transmission of information under noise as is often done by other authors, since I regard this approach as misleading: the set of indexes is *not*, in any serious sense, a transform of the document, but only a set of clues to it. Though then a certain number of false drops, as these unwanted references are often called, is unavoidable and therefore not a cause for any special worry, it may happen that under certain indexing systems and/or coding systems this number of false drops may come to obtain alarming proportions. Again, as so often before, the problem is purely a question of degree and economics. In this I agree with KOLLER et al. [80] who state as one of the questions that have to be considered for the design of a retrieval system: "*How much 'noise' and what per cent of 'false drops' are tolerable?*" But they fail, unfortunately, to give reasons for their subsequent statement: "*It is not true that the large-scale searching system must have some degree of each of these disturbing characteristics.*"

It seems, incidentally, that these authors distinguish between two types of unwanted references: those resulting from an inadequate formulation of the request and those resulting from "ambiguities in the (indexing?) system", which alone they call "false drops". I am not sure that this distinction is justified. The inadequacy of a request formulation is itself often only relative to a certain indexing system, and seems to me therefore strongly connected with the specific form of the system.

If a certain document collection contains both documents dealing with the Export of Cars from France to the USA and the Export of Cars from the USA to France, and if both kinds of documents are indexed, in uniterm or descriptor fashion, by *export, cars, France* and *USA*, then clearly any request for a list of documents dealing with one topic will be answered by a reference list containing also references to documents dealing with the other topic. With this simple observation the theoretical case rests. It is not true, of course, that therefore uniterm indexing is inferior to indexing by subject headings where this kind of false drop is avoided. If it can be shown that the cost incurred by these false drops is less than the difference in cost between the uniterm indexing and subject-heading indexing, for certain specified conditions, then uniterm indexing would still be superior under these conditions. More interesting from the theoretical point of view is, therefore, the fact that the choice is not necessarily between a uniterm system with its many incident false drops of this specific kind and a subject-heading system or classification system with their own well-known shortcomings, but that any number of alterations of a simple uniterm indexing system are possible which would reduce the number of false drops. Many such systems have been proposed in the past, sometimes couched in strange-looking terminology and based upon faulty and naive semantics, and many others will no doubt be proposed in the future. The common point of all these proposals is that through some appropriate tagging of the codes for the uniterms, the specific connection of these terms within the subject headings, lost in the transition from this heading to the unordered set of uniterms, is being re-established without damage to the possibility of approaching this document from these uniterms as such. To illustrate: False drops of the above-mentioned kind in a request for a reference list of documents dealing with the export of cars from France to the USA can be avoided if the indexing terms are taken to be *export, (of) cars, (from) France, (to) USA,* or rather their equivalents in some coding system, where suitable precautions will have to be taken in order to ensure the inclusion of this document in any request for literature on cars. It is easy to see that this method, though effective to a certain degree, is not fully so, since one and the same document could conceivably simultaneously deal with both the export of cars from the USA to France and the export of wine from France to the USA. Indexing this document by *export*, *(of) cars*, *(from) USA*, *(to) France*, *(of) wine*, *(from) France*, *to (USA)* would clearly cause this document to be referred to in a list provided in request for literature on the export of cars from France to the USA. Now it is not too difficult to think up an indexing system which would eliminate this kind of false drops too, but every such system has its price in terms of more complex coding, more complex retrieval operations, more complex rephrasal of the search question in preparation for the retrieval, etc. Some knowledge of linguistics, semantics and symbolic logic could conceivably be of some help in finding a more efficient indexing system, but I have no specific suggestions to make in this connection.

It is interesting, though on second thought not really surprising, that the specific methods for encoding relationships among uniterm-type index terms proposed by the Western Reserve University Group, by the U.S. Patent Office Group and already in current use in some non-conventional technical information systems, viz. by expanding the codes of these index terms to contain "role indicators", "interfixes", etc. —in our illustration, 'of', 'from', and 'to' are interfixes, of a kind, whereas 'item manipulated', 'country of origin', and 'country of destination' would be role indicators—come rather close to variants of the "conventional" classification systems like the Colon system or the faceted classification system, thereby completing the circle. If someone cherishes a generalized fear of false drops he will have to forego the advantages of an unadulterated uniterm indexing system. But it has already been pointed out before (Section 4) that the problem of false drops can presumably be more sensibly handled through a multi-stage information system, combined with a judicious use of cross-references. It stands to reason, however, that coding of chemical formulae, e.g., for Patent Office purposes, will have best to be done through indicating both useful substructures and their mode of combination.

A great majority of the non-conventional technical information systems in current use make no provision for encoding relationships among terms for machine manipulation. There can be little doubt that the directors of these systems feel that the additional cost incurred by incorporating such a provision would not pay off in terms of the savings achieved by a reduction in the number of false drops. I do not know whether this feeling has been put to an objective test, but I am sure that such a test would be very difficult and costly.

A sober and unpretentious approach to this question is exhibited by KOELEWIJN [79]: *"The final answer to this question (whether an indexing*

system for patent search would not be sufficiently selective without interfixings)
can... only be given by comparative tests".

False drops may occur not so much as a consequence of an indexing system as of the coding system employed. Superimposed coding, as has been shown and discussed many times, will yield a certain number of false drops. However, it is known that this number can be kept under control so that this issue is not a decisive one for the general question of the practicality of superimposed coding.

22. BLANK SORTS

Another issue which has gotten more publicity and discussion than it deserves is that of blank sorts, the technical term often used for denoting a situation where the reference list supplied in answering a request for literature is empty. Such an occurrence is often regarded as a black mark on the reputation of the indexing system in use. Now, if the requester is convinced that the document collection he wants to have searched does contain information relevant to his request, he has, of course, good reason to be dissatisfied. He then has the choice of either blaming himself for an inept formulation of his request or of blaming the indexing and/or retrieval system in use. But then this may and will also happen if the reference list is not empty but is only more meager than the requester expected it to be. A blank sort is then nothing more than a psychologically more shocking sign for a defect in the system. However, if the requester has no good reason to doubt the quality of the retrieval system, a blank sort is as good an answer to his request as a list containing 1, 10 or 1000 references. I can easily imagine that a research scientist, having gotten hold of what seems to him to be a completely brand-new idea will sometimes be rather happy to find out that the request for literature on this idea yields a blank sort.   This is in complete agreement with CRANE and BERNIER [43] who state: "*A genuine blank sort is a desirable outcome of many searches*". But they seem still to be under the contrary impact of earlier views, when the next-but-one sentence goes: "*Time for a search terminated by a blank sort is lost*". Altogether I am really convinced that there is absolutely nothing of specific importance to this issue of blank sorts, and that it should better be dropped from further theoretical discussions.

Is Information Retrieval Approaching a Crisis?*

20

Whenever the case for the urgency of mechanizing translation, information retrieval, and other kinds of linguistic data processing is argued in public—whether in popular articles or in research proposals; before congressional committees or scientific gatherings; in the United States, Soviet Russia or any other major country—it is an almost invariable practice to open the argument with the quotation of certain statistics about the prodigious rate of increase in the number of scientific, technological, and other kinds of publications during the last decades. Authorities are then cited which predict that this rate will remain constant, or even increase, during the coming years. In due course, and especially before an American audience, one of the many pertinent *obiter dicta* of Vannevar Bush will be invoked, perhaps the one in which he warns that "science may become bogged down in its own products, inhibited like a colony of bacteria by its own exudations."

On many such occasions, the situation will be described as approaching a crisis where the documentary explosion will lead to a complete breakdown of scientific communication. Scientists, so is claimed, simply will not any longer be able to handle the flood of information, should they continue to gather and retrieve it in their accustomed ways. Only a radical change in these customs will be able to save the situation. This change, to bring the argument to its climax, can be brought about only by the mechanization of abstraction, extraction, indexing, translation, the provision of reference lists, and the other aspects of processing linguistic data.

I am quite convinced that this argument is almost totally fallacious. I would have tended to dismiss it as pure propaganda and no more than an expression of rather obvious vested interests, if it were not the case that many competent scientists not only subscribe to it but are even among its originators. As a matter of fact, there are few scientists who do not occasionally complain about the unsatisfactory state of information retrieval

---

* First appeared in **American Documentation**, vol. 14 (1963), pp. 95-98.

and literature searching, or about the unreliability of translations. They are quite ready to testify that matters constantly get worse in these fields. Though the baselessness of these complaints should be quite obvious after only a little analysis and reflection, I intend, because of the importance of the point, to belabor the issue far beyond its intrinsic merit. In addition, an explanation is mandatory as to why so many scientists invoke these complaints and in all seriousness believe in the imminence of a crisis in the field of scientific information.

Though I shall restrict myself to the discussion of scientific information, most of the following counterargument should apply equally to the processing and evaluation of nonscientific linguistic data, of the kind in which intelligence agencies, for instance, are interested.

My counterargument against the 'flood-of-information' argument is, in essence, extremely simple: This argument, in the form presented above, is irrelevant. Let us see this in more detail. The standard figures quoted are usually given in a rate-of-increase-per-annum form or in the form of a time span of doubling. These forms and others are, of course, mathematically equivalent and differ from each other, if at all, only with respect to the expected psychological shock effect. The estimates range from 5% to 8% annual increase and from 10 to 15 years doubling span. I shall not doubt here the correctness, or even the meaning of these figures, since this makes no difference to the validity of my criticism. What, then, is proved by a statement that "if the scientific output is 2,000 pages a minute today, it will be 4,000 pages a minute some time before 1975"? As such, exactly nothing. That something increases geometrically (or "exponentially', to increase the awe-inspiring impression) may be bad but may also be good or neutral. What about "if personal income is $4,000 a year today, it will be $8,000 a year some time before 1975"? And what about "if annual automobile production is 6,000,000 at present, it will be 12,000,000 some time before 1975"? The second development can become critical if certain other things, such as road construction, do not develop accordingly. But increased road construction may itself become critical, unless..., and so on. However, anything may become critical, even stagnation. It can hardly be doubted that a continuation of the present rate of automobile production will very quickly create a crisis (or worsen the existing crisis, according to some) if extant roads are not kept in good repair. (Let me beg the reader's forgiveness for the somewhat childish level of my present counterargument. But I am afraid that its point has to be driven home, even by childish means.)

That, then, is in the back of the mind of proponents of the 'flood-of-information' argument; why are so many people impressed by it? With some of them it is probably something like the following: A scientist who finds it necessary to read 20 pages a day, on the average. to 'keep up' with the research going on in his field in 1961 will have to read 40 pages a day in 1973 for this purpose, assuming that the total number of publications in his field will double during this period. Assuming also, as we well may, that reading time per page will not change noticeably during these 12 years, the scientist is supposed to find himself in the following dilemma: either he will indeed double the time spent on reading and therefore (if his total research time is kept constant) have much less time to spend on 'creative' research, or the quality of his research will suffer, since he will not be as well informed on what is going on in his field as he should. In addition, he will, in both cases, but particularly in the first, have to spend more time in selecting his reading, since he will have to scan double the published material in order to determine what he will study with more care. Whatever his course of action, not only will his creative effort suffer—which he might not mind, there being quite a number of scientists who would be happy to spend more of their time on reading—but so will the total effort of the society to which he belongs, with obvious detrimental effects to this society.

While formulating this argument, I had to beware not to succumb to its superficial force and attractiveness. But it is still all wrong, of course. It is a matter of simple fact, which I know from personal experience and observation and which the reader will be able to check similarly, that scientists did not spend on the average in 1961 more time on reading than they did 12 years ago, though printed scientific output has indeed almost doubled during this period. On the other hand, I don't think that anybody seriously believes that the quality of scientific research has deteriorated during this period. There must therefore have been a way out between the horns of the dilemma. What is it? Everybody knows it: *Specialization.* In 1961, a scientist's area of research had, on the average, half the width it had in 1949, and this width will be halved again by 1973. It is as simple as that. Or is it? If the situation were really so simple, how can one explain the complaints and worries of the scientists about the situation in scientific information? There are various explanations. None is sufficient by itself, but their combination should be adequate.

First, 'specialization' has become a dirty word among many people, scientists included. I shall not go into the origin of this interesting sociological fact here. At any rate, many scientists are emotionally convinced that specialization is evil and even resent its being regarded as a necessary evil. Though every scientist who has been in business for a long period knows perfectly well that in order to remain an expert in some area he has to cut down the width of his interests more or less continuously, he has been exposed for such a long time to the propaganda of so-called humanists, perhaps best expressed in that silly saying about 'knowing more and more about less and less,' that he has become subconsciously convinced of its truth. He is quite ready to blame society for this development and to listen with attention to those who offer him a remedy for this supposed disease.

Second, this propaganda effect is enhanced by a perfectly natural emotional reaction to the objective pressure for continuous specialization: "What the hell; there is nothing wrong with me, is there? If I am unable today to cope with the literature in a field I could easily master ten years ago, this is surely the fault of those guys there who are supposed to translate, abstract, extract, condense, index, summarize, review, and criticize the literature and are not doing their job properly, probably because they are still using their medieval or 19th-century methods instead of waking up to 20th-century technology. Have they never heard of computers?" One now often hears described the feelings of guilt which the scientist experiences upon entering his office and being confronted with the mountain of reprints with which his well-wishing friends and colleagues seem to be so anxious to supply him and the pile of recent issues of journals to which he is subscribing but somehow never quite manages to read through as carefully as he wishes. He finally does something about it, perhaps cancels once in a while his subscription to a journal; or he hires a new assistant, if he can get the necessary money, and delegates to him part of his own original direct area of interest; but he does this always reluctantly and therefore with a timelag often sufficient to create tensions.

Third, there is a good objective reason why scientists in the United States and in a few other countries, among which Soviet Russia is already included, should have the feeling that something is getting worse in the field of information retrieval. It is perhaps the same reason which is responsible for the fact that the U.S. government and its military agencies are particularly interested in the 'information problem,' and are ready to spend a lot of money and time on research leading to its solution through automation. The reason is the following: Though on a global scale the number of publications increases at about the same rate as the number of scientists, and though the number of scientific publications by Americans increases at the same rate as the number of American scientists, it is not true that the number of scientific publications in general increases at the same rate as the number of American scientists. On the contrary, it is well known that scientific publication on a global scale increases faster than in the United States, due to the fact that the number of scientists outside the United States has been growing during the last years at a higher rate than within the United States, for reasons which are too well known to need exposition here. Since non-American publications are, of course, harder to get and, most of the time, harder to read because their language is not necessarily English, the *American* scientist has a harder time in obtaining and using the publications which are relevant to his work. He might well have to spend today more time for this purpose and therefore less time for his other activities than he had to twelve years ago.

Non-American scientists, on the other hand, have it proportionally easier, but things being as they are, this is probably not much of a consolation to the Americans.

Until recently, many American scientists (and technologists) could very well get along with reading publications originating in the United States, and a still larger number of them could get along with reading publications written in English. I understand that according to the current estimate, close to 60% of all scientific publications are in English, which is a much larger percentage than that of the Anglo-Americans among the scientists. The fact that the American scientist will have to spend more of his time in obtaining pertinent publications will indeed reduce, in some sense, his creative output, and the total effect might very well be that the scientific supremacy of the United States will be reduced before a new equilibrium is established.

In the existing political situation, this development, which in different circumstances might have been welcomed as an indication of the progress in science and technology made by developing countries which would cause in its wake an increase in the standard of living of the world population at large, is certainly, in all-too-obvious sense, potentially dangerous for the United States. It is therefore perfectly intelligible that the U.S. government and military agencies should be ready to take strong countermeasures. It is equally intelligible that they should think, in the first line, of utilizing their great supremacy in financial resources and computer technology for counterbalancing this turn of the tides. But it cannot be too strongly emphasized that wishful thinking might do more harm than good; the belief that a solution will be found simply because it is so urgent to find one might well cause a diversion of financial resources and, more importantly, of valuable scientific research time into a direction which carries very little objective hope of success.

On other occasions (Chapter 19) I have tried to show that full automation of many aspects of the information retrieval field, such as translation, abstraction, or indexing, is not feasible. Partial automation, on the other hand, is theoretically feasible and might also be so economically. But the needed investigations should be carried out in suitable institutions of higher learning and in accordance with standard scholarly methods. The problem, with the exception of certain small portions, is certainly not yet ripe for being transferred to industrial research organizations; even less so has the solution of the problem reached a stage where actual development should be encouraged.

It is certainly not true that the world is about to go to the dogs or to suffocate in its information flood unless information processing is mechanized or otherwise totally overhauled. There is, of course, no doubt that information processing, like any other conceivable human activity, could be improved. It is very easy to point out innumerable aspects which could be done better, and it is often quite easy to show how such local improvements could be made and which should be made. It is another thing to show that these local improvements will not lead to an overall deterioration. It is well known that sub-optimization does not necessarily mean optimization. The situation becomes even more complicated when, as in our case, political considerations intrude and introduce a factor of imponderability which makes it rather hard to evaluate rationally certain proposals. There could, for instance, hardly be any doubt that the establishment of an institution corresponding to the Russian All-Union Institute of Scientific and Technological Information could greatly improve the existing situation in the information field in the United States and could most probably be even an overall improvement. But it is very hard to cope with counter-arguments that are put in terms of the danger in such centralization for the American way of life.

Though I think that on a global scale there exists no crisis in the information-retrieval field, this may not be the case for certain areas in which, for some reason or another, particular conditions prevail which have what we might call *cumulative effect.* I have in mind such areas as patents, and on a local Anglo-Saxon scale, the law.

Whereas, in standard scientific procedure, older publications are consulted at a rate which is roughly inversely proportional to their age, so that for many research problems the literature more than ten years old is hardly consulted at all, this is notoriously not the case in patent searching or in searching the legal literature, especially in those countries whose jurisdiction is based upon precedents. It might, therefore, indeed be the case that not only does the number of patent searches constantly increase, presumably again at approximately the same rate as other scientific and technological activities, which is nothing but a sign of a healthy and natural development, but that the time spent on each search increases too, due to the mentioned cumulative effect. As long as for extrascientific reasons the patent laws are not changed, the effect of this will indeed be that the number of employees of the patent office will have to increase at a greater rate than the number of inventors. This sounds disturbing, but it must be borne in mind that it is not the result of some tumor in the scientific information process but only of certain social conventions which need perhaps to be scrutinized again.

The situation is similar with regard to the legal field. Not only does the number of legal suits constantly increase (leaving aside the question of whether this development is to be welcomed or regretted), but the time spent in preparing each suit constantly increases too, due again to the above-mentioned cumulative effect. It is indeed possible that legal procedure might be suffocated, especially in Anglo-Saxon countries, unless this procedure is revised. But once more the source of the problem is a political and not a scientific one.

Cumulative effects are also noticeable in many libraries. The above-mentioned inverse relationship between the age and the use of documents for scientific research is seldom taken into account in extant library practices. Older books occupy the same space as new books and are usually located with equal accessibility. Under such practices, allocations for library facilities occupy a constantly increasing percentage in the general budget of universities and industrial institutions. The problems created thereby are not negligible, but they are nevertheless less serious than those in the legal and patent field, because no radical change of policy is required in order to make the necessary adjustment. As a matter of fact, these adjustments are being slowly introduced in various institutions, and one may now expect that, even without outcries of 'crisis' and 'breakdown,' the situation will shortly reach a tolerable equilibrium.

To summarize: the geometrical rate of increase in scientific and technological publications raises no particular problems, does not create any particular threatening situations, and does not require crash programs. This increase is commensurate with the increase in scientific and technological manpower and is, in fact, nothing more than its direct result. The feeling of an impending crisis, widespread even among competent scientists, is due to propaganda by vested interests which falls on fertile ground because of the psychologically perfectly intelligible attitude of the scientists towards specialization, but most of all because, on a local scale, in countries which have already achieved a high level of scientific and technological activity, the rate of increase in scientific publications is less than in countries which up to now have lagged behind in this respect, thereby forcing the scientists of the already highly developed countries to spend an increasingly larger percentage of their time in searching the literature originating in other countries and written in foreign languages. The so-called problem of information retrieval is therefore, to the degree that it is a problem at all, of a sociological, psychological, and, most of all, of a political nature and should be attacked on those levels. The only areas in which the retrieval situation is intrinsically worsening are those which exhibit the 'cumulative effect,' especially the areas of law, patent searching, and library acquisitions. But in these areas the natural remedy lies in a change of policy and practices rather than in a revolutionary change of the retrieval operations. The attitude which sees in mechanization the only hope of solving the impending crisis in information retrieval is objectively unjustified and subjectively dangerous, because it tends to replace dispassioned scientific analysis by wishful thinking and therefore diverts valuable research time into utopian speculations. Partial mechanization of various aspects of the information-retrieval field is theoretically feasible, but its economic feasibility can be determined only by extensive research and experimentation to be carried out at scientific institutions that have no vested financial interests in the field.

References

[1] K. AJDUKIEWICZ. *Die syntaktische Konnexität.* **Studia philosophica,** vol. 1 (1935), pp. 1–27.

[2] YEHOSHUA BAR-HILLEL. *Analysis of "correct" language.* **Mind,** vol. 55 (1946), pp. 328–340.

[3] YEHOSHUA BAR-HILLEL. *Recursive definitions in empirical sciences.* **Proceedings of the eleventh international congress of philosophy,** Brussels 1953, vol. 5, pp. 160–165.

[4] YEHOSHUA BAR-HILLEL. *Some linguistic problems connected with machine translation.* **Philosophy of science,** vol. 20 (1953), pp. 217–225.

[5] YEHOSHUA BAR-HILLEL. *Indexical expressions.* **Mind,** vol. 63 (1954), pp. 359–379.

[6] YEHOSHUA BAR-HILLEL. *Can translation be mechanized?* **American scientist,** vol. 42 (1954), pp. 248–260.

[7] YEHOSHUA BAR-HILLEL. *Three remarks on linguistic fundamentals.* **Word,** vol. 13 (1957), pp. 323–335.

[8] YEHOSHUA BAR-HILLEL. *The mechanization of literature searching.* **Proceedings of symposium on the mechanization of thought processes** (Teddington/Middlesex 1958), vol. II, Her Majesty's Stationery Office, London 1959, pp. 789–802.

[9] YEHOSHUA BAR-HILLEL. *Decision procedures for structure in natural languages.* **Logique et analyse,** vol. 2 (1959), pp. 19–29.

[10] YEHOSHUA BAR-HILLEL. *The present status of automatic translation of languages.* **Advances in computers,** vol. I (F. L. Alt, ed.), Academic Press, New York 1960, pp. 91–163.

[11] YEHOSHUA BAR-HILLEL. *Some linguistic obstacles to machine translation.* **Proceedings of the second international congress on cybernetics** (Namur 1958), Namur 1961, pp. 197–207.

[12] Y. BAR-HILLEL, A. KASHER and E. SHAMIR, *Measures of syntactic complexity.* Technical Report No. 13 (prepared for the U.S. Office of Naval Research, Information Systems Branch), Applied Logic Branch, Hebrew University, Jerusalem 1963.

[13] C. L. BERNIER and K. F. HEUMANN. *Correlative indexes III; semantic relations among semantemes—the technical thesaurus.* **American documentation,** vol. 8 (1957), pp. 211–220.

[14] MAX BLACK. *Russell's philosophy of language.* **The philosophy of Bertrand Russell,** Tudor Publishing Company, New York 1951, pp. 227–255.

[15] LEONARD BLOOMFIELD. **Linguistic aspects of science.** International encyclopedia of unified science, vol. I, no. 4, University of Chicago Press, 1939.

[16] L. M. BOHNERT. *Two methods of organizing technical information for search.* **American documentation,** vol. 6 (1955), pp. 135–150.

[17] C. W. BRENNER and C. N. MOOERS. *A case history of a Zatocoding information retrieval system.* **Punched cards, their application to science and industry,** 2nd edition (R. S. Casey, J. W. Perry and M. Berry, eds.), Reinhold Publishing Company, New York 1958, pp. 340–356.

373

[18] LEON BRILLOUIN. *Thermodynamics and information theory*. **American scientist,** vol. 38 (1950), pp. 594–599.

[19] W. E. BULL, C. AFRICA and D. TEICHROEW. *Some problems of the "word"*. [89], pp. 86–103.

[20] VANNEVAR BUSH. *As we may think*. **Atlantic monthly,** vol. 176 (1945), pp. 101–108.

[21] RUDOLF CARNAP. **Der logische Aufbau der Welt.** Weltkreis-Verlag, Berlin-Schlachtensee 1928; 2nd edition, Felix Meiner, Hamburg 1961.

[22] RUDOLF CARNAP. **Logische Syntax der Sprache.** Springer-Verlag, Vienna 1934.

[23] RUDOLF CARNAP. *Testability and meaning*. **Philosophy of science,** vol. 3 (1936), pp. 419–471; vol. 4 (1937), pp. 1–40.

[24] RUDOLF CARNAP. **The logical syntax of language** (Enlarged English translation of [22]). Harcourt, Brace & Co., New York 1937.

[25] RUDOLF CARNAP. **Foundations of logic and mathematics.** International encyclopedia of unified science, vol. I, no. 3, University of Chicago Press, 1939.

[26] RUDOLF CARNAP. **Introduction to semantics.** Harvard University Press, 1942.

[27] RUDOLF CARNAP. **Meaning and necessity.** University of Chicago Press, 1947.

[28] RUDOLF CARNAP. **Logical foundations of probability.** University of Chicago Press, 1950.

[29] RUDOLF CARNAP. **The continuum of inductive methods.** University of Chicago Press, 1952.

[30] RUDOLF CARNAP. *Meaning postulates*. **Philosophical studies,** vol. 3 (1952), pp. 65–73.

[31] E. C. CHERRY. *A history of the theory of information*. **Proceedings of the Institute of Electrical Engineers,** vol. 98 (III) (1951), pp. 383–393; reprinted with minor changes as *The communication of information*. **American scientist,** vol. 40 (1952), pp. 640–664.

[32] E. C. CHERRY, M. HALLE and ROMAN JAKOBSON. *Toward the logical description of languages in their phonemic aspect*. **Language,** vol. 29 (1953), pp. 34–46.

[33] NOAM CHOMSKY. *Three models for the description of language*. **IRE transactions on information theory,** IT-2 (1956), pp. 113–124.

[34] NOAM CHOMSKY. **Syntactic Structures.** Mouton & Co., s'Gravenhage 1957 (2nd printing, 1962).

[35] NOAM CHOMSKY. *On certain formal properties of grammars*. **Information and control,** vol. 2 (1959), pp. 137–167.

[36] NOAM CHOMSKY. *A note on phrase structure grammars*. **Information and control,** vol. 2 (1959), pp. 393–395.

[37] NOAM CHOMSKY. *On the notion "rule of grammar"*. **Twelfth symposium in applied mathematics** (R. Jakobson, ed.), American Mathematical Society, Providence, R.I. 1961, pp. 6–24.

[38] NOAM CHOMSKY. *Explanatory models in linguistics*. **Logic, methodology and philosophy of science: proceedings of the 1960 international congress** (E. Nagel, P. Suppes and A. Tarski, eds.), Stanford University Press, 1962, pp. 528–550.

[39] NOAM CHOMSKY. *Formal properties of grammars*. **Handbook of mathematical psychology,** vol. 2 (Bush, Galanter and Luce, eds.), Wiley, New York 1963.

[40] NOAM CHOMSKY and GEORGE A. MILLER. *Finite state languages*. **Information and control,** vol. 1 (1958), pp. 91–112.

[41] ALONZO CHURCH. **Introduction to mathematical logic,** vol. I. Princeton University Press, 1956.

[42] C. W. CLEVERDON. *The evaluation of systems used in information retrieval*. [123], Area 4, pp. 687–698.

[43] E. J. CRANE and C. L. BERNIER. *An overall concept of scientific documentation systems and their design*. [123], Area 5, pp. 1047–1069.

[44] HASKELL B. CURRY. **A theory of formal deducibility.** Notre Dame mathematical lectures No. 6, University of Notre Dame, 1950.

[45] HASKELL B. CURRY. *Mathematics, syntactics and logic.* **Mind,** vol. 62 (1953), pp. 172–183.

[46] HASKELL B. CURRY and ROBERT FEYS. **Combinatory logic.** Studies in logic and the foundations of mathematics, North-Holland Publishing Company, Amsterdam 1958.

[47] MARTIN DAVIS, **Computability and unsolvability.** McGraw-Hill, New York 1958.

[48] S. C. DODD. *Model English.* University of Washington (mimeographed), 1949.

[49] L. E. DOSTERT. *The Georgetown-IBM experiment.* [89], pp. 124–135.

[50] G. ESTRIN. *Maze structure and information retrieval.* [123], Area 6, pp. 1383–1393.

[51] R. A. FAIRTHORNE. *The problems of retrieval.* **American documentation,** vol. 7 (1956), pp. 65–75.

[52] R. A. FAIRTHORNE. *Delegation of classification.* **American documentation,** vol. 9 (1958), pp. 159–164.

[53] R. FLESCH. *A new readability yardstick.* **Journal of applied psychology,** vol. 32 (1948), pp. 221–233.

[54] D. J. FOSKETT. *The construction of a faceted classification for a special subject.* [123], Area 5, pp. 867–888.

[55] C. FRIES. **The structure of English.** Harcourt, Brace & Co., New York 1952.

[56] D. GABOR, *A summary of communication theory.* **Proceedings of the second symposium on applications of communication theory,** London 1953.

[57] CHAIM GAIFMAN. *Dependency systems and phrase-structure systems.* P–2315, Rand Corporation, Santa Monica, Cal. 1961.

[58] S. GINSBURG and H. G. RICE. *Two families of languages related to ALGOL.* **Journal of the Association for Computing Machinery,** vol. 9 (1962), pp. 350–371.

[59] S. GINSBURG and G. F. ROSE. *Operations which preserve definability in languages.* **Journal of the Association for Computing Machinery,** vol. 10 (1963), pp. 175–195.

[60] E. DE GROLIER. *Problems in scientific information.* **IBM journal of research and development,** vol. 2 (1958), pp. 276–281.

[61] DAVID HARRAH. **Communication: a logical model.** M.I.T. Press, Cambridge, Mass. 1963.

[62] ZELLIG S. HARRIS. **Methods in structural linguistics.** University of Chicago Press, 1951.

[63] ZELLIG S. HARRIS, *Discourse analysis.* **Language,** vol. 28 (1952), pp. 1–30.

[64] ZELLIG S. HARRIS. *Co-occurrence and transformations in linguistic structure.* **Language,** vol. 33 (1957), pp. 283–340.

[65] ZELLIG S. HARRIS. *Linguistic transformations for information retrieval.* [123], Area 5, pp. 937–950.

[66] R. V. L. HARTLEY. *Transmission of information.* **Bell System technical journal,** vol. 7 (1928), pp. 535–563.

[67] D. G. HAYS. *Grouping and dependency theories.* P–1910, Rand Corporation, Santa Monica, Cal. 1960.

[68] LOUIS HJELMSLEV. **Prolegomena to a theory of language** (tr. by F. J. Whitfield). Waverly Press, Baltimore 1953.

[69] CHARLES F. HOCKETT. *An approach to the quantification of semantic noise.* **Philosophy of science,** vol. 19 (1952), pp. 257–260.

[70] CHARLES F. HOCKETT. *Two models of grammatical description.* **Word,** vol. 10 (1954), pp. 210–231; reprinted as Ch. 39 in **Readings in linguistics** (M. Joos, ed.), American Council of Learned Societies, Washington 1957.

[71] CHARLES F. HOCKETT. **A course in modern linguistics.** Macmillan, New York 1958.

[72] R. C. JEFFREY. *Some recent simplifications of the theory of finite automata.* Technical Report No. 219, Research Laboratory of Electronics, Massachusetts Institute of Technology, 1959.

[73] A. KAPLAN. *Definition and specification of meaning.* **Journal of philosophy,** vol. 43 (1946), pp. 281–288.

376   REFERENCES

[74] A. KAPLAN. *An experimental study of ambiguity and context.* **Mechanical translation**, vol. 2 (1955), pp. 39–46.

[75] A. KASHER and D. LOUVISH. *Syntactic simplification.* Technical Report No. 14 (prepared for the U.S. Office of Naval Research, Information Systems Branch), Applied Logic Branch, Hebrew University, Jerusalem 1963.

[76] J. KATZ and J. FODOR. *What's wrong with the philosophy of language?* **Inquiry**, vol. 5 (1962), pp. 197–237.

[77] J. G. KEMENY. *A logical measure function.* **Journal of symbolic logic**, vol. 18 (1953), pp. 289–308,

[78] STEPHEN C. KLEENE. *Representation of events in nerve nets and finite automata.* **Automata studies** (C. E. Shannon and J. McCarthy, eds.), Princeton University Press, 1956, pp. 3–41.

[79] G. J. KOELEWIJN. *The possibilities of far-reaching mechanization of novelty search of the patent literature.* [123], Area 5, pp. 1071–1096.

[80] H. R. KOLLER, E. MARDEN and H. PFEFFER. *The Haystaq system; past, present and future.* [123], Area 5, pp. 1143–1179.

[81] S. KUNO and A. G. OETTINGER. *Multiple-path syntactic analyzer.* **Information processing 62: Proceedings of the IFIP Congress 62,** North-Holland Publishing Company, Amsterdam 1963, pp. 306–312.

[82] JOACHIM LAMBEK. *The mathematics of sentence structure.* **American mathematical monthly**, vol. 65 (1958), pp. 154–170.

[83] JOACHIM LAMBEK. *Contributions to a mathematical analysis of the English verbphrase.* **Journal of the Canadian Linguistic Association**, vol. 5 (1959), pp. 83–89.

[84] JOACHIM LAMBEK. *On the calculus of syntactic types.* **Twelfth symposium in applied mathematics** (R. Jakobson, ed.), American Mathematical Society, Providence, R.I. 1961, pp. 166–178.

[85] Y. LECERF and P. IHM. *Eléments pour une grammaire générale des langues projectives.* **Rapport GRISA**, No. 1 (1960), pp. 11–29.

[86] R. S. LEDLEY. *Tabledex: a new coordinate indexing method for bound book form bibliographies.* [123], Area 5, pp. 1221–1243.

[87] R. B. LEES. Review of *"Logique, langage et théorie de l'information"* (by L. Apostel, B. Mandelbrot and A. Morf), **Language,** vol. 35 (1959), pp. 271–303.

[88] STEFAN LEŚNIEWSKI. *Grundzüge eines neuen Systems der Grundlagen der Mathematik.* **Fundamenta mathematicae**, vol. 14 (1929), pp. 1–81.

[89] W. N. LOCKE and A. D. BOOTH (editors). **Machine translation of languages.** Technology Press of the Massachusetts Institute of Technology and John Wiley and Sons, Inc., New York, London 1955.

[90] H. P. LUHN. *The automatic creation of literature abstracts.* **IBM journal of research and development**, vol. 2 (1958), pp. 159–165.

[91] H. P. LUHN. *Keyword-in-context index for technical literature (KWIC index).* ASDD Report RC-127 (1959), IBM Advanced Systems Development Division, Yorktown Heights, New York.

[92] D. M. MACKAY. *Quantal aspects of scientific information theory.* **Philosophical magazine**, vol. 41 (1950), pp. 289–311.

[93] D. M. MACKAY. *In search of basic symbols.* **Transactions of the eighth conference on cybernetics**, New York 1952, pp. 181–221.

[94] D. M. MACKAY. *Generators of information.* **Proceedings of the second symposium on applications of communication theory**, London 1953, pp. 475–485.

[95] M. E. MARON, J. L. KUHNS and L. C. RAY. *Probability indexing—a statistical technique for documentation and retrieval.* Technical Memorandum No. 3, Data Systems Project Office, Ramo-Wooldridge, Los Angeles 1959.

[96] M. MASTERMAN, R. M. NEEDHAM and K. SPÄRCK-JONES. *The analogy between machine translation and literary retrieval.* [123], Area 5, pp. 917–935.

[97] R. MCNAUGHTON. *The theory of automata, a survey.* **Advances in computers,** vol. II (F. L. Alt, ed.), Academic Press, New York 1962, pp. 379–428.

[98] J. METCALFE. **Information indexing and subject cataloguing; alphabetical, classified, coordinate, mechanical.** The Scarecrow Press, Inc., New York 1957.

[99] GEORGE A. MILLER. **Language and communication.** McGraw-Hill, New York 1951.

[100] GEORGE A. MILLER. *What is information measurement?* **American psychologist,** vol. 8 (1953), pp. 3–11.

[101] GEORGE A. MILLER and NOAM CHOMSKY. *Finitary models of language users.* Handbook of mathematical psychology, vol. 2 (Bush, Galanter and Luce, eds.), Wiley, New York 1963.

[102] C. N. MOOERS. *Zatocoding and developments in information retrieval.* **ASLIB Proceedings,** vol. 8 (1956), pp. 3–22.

[103] C. N. MOOERS. *Retrieval by the method of proximity transformations.* Unpublished, Cambridge, Mass. 1958.

[104] C. N. MOOERS. *A mathematical theory of language symbols in retrieval.* [123], Area 6, pp. 1327–1364.

[105] C. N. MOOERS. *The next twenty years in information retrieval; some goals and predictions.* ZTB-121, Zator Company, Cambridge, Mass., 1959.

[106] G. E. MOORE. *Russell's "theory of descriptions".* **The philosophy of Bertrand Russell** (P. A. Schilpp, ed.), Tudor Publishing Company, New York 1951, pp. 175–225.

[107] J. MYHILL. *Linear bounded automata.* Wright Air Development Division, Technical Note 60–165, 1960.

[108] *Nonconventional technical information systems in current use.* Office of Science Information Service, National Science Foundation, Washington D.C. 1959.

[109] A. G. OETTINGER. *The design of an automatic Russian-English technical dictionary.* [89], pp. 47–65.

[110] A. G. OETTINGER. **Automatic language translation.** Harvard University Press, Cambridge 1960.

[111] A. OPLER and N. BAIRD. *Experience in developing information retrieval systems on large electronic computers.* [123], Area 4, pp. 699–710.

[112] V. A. OSWALD, JR., and S. L. FLETCHER, JR. *Proposals for the mechanical resolution of German syntax patterns.* **Modern languages forum,** vol. 36 (1951), pp. 1–24.

[113] J. W. PERRY and A. KENT. **Documentation and information retrieval.** Western Reserve University Press and Interscience Publishers, Inc., New York 1957.

[114] J. W. PERRY and A. KENT. **Tools for machine literature searching; semantic code, dictionary, equipment, procedures.** Interscience Publishers, Inc., New York 1958.

[115] J. W. PERRY, A. KENT and M. M. BERRY. **Machine literature searching.** Western Reserve University Press and Interscience Publishers, Inc., New York 1956.

[116] K. L. PIKE. **The intonation of American English.** University of Michigan Press, 1945.

[117] K. L. PIKE. *More on grammatical prerequisites.* **Word,** vol. 8 (1952), pp. 106–121.

[118] C. V. POLLARD. **A key to rapid translation of German.** University of Texas, 1947

[119] K. R. POPPER. **The logic of scientific discovery.** Hutchinson, London 1959.

[120] EMIL L. POST. *Finite combinatory processes—formulation I.* **Journal of symbolic logic,** vol. 1 (1936), pp. 103–105.

[121] EMIL L. POST. *Formal reductions of the general decision problem.* **American journal of mathematics,** vol. 65 (1943), pp. 197–215.

[122] EMIL L. POST. *A variant of a recursively unsolvable problem.* **Bulletin of the American Mathematical Society,** vol. 52 (1946), pp. 264–268.

[123] **Proceedings of the International Conference on Scientific Information, Washington, D.C., Nov. 16–21, 1958.** National Academy of Sciences—National Research Council, Washington, D.C. 1959.

[124] W. V. QUINE. *Notes on existence and necessity.* **Journal of philosophy,** vol. 40 (1943), pp. 113–127; reprinted in Semantics and the philosophy of language (L. Linsky, ed.), University of Illinois Press, 1952, pp. 77–91.

[125] W. V. QUINE. *Two dogmas of empiricism.* **Philosophical review,** vol. 60 (1951), pp. 20–43; reprinted in [126], pp. 20–46.

[126] W. V. QUINE. **From a logical point of view.** Harvard University Press, 1953 (2nd edition—1961).

[127] W. V. QUINE. **Word and object.** Technology Press of the Massachusetts Institute of Technology and John Wiley and Sons, Inc., New York, London 1960.

[128] MICHAEL O. RABIN and DANA SCOTT. *Finite automata and their decision problems.* **IBM journal of research and development,** vol. 3 (1959), pp. 115–125.

[129] HANS REICHENBACH. **Experience and reality.** University of Chicago Press, 1938.

[130] HANS REICHENBACH. **Elements of symbolic logic.** Macmillan, New York 1952.

[131] ERWIN REIFLER. *M.T.* University of Washington (mimeographed), 1951.

[132] BERTRAND RUSSELL. **A history of western philosophy.** Allen and Unwin, London 1947.

[133] GILBERT RYLE. **The concept of mind.** Hutchinson University Library, London 1949.

[134] ARTHUR L. SAMUEL. *Programming computers to play games.* **Advances in Computers,** vol. 1 (F. L. Alt, ed.), Academic Press, New York 1960, pp. 165–192.

[135] E. SHAMIR. *On sequential languages.* Technical Report No. 7 (prepared for the U.S. Office of Naval Research, Information Systems Branch), Applied Logic Branch, Hebrew University, Jerusalem 1961.

[136] CLAUDE E. SHANNON and WARREN WEAVER. **The mathematical theory of communication.** University of Illinois Press, 1949.

[137] JOHN C. SHEPHERDSON. *The reduction of two-way automata to one-way automata.* **IBM journal of research and development,** vol. 3 (1959), pp. 198–200.

[138] ALFRED TARSKI. *Der Wahrheitsbegriff in den formalisierten Sprachen.* **Studia philosophica,** vol. 1 (1936), pp. 261–405; English translation in **Logic, semantics, metamathematics,** Oxford University Press, 1956, pp. 152–278.

[139] ALFRED TARSKI. *The semantic conception of truth and the foundations of semantics.* **Philosophy and phenomenological research,** vol. 4 (1944), pp. 341–376; reprinted in **Readings in philosophical analysis** (H. Feigl and W. Sellars, eds.), New York 1949, and in **Semantics and the philosophy of language** (L. Linsky, ed.), University of Illinois Press, 1952.

[140] M. TAUBE and ASSOCIATES, **Studies in coordinate indexing,** vols. I-V, Documentation Inc., Washington D.C. 1953–1957.

[141] L. TESNIÈRE. **Elements de syntaxe structurale.** Klincksieck, Paris 1959.

[142] H. ULDALL. **Outline of glossematics.** Sprog- og Kulturforlag, Copenhagen 1957.

[143] UNESCO. **Scientific and technical translating and other aspects of the language problem, documentation and terminology of science.** Paris 1957.

[144] W. M. URBAN. **Language and reality.** Allen and Unwin Ltd., London 1939.

[145] B. C. VICKERY. *Subject analysis for information retrieval.* [123], Area 5, pp. 855–865.

[146] B. C. VICKERY. *The structure of information retrieval systems.* [123], Area 6, pp. 1275–1289.

[147] JEAN VILLE. *La formation de la connaissance envisagée du point de vue probabiliste.* **Actualités scientifiques et industrielles,** vol. 1145 (1951), pp. 101–114.

[148] WARREN WEAVER. *Translation.* [89], pp. 15–23.

[149] RULON S. WELLS *A measure of subjective information.* **Twelfth symposium in applied mathematics** (R. Jakobson, ed.), American Mathematical Society, Providence, R.I. 1961, pp. 237–244.

[150] NORBERT WIENER. **The human use of human beings.** Houghton Mifflin Company, Boston 1950.

[151] NORBERT WIENER. **Cybernetics.** 2nd edition, The M.I.T. Press and John Wiley and Sons, Inc., New York, London 1961.

[152] V. H. YNGVE. *The feasibility of machine searching of English texts.* [123], Area 5, pp. 975–995.

[153] V. H. YNGVE. *A model and an hypothesis for language structure.* **Proceedings of the American Philosophical Society,** vol. 104 (1960), pp. 444–466.

[154] V. H. YNGVE. *The depth hypothesis.* **Twelfth symposium in applied mathematics** (R. Jakobson, ed.), American Mathematical Society, Providence, R.I. 1961, pp. 130–138.

[155] PAUL ZIFF. **Semantic analysis.** Cornell University Press, 1960.

379

ABCDE69876